EPICS OF THE WESTERN WORLD

E P I C S
OF THE WESTERN WORLD

ARTHUR E. HUTSON
Associate Professor of English,
University of California

AND

PATRICIA McCOY

J. B. LIPPINCOTT COMPANY
PHILADELPHIA AND NEW YORK

CONTENTS

GENERAL INTRODUCTION

An epic is a poem embodying a noble story told in noble verse. A more stringent definition is almost impossible; yet any attempt at such definition must use words like grand, noble, universal. Poetry, to attain epic stature, must possess above all else the qualities contained in these words, and the epic poet must tell of people, their actions and emotions, in such a way that his story expresses everything about his world. The materials of the epic poet are the ideals, customs, traditions, mythology, and—basic to and informing all these—the moral values of a whole society. Obviously, such a poet can soar with "no middle flight." His hero must be a man whose actions are important to the poet's audience, for no one wants to listen to or read a poem about someone who does not matter very much. And the epic poet, though he may pause for the exploration of a detail, does so only because the detail is important to the larger picture. He keeps us constantly aware of the greater field, the larger action.

Although the epic usually contains historical materials, it is not a history. All its elements—historical, fictional, mythological—must unite to produce a single impression of truth greater than fact, which history, because of its concern with diffuse accuracy, can never do. Historical fact, to an epic poet, is merely a basic material, important only so far as it serves his larger purpose. It is interesting that Troy actually existed, but not so important as that the *Iliad* exists.

It is easy to become impatient with Achilles for his resentment at Agamemnon's treatment of him, and to wish that he had stifled his feelings until the war had been brought to a successful conclusion. The emotions of the epic hero, however, are never less than heroic. Ordinary men, like ourselves, may through prudence knuckle under to authority. But we are not heroes, and none of us is capable of Achilles' greatness in the battlefield before Troy, and in that of his mind. Other heroes, though not less in stature, are more easily understood: Odysseus, for example, or Beowulf, because neither of them must conquer himself. Each of these meets dangers as they arise, and each solves his problem in a thoroughly human and comprehensible fashion. The dangers are not small; they may be increased or lessened by the hindrance or the help of the gods. But neither hero has the interior problems of Achilles (or, for that matter, of Roland or Dante) which must be solved before the epic can reach its conclusion. Not every man may expect to fight and kill dragons; but each man has within him his private dragon. The more heroic the man, the bigger the dragon; and from such conflict arises the most glorious and universal of victories.

One source of the importance of the epic hero is his identification with national or cultural heroes. Whether or not the epic is composed before the emergence of a nation, the hero displays something like national spirit. Thus Achilles, Roland, and Beowulf, although they live in epics composed before there was a Greek, a French, or an English nation, are essentially national heroes, men who exemplified the heroic and moral values of the people who gave them birth. So also Aeneas and Vasco da Gama, heroes of epics deliberately composed to exalt the fame of already founded nations, embody the virtues which the epic poet thinks of as peculiar to his own people. A nation may not be the only unit; the *Song of Roland* praises "sweet France," but its country is less France than all Christendom. Its patriotic feeling is in accord with that of its time, less nationalistic than religious:

> *Païen ont tort, et Chretien ont droit:*
> "The pagans are wrong, the Christians are right."

Again, in the *Beowulf,* there is little of the nationalistic feel-

ing one encounters in the *Cid* or the *Lusiads*, for the concept
of nationalism was foreign to the medieval mind. Yet whether
or not a nation is a part of the picture, the hero is always
identified with a single people.

The forces uniting the epic may be the personality of the
hero, as in the *Odyssey* or the *Cid*, or the beginnings of a nation, as in the *Aeneid*, or the fate of mankind, as in the *Divine
Comedy* and *Paradise Lost*. The narrative device which holds
them together is invariably that of the journey. The symbolism
is apt, for the journey is the symbol of man's life. Dante recognizes this in the first line of the *Divine Comedy:*

> *Nel mezzo del cammin di nostra vita:*
> "Midway upon the journey of our life."

The *Iliad's* journey ends before the beginning of the work, and
is only briefly mentioned; but it is the one from which Achilles
did not return. The *Odyssey* and *Lusiads* are very largely
stories of journeys and the adventures which their heroes encountered. Beowulf's journeys are short, but they serve to bind
the episodes together as no other device could do. The paths
of Dante and of Milton's Satan are longer than any others, for
they extend through the whole universe. It is in the *Divine
Comedy* that the epic voyage is given the greatest significance.
Every epic journey is, in a sense, a pilgrimage of the spirit, but
only Dante clarifies and expands the symbol to its fullest extent. Most of us take Odysseus' journey, or Vasco da Gama's,
to known destinations; we meet and overcome perfectly nor-
mal monsters, Cyclopes and the like. Only Dante took the
journey to the point where his will and his desire were moved
by "that Love which moves the sun and the other stars."

Because of the universality of the epic, mythology is basic to
it. Nothing is more important to a people than the activities of
its gods, because these activities explain the things which happen without apparent cause, and help men to explain the problem of evil. These gods, of course, were often made in the
likeness of men. Those of Greece and Rome were very like
their creators: they could be flattered or deceived, but they

could not be ignored or insulted. Ares and Aphrodite, as Demodocus sings in the eighth book of the *Odyssey*, were trapped in adultery by Aphrodite's jealous husband, Hephaestus; their reaction, on being taken *flagrante delicto*, was very human: they ran away in shame. Had not Paris awarded the golden apple to Aphrodite, Athene might have listened to the prayers of the Trojan matrons, and Hera, whom the Romans called Juno, might have helped Aeneas instead of putting every possible obstacle in his way. But that apple was inscribed: "To the Fairest"; and Paris' decision had far-reaching consequences for literature, consequences arising from the hurt pride of the losers.

In the medieval Germanic epic, the Christian mythology lies rather uneasily upon the underlying pagan substructure. Beowulf's enemies are "of the tribe of Cain," and he himself seems devoted to the Christian God. It is interesting in this connection, however, that in other Anglo-Saxon Christian poems and in the Old Saxon *Héliand* (*The Savior*) the poets regularly employ such phrases as "ring-giver" or "leader of warriors" to describe indiscriminately God or human leaders. And when Wagner composed his operas centered in the Ring of the Nibelungs, he felt constrained to go for source-material to the *Volsungasaga*, the product of a not-yet-Christian Norway, which retained the Germanic gods in its mythology. Roland, Oliver, and Charlemagne are good medieval Christians, for France had become a center of Christian culture very early in its history. They, and the Cid, approach more closely to the Greek and the Roman in their unquestioning acceptance of the place of Deity in man's daily existence. Camoens, a child of the Renaissance, has the gods of Greece and Rome meddling with the destinies of Christians, whose efforts were bent to the spread of the Faith, and who heard Mass every day as naturally as (and perhaps more often than) they had breakfast.

It is in the *Divine Comedy* and *Paradise Lost* that we find mythology most intimately a part of the work; indeed, it is the subject. No Christian can look upon his God in the way that Homer and Vergil looked on their many deities. It is unthinkable to see the First Cause as a sort of oversized man, endowed with every human virtue and frailty except sickness, old age, and death. Here lies the great difference between the earlier and the Christian epics. Achilles, Odysseus, and Aeneas lived in and for this world, and saw the next as an inferior copy of it. Beowulf and Roland felt that by their heroism they could be saved; but it remained for Milton to create an epic without a hero of this world, and for Dante, at the farthest extreme from the pagan imagination of the divine, to perceive the Beatific Vision.

Important as the mythological element is in the epic, the poem can never ignore entirely the world of men. It is precisely because Spenser ignored this rule that the *Faerie Queene* is not the second epic of England. Both levels must be held in focus, though the action may at will leave this world behind; in some poems, as in the *Divine Comedy,* there is a third level, that of allegory. Dante's poem has no earthly hero save the narrator himself, nor do any of its scenes (except, perhaps, that of Canto I of the *Inferno*) lie in our world. The earthly level, however, is maintained by the stories of the spirits to whom Dante talks, by imagery based on life and daily experience, or by references to his own life. Milton's devils at Pandemonium are like the political sharks of the English Parliament; his Eden is a real world, and Adam and Eve warmly human figures. Some epics, on the other hand, take place entirely on earth; in them, however, the mythological level comes through, as in the *Tarnkappe* of the *Nibelungenlied,* or the heavenly messengers who appear to Charlemagne and Roland. The epic world-picture must include the realms of fact and of myth, no matter which is given the greater emphasis.

Most epics are composed at a time when history is in a fluid rather than a static phase of development. The old order is changing, and the epic poem both ennobles the old and rationalizes the new. The kingdom of the Geats is declining; Beowulf arises, the last, greatest hero-king of the old dynasty, and with his death, the people, bereft of leadership, must perish. Dante, while medieval social, economic, and religious standards dissolve in revolution, harmonizes past and future. The battle in the epic is always a crucial one; it parallels the conflict faced by its hearers. The problem, whether it be the winning of a new crusade or of individual salvation, is always the one of greatest urgency and immediacy to the audience. When people have needed a summary of the past and reassurance for the future, the epic has often provided both.

Although the element of humor is not totally absent from the epic, it has little place there. In earlier epics, those closer to a primitive society, humor usually results from someone's discomfiture, as when Thersites, beaten by Ulysses, roars in pain and tries to escape while the soldiers laugh, or Hephaestus tells the gods how Zeus grew angry with him and threw him from Olympus; he fell the whole day, and has limped ever since. There are practically no humorous lines in the *Aeneid;* even Iulus' remark as he devoured the cake used for a dish, "Now we are eating our platters!" though intended as a mild pleasantry, is really a signal to Aeneas that a prophecy is fulfilled. The humor of the *Beowulf* is the grim humor of the battlefield: Grendel did not much enjoy having his arm torn off. Considering the subject matter of the *Divine Comedy* or *Paradise Lost,* there is scant room for humor. Perhaps the comment on Adam and Eve's dinner of fruit, "No fear lest dinner cool," or the statement that the elephant, to make them sport, wreathed his lithe proboscis, were intended to be funny. And Dante's description of his terror as he rode the back of Geryon, or his description of Malebranche, have their amusing side. The Homeric epics show that humor need not be out of place in an epic, but the epic hero can never be taken lightly. He amuses himself with hunting, racing, or feats of arms, not by telling funny stories. Humor in the epic is always a digression; and the epic poet has other uses for his digressions.

The greatest epics of Western culture are the oldest, the *Iliad* and the *Odyssey.* Behind these there may lie other, shorter poems of great deeds, called heroic lays; such lays may also be the basic stuff of the *Beowulf.* These may have been songs chanted at the court of a great hero, to celebrate his virtues and exploits. Perhaps, again, they were composed by a bard in hope of reward, as blind Demodocus was rewarded with a good dinner for his song of Ares and Aphrodite, or the minstrel who sang of the fight at Finnsburh. Some of them may have been sung or recited at festivals, to recall to men's minds the deeds of their heroes or the divine attributes of their gods. For all these suppositions we have only the slenderest evidence, for it is clear that the lays, once combined in a great poem, would have ceased to exist independently.

An epic requires a highly-developed society, with mature artistic standards, for its growth. It is fruitless, then, to attempt a division of epics into "primitive" and "artificial" categories. Classification by subject-matter is also unprofitable; in fact, every attempt to fit the examples of this form of literature into classes has been found, in one way or another, unsatisfactory. But without attempting to give names or make any formal categories, we know that there are at least three kinds of epics: the first contains the great classical epics and the *Beowulf;* the second, the medieval epics of chivalry; and the third, the *Divine Comedy* and *Paradise Lost.*

The purpose of this book is to introduce the reader to the greatest literary form of all. The poems we have chosen, we think, represent the best of their kind in the Graeco-Roman tradition which is a central part of our cultural heritage. There are, of course, other epics, and great ones; instead of the *Divine Comedy,* for example, we might have included the epic of the Crusades, the *Gerusalemme Liberata.* But of the two, the *Divine Comedy* is the greater, whether one believes it to be strictly an epic or no. We might have gone further afield, and given an account of the Indian epics, the *Ramayana* and the *Mahabharata,* both very important literary productions. Unfortunately, both are very long; in either of them any of our epics would be mere episodes. And neither of them is really satisfying, in the way a great epic must satisfy; for neither of them seems to have been the product of a single mind. They are episodic in nature; not formless indeed, but without strict confinement to a single important action. The *Kalevala*, too, the Finnish epic, might have found a place here; but it also is not the product of a single great poetic mind. For centuries the Finns had sung songs of the deeds of their cultural heroes, but it was not until 1835 that the scholar Elias Lönnrot collected these into a single work. This had some literary influence— Longfellow's *Hiawatha* owes it much—but it is not an epic within our definition. Some might ask why we have included the *Nibelungenlied* instead of the *Volsungasaga:* surely the second is the greater of the two? But it is not epic, it is saga, a prose story. Sagas have, often, epic elements and epic qualities, and are among the best stories told, but they are usually in prose, and we have defined an epic as a noble poem.

The sort of writing which we attempt here has its own, very special problems. We are trying to translate and summarize simultaneously, to present an outline of the original as clearly as we can, at the same time bringing over into English as much of the quality and flavor of the original as the limitations of the form allow. Line-for-line accuracy is obviously impossible; mere summary of fact is insufficient. Each of these works has a very definite style and flavor of its own, and these we have tried, by one device or another, to catch.

Because the *Paradise Lost* is in English, we solved the problem—so far as it can be solved—by the inclusion of rather generous quotations. Earlier translations of the *Aeneid* and the *Divine Comedy* provided verse-passages which attain to some similarity with the originals. The medieval epics, the *Roland,* the *Cid,* the *Beowulf,* the *Nibelungenlied,* and the Renaissance *Lusiads,* could, without too great loss, be presented entirely in prose. The *Iliad* and the *Odyssey,* however, offered much more difficult problems. In the first place, they are the greatest. Again, their style is rapid and virile; not slangy, but often colloquial. This style is natural, for much of these poems is in direct discourse; and if a colloquial style is found anywhere, it is found in colloquies. We have seen no verse translation which has caught the true Homeric flavor of these epics; for that reason, we have presented them entirely in prose, and have striven hard to write a prose which gives, if even in small part, some tang of the original.

The brief essays which precede the summary of each poem are intended to acquaint the reader with, first, the social and cultural matrices from which the poems grew; second, with a few facts concerning the ways by which these poems reached us, and something of their influence on later readers and writers; and third, with some of the problems which scholars have had to solve in making these poems comprehensible to readers of later times. These essays, being brief, are incomplete; but at the end of each summary we have listed a few books which may assist the curious reader to find out more than we could give him. There is so much to be said about any of these poems that our principal difficulty has been to exclude all but the most important material. Though we could not make these essays complete, we tried to make them accurate, basing our statements upon the best scholarship available to us. We hope that our readers will find the essays an introduction to the exciting world of scholarship as fervently as we hope that they will find the summaries of the stories an introduction to the glorious world of the epic.

A.E.H.

P.A.McC.

SUGGESTIONS FOR FURTHER READING

Ker, W. P. *Epic and Romance,* New York, 1922
Chadwick, H. M. *The Heroic Age,* London, 1921
Van Doren, Mark. *The Noble Voice,* New York, 1946
Bowra, C. M. *From Virgil to Milton,* New York, 1946

THE
ILIAD
AND THE
ODYSSEY

INTRODUCTION: ON THE GREEK EPIC

The times celebrated in the Greek epic were violent and dis-
organized. The tribes were on the march, the older civilizations falling before them. Egypt was in the last glorious days
of the New Kingdom; within a century she was to enter on a
period of civil war and anarchy, after which the long ages of
foreign domination were to begin. Crete, with its centuries-old
civilization, had been only recently overcome and Cnossos, its
capital, sacked by roving savages from the mainland. The
glory that was to be Greece was still far off, and Rome many
centuries in the future.

Somewhere in the middle of Europe a new tribe was growing. As its population increased, the groups on the tribal
perimeter were forced outward to find new dwelling-places, in
their turn to become the ancestors of other tribes. Over a
period of centuries, these people rolled outward from their
centers in successive waves: in the East, they reached the
Ganges; in the West, they were stopped by the gray seas washing the west coast of Ireland. Northward, they moved through
Europe and into Scandinavia; and to the south, they poured
over the mountain-passes into what is now Greece, where they
took up their dwelling around Mycenae and Argos. For want
of a better name for these wandering people, we give them that
of Aryans, a Sanskrit word meaning the "noble ones," or, more
clumsily, we call them Indo-Europeans. Their language was
the ancestor of Sanskrit, Greek, Latin (with its offshoots, the
Romance languages), Celtic, Slavic, and Germanic, which includes our own tongue.

From a study of the words common to all these languages in

their earliest known stages, we learn that these Aryans had dogs and horses, but no cats; honey, grain, and cattle, but no olives, grapes, or camels. In their forests of oak or pine, they fought bears and wolves; but they did not know of lions, tigers, or the cypress. They had a word meaning "to get drunk," but no word for wine. They had swords, but in the earliest period no battle-axes; bronze and tin, but no word for copper. Obviously they traded for battle-axes, wine, and copper, but they had no words for such commercial matters as ships or sacks. They were on the frontiers of a commercial civilization, but they had not yet developed an economy which required peace in order to flourish. In other words, they were just emerging, or perhaps had just emerged, from barbarism.

In their wanderings, these barbarians came into conflict with already established civilizations, with which they fought. When they had the upper hand in battle, they moved into the cities of their late enemies, took over their houses, possessions, and women, and settled down to a civilized life. It was then that they had leisure to remember their past deeds, and to make lays celebrating their ancient heroes.

These lays were the very beginning of literature. They were short poems, usually dealing with a single exploit. We can, perhaps, recognize one in Book X of the *Iliad,* which is the story of a cleverly-handled night-raid, well told, but not serving to advance the action of the epic. Perhaps we can also trace them in some of the ventures of Odysseus. In such song-stories, the narrator told of the gods and heroes of his people: how they overcame difficulties, or how, unable to conquer their enemies, the heroes died bravely. Often the tribal gods warred beside the heroes: sometimes they helped, sometimes they hindered. Always the actions were those of important people, and nearly always they are inspired by noble motives. From these stories, we learn how men lived and died, and we see something of the beginnings of our own ideas of what is right, good, and heroic.

Someone, whom we agree to call Homer, saw the possibility of taking these stories, imposing upon them the unity and order of artistic structure, and making a longer story centered in a single hero. Of the author himself we know little or nothing. Seven cities claim his birthplace. Some scholars think of him as one man, some as two, some as a whole group of singers, each adding his own bit to the story until it was finally reduced to form and order long after its first version was composed. (We shall say more of this later.) But facts of this sort about Homer are unimportant, as are the facts about the individual lays which he used. What matters—and has mattered for nearly three thousand years—is that he composed the first and greatest epics in the Western world. These are the *Iliad*, which means the story about Ilium, or Troy, and the *Odyssey*, the story about Odysseus.

The language which Homer used was Greek, but it was not of the same period, or the same dialect, as that used in Athens during the great period of Greek culture. It is earlier in form, and incorporates many words from dialects other than classical Attic Greek. Nor does Homer, though he surely thought of himself as a Greek, employ the classical word "Hellenes" to describe his heroes; he calls them Argives, Danaäns, or Achaeans. These names tell us the places from which they came to the war. The Argives and the Danaäns were from Argos, a city in southeastern Greece; the name Danaän comes from the old story of King Danaus, who fled to Argos with his fifty daughters, who married the princes of the town. The Achaeans came from Achaea, a district of northern Greece, and from Mycenae, a city to the south. His verse-form is the dactylic hexameter: the biblical line is a good example:

> How art thou fallen from Heaven, O Lucifer, son
> of the morning!

It is admirably adapted to telling a story, for the meter is capable of very large variations. It is musical, yet masculine; subtle in arrangement, sinewy and muscular.

Many of us, without knowing we are quoting Homer, use phrases from his work. We speak of being caught between Scylla and Charybdis, often not remembering that Odysseus had to sail—and did sail—between these two; or we refer to a lady as a Siren, not remembering that the Sirens were a particularly repulsive lot of hags, whose only charming feature was their voices. Again, we may speak of Achilles' heel, or say that people work like Trojans, just because men have been using these phrases for nearly three thousand years.

Others, more learned, may refer to the wine-dark sea, aware that they are using a phrase from the *Odyssey,* or speak wingèd words. These are conscious literary references, part of the cultural inheritance of Western man.

They are the more easily remembered because they are a part of Homer's tag-lines, phrases which he took over, probably, from the composers of earlier lays, who used them as devices to aid the memory. They are not, however, mere line-fillers, employed when Homer could not think of a good way to say something; they are bits of literature, the result of close observation of natural phenomena. The "well-greaved" Achaeans were precisely that; Homer is recalling in vivid phrase the appearance of the warriors. "Then to him, with wingèd words, replied swift-footed Achilles" is a line which occurs more than once; but it says something well, for we are reminded that it was Achilles' fleetness of foot which kept Hector from seeking shelter within the walls of Troy. The many references to Odysseus as *polymêtis*—the man who has many tricks—reinforce in our mind the impression of Odysseus which Homer wants us to have. And so on. In the Greek, these phrases lend flavor and salt to the story.

The text of Homer, who may have written as early as 800 B.C., is better established than that of many later writers, far better than that of Shakespeare, for example. The earliest attempts at making a complete and accurate version of the epics may well have taken place in the time of Peisistratus, Tyrant of Athens (560-528 B.C.). This text was based on the recitations of the Rhapsodoi, professional declaimers of the Homeric poems, who learned them from the bards. In the third century B.C., the scholars of Alexandria, in Egypt, divided the two poems into twenty-four books each, but this division, made with taste and discrimination, is a relatively minor matter. Although the oldest complete manuscript copy of the poems is very much later, we know them now, essentially, as the Greeks knew them twenty-five hundred years ago.

Scholars of the last few centuries have concerned themselves with other problems, with minor textual changes, for example (which need not concern us here), or with the larger questions: Could Homer write? Did he compose both the *Iliad* and the *Odyssey?* Did he compose them as they now exist, or was he the author of shorter versions, to which later poets made additions? This last question was raised by the philologist Wolf, whose *Prolegomena* (1795) was followed by the work of many scholars. Briefly, Wolf's theory was that Homer had composed short poems on the subject of the Trojan War and Odysseus' return, and that later poets had expanded these by grafting on other poems on related subjects. Then, in the time of Peisistratus, a commission was appointed to establish the true version of the poems. Wolf's theory was based partly on the premise that, before the fifth century B.C., very few people could write, and that certainly Homer could not. Nor was it possible, he thought, for any man to hold in his memory the two long poems. Later scholars, following out Wolf's arguments, dissected the *Iliad* and the *Odyssey* into what they believed to be the original portions, and for a time Homer, as a true epic poet, was threatened with extinction. Toward the end of the nineteenth century, however, a reaction against this kind of fragmenting scholarship set in, and for the past fifty years or so it has been the general belief that Homer was the author of the *Iliad,* and probably of the *Odyssey.*

The question of the single authorship of both poems is a harder one. The arguments for it are partly linguistic (which to discuss would require comments on the history of the Greek language), partly mythological, and partly a matter of narrative vision. To consider the mythological arguments: in the *Iliad*, the messenger of the gods is usually Iris; in the *Odyssey,* usually Hermes. But both are known as messengers in both works. The gods are angrier with each other in the *Iliad* than in the *Odyssey*. But the only god much involved in the *Odyssey* is Poseidon, the only goddess, Athene; in the *Iliad*, on the other hand, the war before Troy is reflected in the quarrels of all the gods on Olympus. It is probable that the *Odyssey* was written later than the *Iliad*, but the arguments based on language and mythology do not serve to weaken our belief in the single authorship of both poems.

It has been suggested that the two poems are by different authors because of the way in which each poem looks at its subject. The *Iliad*, it has been said, is heroic; the *Odyssey*, on the other hand, exemplifies the middle-class virtues of careful planning, the acquisition of worldly goods, of prudence in general. Some critics consider the *Odyssey* more carefully planned and plotted, the episodes more carefully selected, as a modern story-teller might select them. Others have considered the differences between the women in the two books: those of the *Odyssey*, they believe, are so much more fully realized than those of the *Iliad* that the same mind could not have created both groups.

It is true that the women of the *Odyssey*, Calypso, Circe, Nausicaä, Eurycleia, and Penelope, are much more carefully portrayed than those of the *Iliad*, Helen, Briseis, and Andromache. Though Helen is the cause of the war, she appears but little, and Briseis is merely something for Achilles and Agamemnon to quarrel about: she might as well have been a suit of armor. But the *Iliad* is a story of war, and women do not go to war. When Hector takes his last farewell of Andromache, the scene is instinct with deep pathos, and Andromache comes alive in a way that neither Helen nor Briseis does. In other words, when Homer looks away for a moment from the battlefield, he shows us that he can create a genuinely feminine character.

The women in the *Odyssey*, also, are necessary to the story in a way that those in the *Iliad* are not. The goddess, the witch, the maiden (and surely Nausicaä is the loveliest girl in all literature), the devoted servant, the faithful wife: each represents a type of woman, and each, in her way, is the best of her type. But surely it is not impossible to believe that the mind which imagined and set down the sorrow of Andromache could also have conceived the wonderful women of the *Odyssey*. To sum it up, it is perhaps safest to follow the tradition, and to think of Homer as the man who composed both poems.

Of the two works, we think the *Iliad* the more mature, for it probes the minds of the Greek chieftains, where the *Odyssey* emphasizes adventure. In the beginning of the story, Achilles and Agamemnon engage in a rather ignoble quarrel over the division of loot, and Achilles, whose temper is never very mild, goes back, in anger, to his own troops, whom he withdraws from the battle. Then for nine books, we hear of the growing power of the Trojans, until Achilles, shot through with grief for the death of his dearest friend Patroclus—the result of his own unreasoning anger—again enters the fight, and kills Hector. With the realization that he has been wrong, he begins his purification. The entire action occupies only some fifty days in a ten years' war, but in that time we explore the whole problem of tragedy. For, although there was no drama when Homer wrote, he perceived that men are not really simple beings but complexes of emotions, motives, reason. He took the occasion of this quarrel between two men—one depending on his rank, the other on his personal prowess and valor—to trace the growth of the mind of one from unreasoning anger and hatred to humility and pity; for when Achilles returns the body of Hector to Priam, he has learned that his earlier emotions have held him back from maturity. Now he is a whole man.

Brooding over the whole story is a sense of fate. We know, and Homer's first audience knew, that Troy must fall, and that Achilles' life, after his conquest, must be short. Homer never lets us forget this, for although he presents both Hector and Achilles sympathetically, so that we hope that both will succeed, he is always ready with a comment on the future. In other words, he is not concerned with "suspense," as the modern writer so often is; he wants us to get into the minds of his people, and see why they do as they do.

He examines the mind of Odysseus as thoroughly as that of Achilles, though the examination is of a different kind. In saying, as we said above, that we consider the *Iliad* the more mature of the two poems, we do not mean to imply that the *Odyssey* is less great. It is simply that the emphasis is different. As the reader knows that Achilles must die shortly after the fall of Troy, so he knows that Odysseus will reach his home after twenty years' absence and will reclaim his birthright. But in the *Odyssey* Homer was making no subtle examination of a man's moral growth and final purification. Rather, he was telling a story—not less than the greatest—of a man's adventures in overcoming monsters not of his own making, defeating them by the use of his human intelligence.

The first word of the *Iliad* is "wrath"; the first word of the *Odyssey,* "man." In the two words, striking the keynote of each poem, we may see, perhaps, the essential difference between the two. The *Iliad,* for all its battles, is really fought out in the mind of Achilles. The *Odyssey,* on the other hand, is pre-eminently the story of a man dealing with external problems. But Odysseus does not solve his problems as, say, Ajax would have done, with a bull-like rush and roar. His weapon (though he is no weakling or coward) is the mind. Homer's favorite epithet for Odysseus is *polymêtis,* the man of many devices. His devices, however, are not base tricks. Like all epic heroes, he exemplifies the virtues of his people, and the Greeks were very much people of the mind. Coupled with their intellectual curiosity was a very high moral sense, and Odysseus, a true Greek, had a sense of responsibility to his moral values which, as much as his intellect, brought him through all perils. His men, deficient in that sense, perished, though Odysseus did his utmost to save them from themselves.

It is this intellect and this sense of values which keep Odysseus from giving in to the obstacles in his path. How easy it would be for any of us to dwell immortally with Calypso on her island, or to give up in despair before Scylla and Charybdis! But Odysseus never yields, either to danger or to the easy alternative. He keeps always before him the goal of his journey, his own Ithaca; he seldom despairs; he lives out his life, never forgetting that he has to perform the duties of a man.

The influence of Homer is apparent in early Greek times. Other authors wrote poems to fill in the gaps left by the *Iliad* and the *Odyssey*, but none of these has been preserved. A prose summary of these supplementary poems was made, probably in the second century of our era, by a man named Proclus; from his work we know all we know about these Cyclic poets, so called because they rounded out the cycle of the stories of Troy and Thebes. The first of these in the cycle is the *Cypria*, by Arctinus, which tells the story of the beginnings of the Trojan War: how, at the marriage of Peleus and Thetis, parents of Achilles, the goddess Eris, or Discord, threw among the guests a golden apple bearing the legend, "For the Fairest." All the goddesses present wanted it, but Hera, wife of Zeus, Athene, goddess of Wisdom, and Aphrodite, goddess of Love (both daughters of Zeus), were the final contestants. They asked Zeus to decide among them, but he preferred to avoid family quarrels, and sent them to Paris, son of Priam, King of Troy. Hera promised power, Athene wisdom, but Aphrodite promised him "the fairest and most loving wife in Greece." This was Helen, wife of Menelaus, daughter of Leda and Zeus, sister of Castor and Polydeuces. She was the most beautiful woman in the world. When it was time for her to marry, there was a great contest for her hand; but Odysseus suggested that she choose her own husband, and that the other contestants (of whom he was one) agree to support him in battle. She chose Menelaus, with whom she lived happily, and had a daughter named Hermione.

Then Paris came to Sparta, and, while Menelaus was away, eloped with Helen. Menelaus immediately demanded that the other kings support him in recovering her, and all did as they had promised, except Achilles and Odysseus. The latter had a wife and a young son in Ithaca, and did not want to go so far as Troy. He pretended madness, plowing the beach and sowing it with salt. Menelaus' heralds placed Telemachus, his infant son, before the plow, and when Odysseus turned it aside, they made him admit his sanity.

Then Odysseus was sent to find Achilles. This hero, as Homer says in the *Iliad*, had a double fate: either a long but inglorious life at home in Phthia, or a short, glorious one before Troy. His mother, while he was a baby, had dipped him in the River Styx, the boundary of the land of Hades, god of the Dead. This action made him invulnerable to weapons, except in one spot, on his heel. Thetis, not wishing him to die before Troy, had sent him to the court of Lycomedes, King of Scyros, where he lived disguised as a girl. There he had a son by Deidamia, one of Lycomedes' daughters. The boy, whose name was Neoptolemus, joined the Greek army late in the Trojan War.

Odysseus came to Scyros disguised as a merchant, selling jewelry, ribbons, and clothing, together with some weapons. He made his way to the women's quarters, where the girls all admired the feminine things, but Achilles gave himself away by selecting the swords to examine.

All the Greeks gathered at Aulis, where Zeus sent them a token of the ten years' war (Book I, *Iliad*). The north wind held them in the harbor, until Calchas, the soothsayer, announced that Agamemnon had offended the goddess Artemis, and must sacrifice his own daughter, Iphigenia, to placate her. Agamemnon sent for the girl, pretending that he was going to marry her to Achilles; she was sacrificed, and the army proceeded.

When they landed at Troy, the first to leap from the ships was Protesilaus, who desired the honor of being first ashore, though the oracle had said that the first ashore should be first to die. His wife, Laodamia, when she heard of his death, prayed that he might return to her if only for three hours. Her prayer was granted, and she joined her husband by committing suicide.

The *Iliad* begins in the last days of the Trojan War, and continues to the death and burial of Hector. After the *Iliad*, there is another minor epic of the cycle, the *Aethiopia*, which tells how Achilles killed Penthesilea, the Queen of the warlike women, the Amazons; how he also killed Thersites, when the latter railed at him for his sorrow over her death; how Achilles was killed by Apollo and Paris, being wounded mortally by an arrow in his only vulnerable spot; and, finally, how Odysseus worsted Ajax in a combat for Achilles' weapons.

The *Little Iliad*, whose author is unknown, follows; it tells of the death of Telamonian Ajax, who committed suicide in mortification at his defeat by Odysseus. The latter also captured the Trojan Helenus, who could see into the future. He prophesied that when Philoctetes should return to the battle, bearing the arrows of Heracles, and Neoptolemus, son of Achilles, should take up his dead father's task, the Greeks should sack Troy. After their arrival, Odysseus went, disguised, into the city, and discovered a way to steal the Palladium, the most precious religious possession of the Trojans, without which their city was doomed. Accompanied by Diomedes, he made his way into the town and carried off the Palladium.

After the theft of the Palladium, Odysseus planned the strategem of the Trojan horse, a great wooden figure whose belly was filled with warriors. The Greeks left it on the plain before the city, and sailed away, ostensibly in defeat. When the Trojans came to the old camp, they found a Greek named Sinon, "who brought Troy all utterly to sorrow." For he told them that the Greeks had built it to appease the wrath of Pallas Athene for stealing her Palladium.

Iliou Persis, The Sack of Troy, takes up the story at this point. Only Cassandra, daughter of Priam, and Laocoön, a priest of Earth-shaking Poseidon, did not believe the Greek's story. But it was Cassandra's fate to prophesy nothing but the truth, and never to be believed; and Laocoön, with his two sons, was strangled by two serpents from the sea. The Trojans accepted this as an omen that Poseidon, the Sea-god, was displeased with his priest, and brought the horse into Troy. That night, they celebrated their supposed victory, and when everyone was well drunk, Sinon opened the horse, the warriors came out and sacked the city, and the other Greeks returned, to complete their victory and to carry off their plunder and their victims.

Then the *Odyssey* begins, and after Odysseus' successful return, the *Telegonia* (the story of Telegonus) by Eugamon of Cyrene, brings the story of Troy to its end. In the *Telegonia,* we hear how Odysseus, after the burial of the suitors, went to Elis to visit Polyxenus, and then returned to Ithaca to make the sacrifices which Teiresias had commanded. After this, he went to Thesprotis, where he married Callidice, the Queen, and engaged in a war. His son by Callidice, Polypoetes, took the kingdom on his mother's death. Odysseus returned to Ithaca to find his son by Circe, Telegonus, ravaging the land. Telegonus killed Odysseus, and when he discovered that he had killed his father, took the body to Circe's island, Aeaea, for burial. Penelope and Telemachus accompanied him. Circe conferred upon them immortality, and, to wind up the whole story, Telemachus married Circe and Telegonus married Penelope. Other writers composed poems (*Nostoi,* or *Returns*), now lost, on the later fates of other heroes; but these, like the other Cyclic poems, must, in comparison with the Homeric epics, have been wretched productions.

The story of Troy has never been forgotten. Vergil took it up (see the *Aeneid*) and made it known throughout the Middle Ages, when for many centuries the knowledge of Greek was lost to the Western world. He modeled his first six books upon the *Odyssey,* giving Aeneas problems very much like those of Odysseus. (He did not like Ulysses, as he calls him, very well, for Vergil was naturally inclined to the Trojan side, and he made Ulysses out to be a rather deceitful fellow.) Books II and III of the *Aeneid* give a summary of the sack of Troy and Aeneas' subsequent wanderings. Two brief accounts, also in Latin, were produced by authors traditionally named Dares of Phrygia and Dictys of Crete; for many centuries these were the main sources of information about the Trojan War. Imitating Vergil, Geoffrey of Monmouth (1100-1154) derived the settlement of Britain from Brutus, a Trojan. He was followed by Wace, who translated Geoffrey into French, and by Lawman, who worked the whole story over into English (about 1200). Many authors in the later Middle Ages told the story in their vernaculars: Benoît de Sainte-Maure's *Roman de Troie* is an example, as well as Boccaccio's *Filostrato*, the source of Chaucer's *Troilus and Criseyde*.

Many authors used Homer's narrative device of the voyage as at least part of their epic framework, from Vergil to Camoens. The best-known example of modern times is James Joyce's great *Ulysses*, the story of a day in Dublin (June 16, 1904), in which Mr. Leopold Bloom may be seen as Ulysses and Stephen Daedalus as Telemachus; and the curious reader may parallel the adventures of Ulysses with those of Mr. Bloom.

There really was a Troy, and the account of its finding is one of the best success-stories ever told. For centuries it had been the general belief of scholars that the towers of Ilium were the cloud-capped pinnacles of myth and legend. A few conceded that there might have been a border-foray by the Greeks against some outlying tribe, but none would go so far as to admit that Troy might have been the capital city of an important civilization. There was some reason for this belief. Although the classical Greek historians, Herodotus and Thucydides, believed that there had been a Trojan War, and although the Romans traced their descent from the Trojans, such evidence as later came to light indicated that, in the days of Troy's greatness, the Greeks had been a people of comparatively primitive culture, unable to produce the beautiful objects of art which are common throughout the epics; and that to marshal and deploy great fleets must have been far beyond the capacities of a wandering tribe groping toward the beginnings of civilization. The constant presence of the divinities in the poems, also, fighting on one side or the other, and acting very like the human beings who created them, argued in favor of the theory that in the Homeric poems we had nothing beyond a collection of lays and ballads, put together over the course of centuries, and finally polished up to their present beauty by one or more professional poets.

It was not until the nineteenth century that these theories were finally disproved and Troy was exactly located and dug up. In 1832, a German clergyman gave his son a book about the Trojan War. The boy, Heinrich Schliemann, believed the stories, and when he learned that no one knew where Troy was, determined that one day he himself should find it, though forty years of an adventurous life were to elapse before he realized his dream.

He left Hamburg in 1841, nineteen years old, on a ship for Venezuela. Like Odysseus, he was wrecked, and like Odysseus he made his way to the nearest town—which, since the wreck took place early in the voyage, was Amsterdam. Here he got a job with an exporting and importing firm, and, in order to advance in business, began his study of languages. By 1844, he had taught himself Dutch, English, Italian, Spanish, Portuguese, French, and Russian. Being the only Russian-speaker available, and being also a good businessman, he was sent, in 1846, as an agent of the company to St. Petersburg. In 1847, at the age of twenty-five, he went into business for himself.

Within the next few years, he traveled over most of the world, prospering as he went—again like Odysseus. In 1850, he had a grocery-shop in the roaring boom-town of Sacramento, now the capital of California, and, because he was there when California was admitted as a State of the Union, he was granted American citizenship. By 1863 he was rich enough to retire—at forty-one—and to give his life to what he had always wanted: to find Troy.

Five years later he was exploring the traditional site of Ilium, the village of Bunarbashi, in Turkey. There were difficulties in believing this to be the right place, however, for in reconnoitering the area Schliemann found that it was too far from the coast, and that, if Homer were to be believed, Achilles could not have pursued Hector around the walls of Troy, unless both heroes had scrambled down the face of a cliff.

Homer mentions no such unheroic scrambling, which was enough for Schliemann.

Casting about in a new direction, he looked at Hissarlik, also called New Ilium, the site of a Phrygian city. He found there a great mound, an hour's journey from the coast, commanding the whole plain, and of about the right size to cover a city as large as Homer described it. This, he decided, was Troy, and he went to work. He struck pay-dirt almost immediately, though his methods would have made a modern archaeologist wince. As he went on digging, he found something he had not expected: city piled on ruined city, nine in all. The lowest was a late Stone Age village; the next showed a great gate, and buildings, scorched by flame. This, he decided, was Priam's Troy. On the last day of his dig he uncovered a great treasure-house, buried for two and a half millennia, which he felt sure was what the "well-greaved Achaeans" had missed in their sack of the city. He had found what he always knew he would one day find.

It hardly matters that later archaeologists, working more carefully, proved that the treasure had been hidden away in another war a thousand years before Priam wept over the dead body of Hector. Nor does it matter that the Troy of the story was the second city below the surface, not the sixth or seventh, as Schliemann believed. What matters is that a boy, reading the stories of gods and heroes, recognized that underneath them, as underneath the great mound of Hissarlik, lay truth— and that he found it.

Like all great stories, those of Troy and of Odysseus remain vital and important almost indefinitely. We do not always remember them exactly as the poems present them; but we never cease to thrill at such lines as Marlowe's

> Was this the face that launched a thousand ships
> And burnt the topless towers of Ilium?

THE ILIAD

Much have I travell'd in the realms of gold,
　And many goodly states and kingdoms seen;
　Round many western islands have I been
Which bards in fealty to Apollo hold.
Oft of one wide expanse had I been told,
　That deep-browed Homer ruled as his demesne;
　Yet did I never breathe its pure serene
Till I heard Chapman speak out loud and bold:
Then felt I like some watcher of the skies
　When a new planet swims into his ken;
Or like stout Cortez, when with eagle eyes
　He stared at the Pacific—and all his men
　Looked at each other with a wild surmise—
Silent, upon a peak in Darien.

　　　　　　　　　　　　　　　——John Keats

THE ILIAD: THE STORY

Book I: The wrath of Achilles I sing—how his quarrel with Agamemnon of the house of Atreus brought sorrow on the Achaeans. For Chryses, the priest of Apollo, came to ask that Agamemnon return his captive daughter, Chryseis; but Agamemnon told the old man to be off—the girl should stay. Then Chryses went by the shore of the murmuring sea, and prayed that vengeance might fall on the Achaeans; and Apollo heard.

For nine days the arrows of pestilence fell on the camp; on the tenth, Achilles summoned all to a meeting. Calchas, the soothsayer, who knew past and present and future, spoke: "It is not lack of prayer or sacrifice which has angered Far-shooting Apollo, but Agamemnon's insult to Chryses, when he refused to send the priest's daughter home. And he will not hold back the sickness from us, until we send the girl, with a sacrifice, back to Chryses."

Then Agamemnon spoke: "You miserable old prophet, who foretell only evil! I like the girl better than my own wife. If I must return her, I shall—but I want a prize in her place."

Achilles spoke, "Where will you find a prize? Everything we have taken has been shared. But give back the girl, and when—Zeus permitting—we take Troy, you shall have three or four times as much."

"Do not speak so to me, Achilles—you only want to keep your prize. I will take what I want from you or Ajax or Odysseus. Now, however, we will send a ship with Chryseis, and one of the lords here shall pacify Apollo with a sacrifice."

Achilles answered, "You greedy, good-for-nothing, dog-faced king! I fight for plunder; you steal it. I might as well go home to Phthia; there is nothing for me here."

"Go and be damned to you! I'll not go on my knees to hold you here. And I tell you this: I will send the girl back, for Apollo has taken her; but I will have your Briseis, and I will come and take her myself."

Achilles half-drew his sword, but Athene came from Olympus, invisible to all but him, and held him back by his red hair. He spoke to her: "Have you come to see me insulted by Agamemnon? One of these days his bad manners will be his death."

But Athene replied, "Queen Hera has sent me; do as I tell you. Stop fighting; tell him off; sheathe your sword: and one day you shall have a threefold payment for this injury."

Achilles did as she commanded, and Athene returned to Zeus on Olympus. But Achilles was still angry, and said to Agamemnon, "You bitch-faced, fawn-hearted wine-bibber! You never fight—you'd rather stay home and rob the fighting men. I tell you—and I swear it—the time will come when you will miss Achilles, when the Greeks are falling before Hector!"

Agamemnon would have answered, but honey-tongued old Nestor rose and addressed them: "Gentlemen! The Trojans would be happy to hear this quarrel. Hear me: I am old; I have seen and known much; I have been honored by better men than you. Agamemnon, do not take Briseis, for she is Achilles' prize. And do you, Achilles, honor your king; for, though you are a great fighter, his rank is greater. I ask you both, let this quarrel pass over."

Then they ceased their quarrel, and Achilles returned to his tents. King Agamemnon sent a ship with a sacrifice, and Chryseis went to Chryses, her father. He prayed that the pestilence might cease, and Apollo heard his prayer. They slew the sacrificial animals, and sang the hymns to Apollo; and the next day the Far-darter sent them a favoring wind, and they returned to Troy.

But, in the meanwhile, Agamemnon sent his heralds to Achilles' tents for Briseis, and Achilles' friend Patroclus gave her to them. Then sorrow overcame Achilles, and he went to the shores of the sea, calling upon his mother, Thetis. She heard him and rose from the depths. Achilles told her the story of his humiliation, and prayed that she would ask Zeus to avenge him on Agamemnon by helping the Trojans. She wept that his life, doomed to be short, should be made sorrowful, and promised to intercede with Zeus, the Thunder-maker, for him.

The Immortals had gone on a visit of twelve days to the land of the Ethiopians; and when they returned, Thetis spoke to Cloud-gathering Zeus, clasping his knees in prayer, "Grant me, Father Zeus, this request: let the Trojans get the upper hand of the Achaeans, until these grant my son the honor he deserves!"

Zeus answered her: "This will make Hera very angry, for she taunts me continually, saying that I help the Trojans. But I give you my word, which cannot be recalled: you shall have what you ask." Then they parted—she to her home in the seadeeps, he to his great hall on Olympus.

As he entered, all the gods arose; but Hera, who had seen Thetis, scolded her husband: "Of what have you and Thetis been speaking? I suppose that she has been coaxing you to harm the Achaeans, and I suppose that you have consented!"

Then Zeus replied, "You are always supposing, always spying; but there is not a god on Olympus who can help you if I grow angry and lay hands on you." Hera was silent and frightened, but Hephaestus spoke up: "Oh, what is the good of all this quarreling? Mother, you might as well give in to Father Zeus, for if you do he will be patient. Once I tried to help you, but he took me by the leg and threw me from Olympus—and I fell the whole day." Then she smiled, and took the cup which her son offered; and unquenchable laughter arose among the gods. They drank and feasted, and at night they slept.

Book II: But alone of gods and men, Zeus could not sleep. He called a false dream, and told it to visit Agamemnon, to say that now was the time to attack Troy. The dream did as he was told, appearing to Agamemnon in the form of Nestor. Agamemnon awoke; he rose, and drew on his clothes; he took the sceptre which Hephaestus had made, and which had been handed down for many generations of the Atreidae.

Now it was dawn, and Agamemnon summoned the chiefs. He told them of the dream, and proposed to test the soldiers' valor by asking whether they wanted to return to Greece. The men were gathered, and Agamemnon addressed them: "Zeus has deceived us! Long ago he promised us victory—now he commands that we return defeated to Argos. After nine years, our ships are rotten, our work unfinished. But there is nothing else—let us sail back!"

Then there was a great shout as the Greeks struggled to launch their ships quickly. Hera saw them and called to Athene, "Look! Are they to go home now, without Argive Helen, leaving so many dead? Go, hold them back!"

Athene plunged from towering Olympus, and found Odysseus standing disconsolately by his unlaunched ships. She called to him to restrain the men; he knew her, and obeyed. From chief to chief he ran, exhorting them to bravery, telling them that Agamemnon had only been testing the men's mettle. So all the men were collected, and sat quietly in their ranks, all save Thersites, a quarrelsome, ugly fellow, who rated his lord Agamemnon with insulting words: "What's the matter with you? Do you want more money, more women, more goods from those who won them in fight? You insult Achilles, a better man than you, and if he were not so noble, he would kill you!"

Odysseus could not endure this. "Thersites," he said, "you speak too freely! Be silent now, or I will beat you back to the ships!" And he thumped Thersites with his sceptre, so that he raised a bloody welt on the man's back, and he sat down, weeping. Everyone said that Odysseus had served him rightly— there would be no more words from him.

Odysseus arose and spoke: "King Agamemnon," he said, "these men are like children. For nine years they have been away from home, and life has been very hard. Perhaps I should not find fault. But remember, friends, the sign which Zeus sent us: the serpent who swallowed the mother-bird and her eight chicks, and then turned to stone. Calchas told us its meaning: for nine years we should fight, and in the tenth year gain the victory. Now, Achaeans, let us stay here, and capture towered Ilium."

Nestor, too, spoke to them. "Are we to fight only with words? What of our vows, of the solemn clasping of hands? King, take the fighters to the fight; let the cowards go home. I tell you the omens are good, the Thunderer has given to us the sacking of proud Troy. Then let us think of vengeance for Argive Helen before we think of flight. Here is my advice, King Agamemnon: let each man fight with his own tribe; so will you know which tribe is to be trusted, and whether it is the will of Zeus or the weakness of men which keeps you out of Troy."

Then the men cheered, and separated for their meal, and Agamemnon gathered the chiefs for the sacrifice. They stood about the bull while Agamemnon prayed for victory over Hector and the Trojans. When the sacrifice was done, the men were summoned. Like flocks of wildfowl, like swarms of flies, they gathered for the battle.[1]

Then Zeus sent Iris, his messenger, to warn Priam that the Achaeans were coming; she appeared to him in the form of his son Polites. Quickly Hector dismissed the assembly, and quickly the Trojans and their allies formed their ranks.

BOOK III: The two armies advanced, the Trojans making a great clamor, as when cranes fly, heralding a storm; the Achaeans grimly silent. Then Paris stepped from the Trojan ranks, and challenged any Greek to a duel. Menelaus was glad, for here was his opportunity to punish his wife's seducer, and he leaped from his war-chariot.

But Paris did not wait—he slipped back into the ranks. Hector spoke to him, "You cowardly boy! I wish that you had never brought the woman here. Those Achaeans are all laughing at you—you who have no fight in you at all! Why not face

---

[1] Here follows the catalogue of the Ships, which is omitted.

Menelaus? After all, your good looks will not help you when you are dead!"

Paris answered, "Do not make fun of Aphrodite's gifts. But if there must be a fight, let there be a duel between me and Menelaus."

Then Hector stepped between the armies, and all men were glad of a duel, for they were weary of war. But Iris came to Helen in the shape of her sister-in-law Laodice, and told her of the duel. Quickly she and Helen ran to the Scaean Gate; there Priam called her to his side, and she told him of the opposing chiefs—who each was, and what sort of man. The messengers came, and Priam went to make sacrifice before the fight, and to swear the oath of peace.

Paris won the first shot; he threw, and Menelaus caught the spear on his shield. Then Menelaus threw, and the spear cut through the shield and the body armor, but Paris twisted away and avoided death. Menelaus drew his sword and struck Paris' helmet, but the sword shattered. He leaped forth and caught Paris by the plume of his helmet, and would have dragged him to the Achaeans' ranks, but Aphrodite broke the chin-strap, and carried Paris off in a mist to his own chamber in Troy. Aphrodite came to Helen in the shape of an old servant-woman; but Helen recognized her, and reproached her for watching so carefully over Paris as to make him an object of scorn. Nevertheless, Helen returned to the chamber, but she spoke harshly to Paris. He replied, "Do not scorn me—Athene was helping Menelaus. Yet come to me, for I love you more than ever." Then her anger was softened, and she went to him.

On the field, Menelaus searched for Paris, raging like a wild beast. Agamemnon cried out, "Menelaus has won! Trojans, Dardanians, allies! Return Helen with her wealth, and pay a great fine!"

BOOK IV: On Olympus, the gods watched the deeds of Achaeans and Trojans. Zeus said, to annoy Hera, "Menelaus has conquered! What now? Shall the war begin again, or shall we make them friends? If friends, then Menelaus may take Helen home."

Athene and Hera were talking together. Athene did not answer, but Hera could not hold in her anger. "How can you say that, after what I have done to destroy Priam!" And they quarreled bitterly.

Then Zeus called to Athene to go to the plains of Troy, and to make the Trojans break their peace-oath. She appeared in the form of Laodocus to the archer Pandarus, and tempted him to shoot Menelaus. The shot was not mortal, for the arrow struck the belt and pierced his groin, but not deeply. Agamemnon saw the hurt, and groaned; he sent for Machaon, most skilful of healers, to tend the injury; and he healed it with salves and drugs given him by old Cheiron.

As Menelaus was being helped, the Trojans moved to the attack. Agamemnon went through the ranks, cheering the brave and encouraging the timid to fight. Idomeneus and Ajax and Nestor, Diomedes and Odysseus and Menestheus were of the chieftains; they led on in their chariots, and behind them the Danaäns moved, rank on rank, as the long lines of waves roll forward, crashing on the shore. Against them came the Trojans. The first to fall was the Trojan Echepolus, slain by Antilochus; then Telemonian Ajax slew Simoeisius. Antiphos cast a spear at Ajax, but missed him, and killed Leucus, a dear companion of Odysseus; then the first rank of the Achaeans surged forward over the Trojans. But Apollo stirred the Trojans to fight harder, while Athene moved through the battle. Many a Trojan and many an Achaean lay side by side in the dust.

Book V: Pallas Athene gave to Diomedes, son of Tydeus, courage and bravery, so that he stood above all in glory. He killed Phegeus, son of Dares, and the Trojans were afraid. The battle wavered to and fro, but Diomedes was everywhere, as a winter torrent breaks out over the dikes and covers the plain.

Pandarus saw him, and aimed his arrow; he struck Diomedes, but Pallas Athene kept up his heart, and he did not flinch from

the battle. He slew Trojans as the lion slays sheep in the fold.
Then Aeneas and Pandarus leaped into a chariot, for they
wanted to engage with Diomedes. Pandarus flung a spear so
that it wounded Diomedes; but Diomedes was not dismayed,
and flung his spear so that it went through Pandarus' face.
Aeneas tried to help his friend, but Diomedes lifted a great
stone and smashed Aeneas' hip-joint. Had it not been for
Aphrodite, who sheltered her son, he would have died. Diomedes followed them, and wounded Aphrodite in the hand,
and the timid goddess fled to Olympus. Apollo, the Far-darter,
saved Aeneas from Diomedes' wrath, for he warned Diomedes
that men are of one race, the gods of another; and the gods
are greater. Apollo called to Ares, god of War, to help the
Trojans; and a phantom created by Apollo appeared to Hector
in the form of the Trojan Aeneas, inspiring the men to battle.
Hector moved among the men, shaking his spears, and the
Trojans again faced the enemy. Apollo cured Aeneas, and
brought him again to the battlefield. Ares and Hector drove
the Achaeans before them, for Diomedes recognized Ares, and
would not fight against a god. The Danaäns would not turn
to run, but were pressed slowly backward.

Then Hera spoke to Father Zeus on Olympus, for she was
angry at the pushing-back of the Achaeans, and begged that
she might oppose Ares. Zeus consented; and Hera and Athene
went in their mighty chariot to the plain before Troy. Athene
went to Diomedes, and Hera, taking the shape of Stentor,
whose voice was that of fifty men, inspired the Achaeans to
fight anew. Athene drove the chariot of Diomedes straight
toward Ares; the god threw a spear, but the goddess shoved
it aside. Then Diomedes threw, and the spear, guided by
Athene, pierced the god's belly. He roared as loudly as nine
thousand men, and all the warriors were frightened; and the
god went up to Olympus, where the Healer cured his wounds.

Book VI: So the battle raged on the plains; only men fought,
for the gods had returned to Olympus. Many a hero was slain,
and the Trojans would have been beaten back to Troy if

Helenus had not inspired Hector and Aeneas. They rallied the men to the battle, and again the Achaean ranks gave back before them as if a god had come to help.

Then Hector, advised by Helenus, went again into Troy, to offer prayer and sacrifice. He asked his mother, Hecuba, to offer her finest robe, brought from Sidon, to Pallas Athene, and to promise a sacrifice of twelve yearling heifers in exchange for victory. She did so, with the matrons of the city, but Pallas Athene would not hear. While she did this, Hector went to Paris' mansion, where he found him polishing his armor. He reproached Paris bitterly for staying in the town while men fought outside the walls, and Helen spoke her own shame at Paris' womanishness. Then Hector left, to see for the last time his wife, Andromache, and his little son, Astyanax.

Andromache begged him not to go forth again, for without him she was alone in the world. Achilles had killed her father, Eëtion, and had sent her seven brothers to the land of Hades in one day, and carried off her mother. Now Hector was father and mother and brothers and husband to her. Hector replied, "I know only that one day Troy must fall. But I shall not grieve for that as I should to know that you are a prisoner in a strange land, when men shall see you weaving or carrying water, and say, 'That was Hector's wife.' Yet I cannot slink from the battle." He held out his arms to Astyanax, but the child shrank back, frightened of the gleaming, horsehair-plumed helmet. Hector and Andromache laughed, and he took it off. Then he kissed the lad, and prayed that Astyanax might be as great among the Trojans as he; that the boy might have praise and victory in war. Then he returned the child to his mother's arms, and told her, "Do not grieve in your heart, beloved, for no man on earth goes to the house of Hades before the appointed time. But no man, hero or coward, may from the day he is born avoid the fate set for him. Do you go home, and see to your tasks; war is men's work, mine especially of all those who live in Troy."

He took up his helmet and went; and those left behind mourned him, for they did not expect to see him again. As he

left Troy by the Scaean Gate, Paris joined him, and they went
to the battle together.

BOOK VII: Hector and Paris made great slaughter among the
Achaeans, until Athene came to help the Greeks. Apollo saw
her come, and came to the aid of the Trojans. The god spoke:
"Have you come here to interfere in the battle, and to help the
Achaeans? Let us make Hector issue a challenge for a duel."
Athene agreed, and Helenus, the soothsayer, brother of Hector,
perceived their meaning. He spoke to Hector, who was glad
of the message, and held back the troops until the battle could
be arranged. Then Hector spoke to both armies: "Hear me
now, Achaeans! If any of you wishes, let him come and fight
in single combat with me. If he slay me, let him keep my
weapons, but send my body to be burned in Troy; if I slay him,
his armor I will hang in the temple of Apollo, but his body I
will give back, so that it may be burned, and a tomb erected
over it; and men will say, 'He was killed by the great Hector.'"
The Achaeans were silent, ashamed to refuse and afraid to
accept the challenge. Menelaus arose and shouted, "You brag-
ging women, not men! I will fight this man myself, for it is the
gods who award victory!" And he would have fought, but the
Achaean leaders held him back; even Agamemnon restrained
him. Nestor arose, and taunted the Achaeans with their cowardice; at his words nine warriors stood up, Agamemnon, Diomedes, both Ajaxes, Idomeneus, Meriones, Eurypylus, Thoas,
and Odysseus. Then Nestor put each man's lot into a helmet,
and shook it; the first to leap out was that of great Ajax. He put
on his armor and prepared for battle, looking like Ares, god
of War. Even Hector's heart beat quickly, but he could not
retreat from his challenge. Hector cast the first dart, and it
pierced through six of the ox-hide coats of Ajax' shield, but
stopped at the seventh. Then Ajax flung his spear, and it
passed through shield and armor, and cut Hector's neck so that
the blood spurted. But Hector seized a great stone and dashed
it against Ajax' shield, and Ajax cast a stone at Hector, so that
he was beaten down; but Apollo raised him up again.

Then the heralds came between, for night had come, and told them to stop the fight. Ajax waited for Hector, the challenger, to give the word; Hector said, "Let us fight again later, until the Fates decide the victor. But let us also give one another a gift, so that men may know we parted friends." Hector gave him his great sword with the silver bosses, and Ajax gave Hector his purple belt; and each returned to his own people.

In the camp of the Achaeans, Agamemnon made a great feast of a five-year-old bull; and when everyone had eaten and drunk his fill, Nestor counseled that next day they should bury the dead, erecting a wall and a moat lest the Trojans should be too much for them; and everyone agreed.

By the Gate of Priam, the Trojans held their assembly. Antenor spoke, and said that it would be best to give back Helen, with her wealth; for they had broken their oaths. But Paris answered that he would never give the woman back, though he would return her wealth, and more of his own. To this Priam agreed, and ordered the herald Idaeus in the morning to bear the offer to the Achaeans at their ships.

But when the herald came at dawn, the Achaeans refused, for Diomedes spoke to them, and said that Troy was doomed to fall. Nevertheless, both sides agreed to an armistice for the burning of the dead. After the bodies were burned, the Trojans returned to their city, and the Achaeans to their ships, protected by the wall and the moat. The ships of Euneus were there, bearing wine; this the Achaeans bought for bronze or iron or captives; and all night they feasted.

But on Olympus, Poseidon, god of the Sea, looked at the wall, and fretted that the Achaeans had built it without sacrifices to the gods. Cloud-gathering Zeus spoke to him and said that the wall was of no moment, for when the Greeks had returned to their cities, Poseidon might easily overwhelm it, so that men should never know it had been.

Book VIII: At dawn, Zeus, the Thunderer, called to him the gods and warned them that on that day none of them should venture to intervene in the battle. "Try if you like," he said, "to draw me down from Olympus; I, alone against you all, would conquer you, and cast you into Tartarus." The gods were abashed, and did not reply, except Athene, who asked Zeus that he not entirely defeat the Danaäns.

Then Zeus went to the slopes of Mount Ida, to behold the fight between the Achaeans and the Trojans. All morning they strove together, and the earth flowed with their blood. But at noon Zeus laid in his scales the two weights, which bear the fates of men; that of the Trojans lifted, and the Achaeans' fell; Zeus thundered from the mountain, so that pale fear seized the Danaän host.

Idomeneus ran for the ships, and the two Ajaxes, and Aga-memnon—even Odysseus had no stomach for the fight that day. Only old Nestor could not escape, for Paris had sunk an arrow into the forehead of one of his horses, so that the horse reared up and tangled the harness. Nestor leaped from the chariot, trying to cut the traces loose with his sword, and Hector bore down on him, shouting. But Diomedes got before Nestor, and called to him to mount on his own chariot, for the chariot of Aeneas was also coming toward them. Nestor and Diomedes, ready again for battle, left the old man's chariot to the squires, and turned toward the Trojans. Diomedes missed Hector with a spear-throw, but killed his chariot-driver; and Hector turned away. Diomedes' valor would that day have won the war, had not Zeus sent a thunderbolt before his chariot, so that Nestor was afraid, and persuaded Diomedes that it is of no avail to fight against the gods—for Zeus is mightier than all. Diomedes answered, "Yes—but men will say that I ran from Hector—and on that day may the earth swallow me up!" But Nestor's counsel prevailed, and they turned back towards the ships.

Hector followed them closely, shouting taunts; three times Diomedes decided to turn and fight, and three times Zeus thundered against him. On Olympus, Hera and Poseidon talked of the battle, how Zeus was giving victory to the Trojans; but they dared not strive against him. On the battlefield, Hector had driven the Argives into the shelter of the wall and moat about their ships, and he would have burned ships and all had not Hera put it in Agamemnon's heart to inspire the Greeks to renewed conflict. He shouted, "You sons of shame! Do you now forget your boastings over the wine—how you would stand one against a hundred? But now none will stand against one! O Father Zeus! Remember the fat sacrifices that I made, and grant that the Achaeans be not destroyed by the Trojans!"

Zeus heard, and sent a sign: an eagle, who dropped a fawn by the altar. The Greeks were encouraged, and turned again upon the Trojans. First of them was Diomedes, who drove out against the Trojans, and killed Agelaus; close behind came both Ajaxes, and Menelaus and Agamemnon, and the other warriors. There was Teucer, the skilful bowman, protected by the shield of Telamonian Ajax. He peeped out from behind the shield, and shot his arrows; with every shot a Trojan fell. Agamemnon praised him, and promised him many prizes when the city should fall.

Teucer shot at Hector, but missed him, and struck his brother Gorgythion; he shot again, and again he missed Hector, but killed his charioteer. Then Hector took up a great stone, and broke Teucer's collar-bone; but Ajax saved the archer again, and he was carried to shelter. Then the Trojans pressed hard upon the Danaäns, and pushed them back toward the boats. Hector led the Trojans in the onrush; he harried the Greeks as a hound harries a boar or a wolf, slashing at his quarters, from every side.

Hera and Athene watched from high Olympus, and were sad at the slaughter of the Argives; they determined to mount their chariot, and, in spite of Zeus' commands, to help the Greeks. But Zeus saw them from Mount Ida, and sent Iris, his messenger, to deter them. Then both were afraid of Aegis-bearing Zeus, and turned back to the council of the gods. Zeus came thither in his golden chariot, and saw their anger. But he told them that on the next day also they should see Hector make havoc among the Greeks, and so it should continue until Achilles, grieving for the death of his friend Patroclus, should again take up the battle.

Now it was dusk, and Hector gathered the Trojans and their allies in a spot near the river, where there was a space clear of dead. He spoke to them, and advised that for the night they should make a camp in the field. Meat and wine should be brought from Troy, and fires should be kindled about the camp. A guard should be set, that there might be no night-attack, and in the morning, refreshed, they should set again upon the Greeks. The Trojans applauded, and did as he had counseled; all night they feasted and offered sacrifice—but the gods would not taste it—and beside them their horses stamped, waiting for the dawn.

Book IX: Outside the wall, the Trojans stood guard over their camp; but within, there was tumult and fear. Agamemnon, struck to the heart with grief, called an assembly, and stood before them weeping, for he thought that now they must indeed turn homeward, beaten. But Diomedes stood up, and denied that they must go; for himself, he and his long-haired Achaeans would stay until they had wasted Troy, and the Achaeans shouted their applause. Then Nestor arose, and spoke wisely: "Diomedes, you are young, and not yet so wise as I. But let us not act in haste; set a watch, and let us eat, and then talk together; for tonight we shall win or lose all." The Achaeans did as he bid, setting a watch of the young men, and brought out food and wine.

When they had satisfied themselves, old Nestor arose again and spoke: "King Agamemnon, it is the taking of Briseis against Achilles' will, and against ours, that has angered the hero; it is my advice that you return her, for Achilles feels himself dishonored, and we must appease his wrath."

Agamemnon spoke: "Sir, it is true that I have been a fool. Now I will try to make up for it: gifts of gold and horses I will give, and seven women whom I took on Lesbos; Briseis also I will send back to Achilles. And beyond this, he may have any of my daughters, when we return to Mycenae, and that without price, but I myself will add a great dowry. Let Achilles be appeased, and these shall be his."

Nestor spoke to great Ajax and to Odysseus, advising them how best to win back Peleus' noble son; and they went through the camp to Achilles' tent. They found him singing to the lyre a lay of heroes of old time; and Achilles sprang to his feet and welcomed them courteously.

He set forth good meat and wine, and when they had eaten, Odysseus spoke: "There is meat and drink also in Agamemnon's tent, and you have treated us well. We do not come to talk of feasting, but of the danger which is near. The Trojans lie outside the camp, waiting for the dawn to fall upon us. Hector especially is anxious for the fight, for Zeus has shown him signs of victory in the thunder. Then surely you cannot sit here idle —give up your anger and help us! Agamemnon has promised great gifts, as well as Briseis herself; and when we return, you shall have any of his daughters, with a great dowry. And even if you cannot bear Agamemnon, think of your friends the Achaeans—and think how you may kill Hector, who thinks himself greatest of warriors."

Achilles replied, "Odysseus, I have no use for a man who says one thing and means another. I tell you plainly that I cannot be persuaded. See how it is: the brave man and the coward are equally rewarded. Twenty-three cities I have sacked and plundered, and, as my duty was, I gave the plunder to Agamemnon. A little of it he gave back; some he gave to other princes; most of it he kept. Then he took from me the girl I most wanted—much good may she do him! And why are we here? Do not other men beside Menelaus love their wives? And he has dishonored me! No, Odysseus—let him defend the ships against Hector, who, though he is the bravest of the Trojans, stayed near the gate when I was in the combat. To-morrow I intend to launch my ships, and depart for Phthia, my home. Never again will I have anything to do with that dog-face, for he has shamed me. I think nothing of him or his presents, and as for wives, there are plenty of fine women in Phthia whom I can have. I have a double fate: either I shall have a short and glorious life here before Troy, or a long life, without glory, in my home. So now return to Agamemnon with

4

this answer—and if your companion, Phoenix, wishes to return with me, I shall be glad to have him."

Then Phoenix, Achilles' old teacher, burst into tears, for he remembered how he had brought up the hero while he was still a lad, and unskilled in war or debate; and he advised Achilles to lay aside his wrath. Achilles replied that he had decided, and asked Phoenix to stay for the night. Then they went to rest, and Ajax and Odysseus returned to the Greek host by the ships. Here they told of Achilles' answer to their prayers. Then Diomedes spoke, "Agamemnon, it had been better for us if you had not begged him for help, for though he is proud, now you have encouraged him in his pride. But let each man now rest; tomorrow we fight—and your place is in the front." So they rested, and waited for the dawn.

Book X: But Agamemnon could not sleep, and he arose to talk with Nestor of what would be best to do. Nor could Menelaus sleep, and he too arose, and put on his armor, meaning to see that the watch was being kept. They met, and decided to call together the chiefs, and Menelaus summoned them.

Agamemnon aroused Nestor, and together they went to the gates, where the others were gathered. Together they stole out onto the plain, and sat down to make a plan; they decided to make a night-raid on the enemy's camp, to discover what they were doing. Diomedes, as leader, chose Odysseus, the wily man, for his companion; they armed themselves, and went out.

But Hector, in the Trojan camp, had also thought of a night-raid. He called together the warriors, and promised any who would reconnoiter, a great gift of two very fine horses and a chariot. Dolon, a swift-footed but ugly man, the one son in a family of six, agreed to go. He armed himself and set out, running very quickly.

Odysseus and Diomedes heard him coming, and turned aside a little until he should pass them; they meant to catch him between themselves and the Greek camp. When he had gone by, they rose and ran after him; Dolon thought they were from the Trojan camp, and waited; but when they were a spear-throw off, he knew they were not Trojans, and turned to run. But Diomedes and Odysseus overtook him, and Diomedes threw his spear so that it stuck in the ground before the runner; he stopped, green with fear, his teeth chattering. Then he offered a great ransom to be released, but Odysseus asked him who were in the Trojan camp, and Dolon told him the names of all the allies, and where they slept. "If you intend to steal into the camp, the finest horses in the world are with Rhesus, King of the Thracians. Take me now to the ships, or leave me here, on my parole, until you find whether I have spoken the truth."

Diomedes answered, "Do not think of escape, for either you will fight against us, or try to steal into the camp again." The other begged for his life, but with one blow Diomedes sheared off his head, and it fell, still talking, to the plain.

They took Dolon's weapons, and marked the place, so that they should see it on their return, and went on to the camp of the Trojans. There were the horses of Rhesus, guarded by thirteen men; Diomedes fell upon and killed twelve of them, and Odysseus dragged the bodies out of the way. Then Odysseus led the horses away, and whistled to Diomedes; swiftly he and Odysseus darted back through the night, beating the horses with the bow to keep them running; when they came to the place where they had killed Dolon, Diomedes picked up his spoils, and gave them to Odysseus, and they sped back to the ships. Odysseus and Diomedes told of their night's work, and the Achaeans laughed to hear of it. Then the two bathed, and ate.

Book XI: When Dawn arose from her couch, bringing light to mortals and Immortals, the goddess Discord, sent by Zeus, clamored from the ships; and the Achaeans were inspired to battle. Quickly they made ready, and sent the charioteers to the gates to await the warriors. And Zeus rained down bloody dew, a sign of slaughter.

Around Hector the Trojans gathered, and the two hosts

rushed together. For the whole morning, the Danaäns broke into the Trojan host, slaying many men; first to fall, killed by Agamemnon, were Bienor, and his charioteer. The King stripped them of their armor, and went on: he killed two of Priam's sons, and Peisandrus and Hippolochus, though these begged for their lives, and offered ransom. As when a forest fire rages through the woods, borne on the swift wind, so Agamemnon raged through the Trojan ranks, laying men low.

But Hector drew aside to the Scaean Gate, near the oak tree; and Zeus sent his messenger, fleet-footed Iris, to say that so long as Agamemnon was unwounded, the Argives should have the upper hand; but when Hector saw him turn, wounded, from the fight, then the Trojans should press in, and they should drive the Greeks to their ships again.

Iphidamas, son of Antenor, came against Agamemnon, and struck him with his spear; but the point was turned against the silver boss of the King's belt. Agamemnon struck back, and night came upon the eyes of Iphidamas. His brother drew the body aside, and with his spear struck Agamemnon on the elbow, so that the point went through the arm. Agamemnon drew the spear out, and cut off his enemy's head. Agamemnon still raged through the hosts, killing with spear and sword, while his wound was yet green; but when it grew cold, he was in pain; he leaped into his chariot, and turned back to the ships.

Then Hector saw him leave the battle, and called terribly to the Trojans and their allies; he led the way, and they followed. Hector killed many a warrior of the Danaäns; like the strong west wind, scattering the spray of the sea, he roared through the lines of the Argives, scattering their heads. Odysseus and Diomedes joined together to fight him off; Diomedes threw his spear, but it was turned by the bronze helmet; nevertheless, Hector was hurt, and retired for a moment from the battle until his eyes cleared. Then he and Diomedes rushed together again with bitter words; but Paris shot an arrow that wounded Diomedes in the foot. Paris laughed, and said, "I wish I had hit you in the heart—that would have ended the war!"

But Diomedes replied, "You coward, if you ever got into a real fight, man to man, your bow would help you not at all. But a wound from a girl, or a man like you, is no wound—you have only hurt my foot a little. When *I* throw a spear, the man dies." Then he drew the arrow from his foot, protected by Odysseus; and he went back to the ships, for he was hurt.

Then the Trojans bore down upon Odysseus, and surrounded him, and Odysseus fought like a boar at bay. Some he wounded, and some he killed. But the Trojans continued to press him hard, and three times he shouted loudly. Then Menelaus and Ajax drove into the press and helped Odysseus, until he could return to the chariot.

Then noble Ajax fell upon the Trojans; but Hector was not there, for he was on the left of the battle, fighting with Nestor and Idomeneus. In that fight, Paris struck Machaon, the healer, with a three-pronged arrow, and the Achaeans were afraid that he should be captured. But Nestor took Machaon in his chariot back to the hollow ships; and Hector, in his chariot, drove to where the fight was thickest.

Ajax was surrounded by Trojans as a lion is surrounded by villagers, who drive him from their herds. Now and again he stopped to face them, and held them at bay. Nevertheless, he moved slowly backward toward the ships, holding the Trojans from them though he himself was in peril. Eurypylus, though wounded by an arrow from Paris' bow, shouted to the Argives to help Ajax, and they stood about him, covering him with their shields against the onslaught of the Trojans.

Among the ships, Achilles had been idly watching the fight. He saw the heroes of the Achaeans return wounded, and sent Patroclus to ask who they were. Nestor said, "Why does Achilles ask? He does not know how it has gone: Diomedes is wounded, and Odysseus, and Agamemnon. Does Achilles intend to wait until we are all killed among the ships?" Then Patroclus went to the camps of the heroes, and Eurypylus, returning wounded from the battle, said, "The Achaeans can defend the ships no longer. Now help me, for Machaon, the healer, is wounded, and the other, Podaleirius, is in the battle."

Then Patroclus helped Eurypylus to his tents, and tended his wounds.

BOOK XII: Outside the wall and the moat which guarded the ships, Hector and the Trojans dismounted from their chariots, for only footmen could fight their way in. Asius, on the left, tried to force his way through the gates in his chariot; but he and his company were held back in the narrow way, while the Danaäns on the wall threw down great stones. As Hector and Polydamas were planning the breakthrough of the wall, a great eagle, bearing a living, red snake, flew over them, and dropped the snake—an omen of Zeus. Polydamas believed it a bad omen, but Hector, trusting in his strength, replied, "One omen only is the best: to fight for our land." Then Zeus sent a great dust into the Achaean camp, frightening the warriors; and Hector and the Trojans tried mightily to break open the wall.

They struggled long and hard, until Sarpedon, King of the Lycians, led his men into the battle; they made their way to the tower guarded by Menestheus. Hector seized a great stone, pointed at one end, and broke in the gates with a terrible smash; the Trojans followed him through the gap, and there was a great fight.

BOOK XIII: Zeus turned his eyes from Troy, for he thought that none of the gods would dare meddle in the war. But Poseidon, the Shaker of the Earth, looked with pity on the Achaeans, and went to their help. He appeared to them in the form of Calchas, the prophet; but Ajax, son of Oileus, knew him, for the gods cannot conceal themselves entirely, and spoke to Telamonian Ajax of what he had seen. Then the Achaeans were cheered, and ready to fight again, and harder. Poseidon moved among the warriors, inciting them to battle—"Shame on you, Argives! I never thought to see the Trojans fighting about your ships! Usually they run like deer from you, but now they are killing you. What if Agamemnon did anger Achilles? We still must fight! Now let every man take heart, for Hector has broken in the gate, and is fighting at the ships."

The Greeks made a stand around the two Ajaxes, fitting their shields together into a wall of defense. Hector led the Trojans against this battle-square, shouting his war-cry, and encouraging his warriors. Deiphobus, son of Priam, met with Meriones, and Meriones' spear broke; he retreated. Then Ajax thrust at Hector, striking him on the boss of his shield—the blow did not wound, but Hector was pushed back, and the Achaeans pulled the bodies away. Poseidon appeared to Idomeneus in the shape of Thoas of Calydon, and stirred him to fight harder. Idomeneus took the spear, and with Meriones went back to the fight.

Zeus helped the Trojans, and Poseidon, feeling pity for the Argives, fought on their side. Zeus was the stronger, and with his help the Trojans were winning. But old Idomeneus, bravest of all that day, entered the battle on the left flank, and pushed them back.

In the center, Hector held his place among the Trojans and their allies. On the other side the Greeks stood them off bravely, and from above the Locrians, skilled with bow and sling, rained darts and stones on the Trojans, so that these were in great disorder. Then Polydamas spoke to Hector: "You are brave, but you should listen to advice. We are not fighting together; some of us are in the fight while others stand by and watch. Now let us assemble the best men, and decide whether to carry on this attack or to retire."

Hector answered, "That is good; I will go and get the captains, and you keep them here when they come." He went out, calling for the chiefs. He could not find Deiphobus and the others who had been killed or wounded, but he met Paris, and blamed him bitterly for their deaths. But Paris had been fighting, and reassured Hector that Deiphobus and Helenus were wounded but alive. Then Hector assembled the Trojans, and led them against the Achaeans; on the other side Ajax led the Achaeans, and they taunted each other with bitter words.

BOOK XIV: In his tent Nestor heard the sound of battle, and asked his guest, Machaon, to wait while he found a place from which to see it. Even from where he stood he could see the Achaeans running, and the Trojans hard after them. He was in two minds, whether to get into the fight, or to look for Agamemnon; and he decided to find the King.

Agamemnon was in great distress, for he thought that surely Zeus had decreed the death of the Achaeans. He would have launched the ships then, hoping to escape under the cover of night; but Odysseus said, "That is mere cowardice. Do you mean to leave this city for which we have suffered so much? How can a king speak in that way? And if the men see the ships being launched, do you think they will stand and fight?"

Diomedes added, "We must get back to the battle. We are wounded, it is true, but, though we cannot fight much, we can encourage the others."

Then they went to the battle; and as they went, Poseidon came to Agamemnon in the shape of an old man, and heartened him with brave words. The god vanished, but the Achaeans could hear his voice, like that of ten thousand men, and their strength increased.

On Olympus Queen Hera saw him in the battle, and on Mount Ida she saw Zeus. Quickly she thought of a trick: to make herself beautiful, and to go to Mount Ida, to entice Zeus into love-making. She borrowed of Aphrodite her girdle, whose possession makes one invincible in love, and went to Lemnos, where she met the god of Sleep. She asked him a favor: when she and Zeus were on Ida together, he should cast sleep upon the Thunderer; in return, she promised him a fine golden throne, and the love of Pasithea, one of the Graces, whom Sleep had long desired. At first he was not willing, for he remembered the time that Zeus had been angry with him before; but when Hera swore by Styx, the oath which no god can break, he agreed. Together he and Hera went to Ida, where he took the shape of a bird. Zeus was overcome with love for Hera, and surrounded them with a bright golden cloud, that they might not be seen. When their love-making was over,

Sleep cast a spell upon Zeus. Then he ran to the ships of the Achaeans, and called to Poseidon that he might do as he wished, for Zeus was asleep.

Poseidon shouted to the chiefs; they rearmed the men, giving the best weapons to the strongest fighters, and led by the Earth-shaker they advanced terribly on the Trojans. As when the sea roars upon the land, driven by the northeast wind, or the forest fire roars up a glen, or the wind roars in the treetops, so the Trojans and Achaeans roared in their mortal fight.

Hector threw a spear at Ajax; the point struck on the sword-strap, and Hector drew back. Ajax seized a great stone, a mooring-stone for a ship, and dashed Hector down. The Achaeans rushed on him, hoping to drag him off, and to seize his armor, but the bravest of Hector's companions surrounded him and held them off until Hector could be got out of the battle. The men took him to the shores of the Xanthos, where they poured water on him; he opened his eyes, and vomited dark blood. When the Greeks saw Hector out of the fight, they fought the harder. The battle raged over the bodies, and the Achaeans drove the Trojans before them.

Book XV: So the Trojans were put to flight. But great Zeus awoke, and saw how things went. He upbraided Hera for her trickery, but she replied, "It is not I, but Poseidon, who is doing all this. If he would only listen to me, he would always obey you."

And Zeus: "Yes—if you would agree with me, he would. But for now, go to Olympus and send Iris and Apollo here. Iris is to tell Poseidon to stop interfering, and to go back under the sea; Apollo is to cure Hector, and to help him drive the Achaeans back to their ships. Then Patroclus will fight for the Achaeans, and Hector will kill him. And when Achilles, in revenge, kills Hector, I shall permit the Danaäns to sack Troy. For the time, however, no one shall help the Achaeans; for I have sworn to Thetis that Achilles shall be honored."

Quick as thought Hera returned to Olympus and told the assembly of the gods what Zeus had said. Then Iris took her message to Poseidon; he was angry with Zeus, but finally Poseidon obeyed.

Apollo came to Zeus, who told him his duties: to revive Hector, and to shake the aegis of Zeus over the Achaeans and put them to rout. Quickly Apollo flew down to Hector, and cured him. Thoas saw him, and wondered that he had been cured; surely a god had helped him. He ordered the best fighters to cover the retreat of the rest to the ships. Ajax and Teucer and Idomeneus and Meriones and Meges stood together against Hector.

With Apollo holding the aegis, the Trojans advanced. Terribly either side shot at the other, and on both sides many fell. Then Apollo shook it before the Greeks, and they turned to run like sheep. Hector urged his men on with his terrible war-cry, and they poured into the Greek camp. Swiftly the Trojans drove across, and up to the ships.

Patroclus saw this, and hastened to urge Achilles to the fight, for now the battle was going strongly against the Greeks. Hector and Ajax fought together by the ships, yet Hector could not get close enough to burn them, nor could Ajax drive him out. The battle raged all about the ships: Hector's Trojans were among the ships, killing and wounding. Ajax ran up and down the line of the ships, leaping from ship to ground and from ground to ship, as a tumbler leaps from a horse's back. He carried a great sea-pike, made of many jointed lengths. Old Nestor called on the men to fight now, and not to give in to fear. Hector cheered on the Trojans, calling for fire to burn the ships, and they swarmed into the battle. Ajax was struck nearly to death, and his eyes were dark; but he defended the ships, keeping the fire-bearers from setting them alight. In that struggle he killed twelve men.

BOOK XVI: As they fought about the well-built ships, Patroclus went to Achilles weeping. Achilles was sorry for him, and asked, "Why do you weep, like a child that runs to its mother for comfort? Your family, they say, are still living; do you weep because of the Achaeans, who have dishonored me? Tell me."

Patroclus answered, "Diomedes and Odysseus, Agamemnon and Eurypylus are all wounded; but you do not seem to care! Surely you were not born of Peleus and Thetis, so hard your heart is, but of gray sea and stony cliff. Now I beg you to give me your armor, and let me lead your Myrmidons into battle, for surely when the Trojans see me, they will think you are fighting, and will be afraid."

Achilles answered, "I still feel bitter in my heart toward Agamemnon for taking Briseis from me. But let bygones be bygones. Take the armor, if you like, and lead my Myrmidons to battle, shouting my war-cry. Indeed, I do not hear the cry of Diomedes or of Agamemnon, but that of Hector as the Trojans win.

"Take the armor, then, and fight the Trojans off. But mind: do not, when you have driven them from the ships, pursue them across the plain to Troy, for Apollo, the Far-shooter, loves the Trojans. Come back, and then, perhaps, the Achaeans will return the girl to me."

As they spoke, Ajax was all but overcome at the ships, for he had encountered Hector, and the Trojan had cut off the bronze head of the spear. Ajax drew back a little out of the fight, and the Trojans brought fire and set it to a ship.

Then Patroclus got on Achilles' armor, and Achilles armed his Myrmidons. From their fifty ships they came in three companies, raging like wolves who have brought down a noble stag, and are drinking his blood.

Achilles went into the tent, and drew from his chests a beautiful cup; he put wine into it, and prayed to Zeus that Patroclus might be victorious, and poured the wine on the ground as a sacrifice. Zeus heard him, and granted that Patroclus have the victory, but he did not intend that Patroclus should return alive.

The fresh troops advanced into the battle, and fell upon the Trojans, who wavered when they saw the leader, and each man looked for his own safety. At the head of his troops

Patroclus drove into the Trojans, and scattered them from about the ships; then he put out the fire. The Danaäns poured after him, and the Trojans turned away.

Patroclus was everywhere in the fight. He struck down everyone who opposed him, eager to find and destroy Hector. Nor would he let the Trojans gather together, and fight their way out of the camp and back to the city; he stayed always between them and the town, and killed many men. When Sarpedon saw his attack, he leaped from his chariot and faced Patroclus on foot. Zeus looked down from Olympus, grieved that his son Sarpedon should fall to Patroclus; but Hera spoke to him, and advised that when Sarpedon was slain, Death and Sleep together should bear his body to his homeland of Lycia, where his kinsmen would rear a monument to him.

Sarpedon cast his spear and missed, but killed the good horse Pedasos; the horse whinnied in his death agony, and the other horses reared, tangling the harness. Automedon, Patroclus' charioteer, cut the traces, and they met again in battle. Sarpedon threw again, and again he missed: but Patroclus struck him with a dart in the middle, and Sarpedon fell as a great oak falls when the shipwrights cut it with their axes. In his agony he called to Glaucus, his companion, to avenge him. Then Glaucus ran to the other Trojans, and called them to help him against Patroclus. Eagerly they ran against the Achaeans, led by Hector, and they shouted terribly as the battle was joined over the body of Sarpedon. At first the Trojans drove back the Danaäns. Hector killed Epeigeus with a great stone, dashing out his brains; but Patroclus killed Sthenelaus, and Hector drew back. They rushed together again, and warriors fell on both sides.

Zeus put fear into the heart of Hector, so that the warrior turned his chariot and ran for the gates of Troy. And as the Achaeans were stripping the armor from Sarpedon, Zeus sent Apollo to carry the body to its native land, that his word might be fulfilled.

When the Achaeans saw the Trojans flee after Hector, they pursued, and Patroclus laid about him terribly, slaying many

Trojans. But when they came to the walls, and Patroclus was trying to scale them, three times Apollo thrust him back. Then the Far-darter appeared to Hector in the form of Asius, his cousin, and incited him to battle against Patroclus. Hector heard, and went forth from the Scaean Gate in his chariot. Seeking for Patroclus, he drove through the ranks of the Argives, who were struck with terror. Nor did Patroclus avoid the fight—he leaped from his chariot, and flung a great stone, which killed Kebriones, the charioteer of Hector. Hector leaped from his chariot, and they fought over the body—Hector at the head, Patroclus at the feet. And around them the battle raged again, from noon until the time when men set their oxen loose to graze. Three times Patroclus rushed upon the Trojans, and three times he slew nine men. But at the fourth onset, Apollo dashed his helmet to the ground, so that he was amazed, and loosened his armor. And as he stood, Euphorbus struck him in the back with a dart, though the wound was not mortal. When Hector saw him hurt, he came before Patroclus, and struck him through the belly with his broad bronze spear. Then Hector exulted over Patroclus, saying, "Surely you meant to sack Troy! But the vultures shall have you. I suppose Achilles sent you out, ordering you not to come back until you had killed me—but it went otherwise!"

Patroclus answered, "You have only a third of my death, for Apollo and Euphorbus also struck me. Yet Achilles will avenge me: for I say to you that you have not long to live before you shall be struck down by the noble son of Peleus." Then he died.

Hector drew out the spear, setting his foot on the body, and would have killed Automedon, the charioteer; but he turned the swift horses aside, and they carried him from the battle.

BOOK XVII: Menelaus came and stood over the body of Patroclus; he killed Euphorbus, who was about to despoil the body of Achilles' armor. None dared approach the King, for he raged like a lion which has just killed an ox, and growls as he devours it. Phoebus Apollo appeared to Hector in the shape of Mentes of Ciconia, and told him of Euphorbus' death.

Hector shouted; swiftly he ran to the body. Menelaus was in two minds—to stand and fight Hector, or to make his way back to the ships, and as he thought, Hector and his men came up. Slowly Menelaus retreated until he saw Telamonian Ajax; he summoned the warrior, most terrible of the Achaeans after Achilles, to help. Ajax came, and Hector, who would have cut off Patroclus' head and thrown it to the dogs, retreated. He put the armor of Achilles into his chariot.

Ajax bestrode Patroclus' body, covering it with his shield. By him stood Menelaus, and when Glaucus, the Lycian, saw them, he taunted Hector: "How will you save Ilium now? For the Lycians will no longer serve with a man who deserted his friend as you deserted Sarpedon. If you Trojans had any courage, we could drag this body into Troy. Then the Achaeans would give back the armor of Sarpedon—but you refuse to fight Ajax, the better man!"

Said Hector, "Why do you speak so foolishly? But if you want to see a fight, come and stand beside me." He called to the Trojans and their allies; quickly he put on the armor of Achilles, and quickly he went to the combat.

Ajax and Menelaus saw the swarm of Trojans, led by Hector, advancing upon them. They called loudly for help, and Swift-foot Ajax came, with Idomeneus and brave Meriones. The Achaeans formed themselves into a solid mass over the body, shield lapped over shield; the Trojans came like a wave of the sea, and pushed them back. Ajax set upon them and scattered them—he killed Hippothoös, who had looped a belt about Patroclus' ankles to drag him away. Hector threw a spear at Ajax, and struck Schedios so that the blade went through the shoulder. Then Hector retreated, and the Achaeans dragged the body of Patroclus away.

The Trojans would have given up, discouraged, had not Apollo heartened them. Aeneas knew the god and cheered on the Trojans, who fell again upon the Achaeans. The battle raged furiously and long; a man could not see the sun, for a dark cloud, sent by Zeus, covered all those fighting about the body. Back and forth they tugged it, as men tug, stretching an oxhide; and over all sounded the clash of weapons.

Desperately the warriors fought over Patroclus. Athene helped Menelaus, and Apollo inspired Hector. Back and forth the battle swept, until Zeus shook his aegis over the Achaeans, and they moved back toward the ships.

Menelaus and Ajax saw the Greeks retreating, and Menelaus called on Zeus to help—or at least to lift the cloud from around them that they might die in the light of day. Zeus heard, and pitied him; he scattered the cloud and the dust. Menelaus called to Antilochus, "Quick! Run and tell Achilles of Patroclus' death. We cannot save the armor, for Hector has stripped it off, but if Achilles will help, we may be able to save the body." Antilochus, heavy-hearted, went to tell Achilles.

Then Menelaus and Ajax took the body and carried it to the ships, fighting off a swarm of Trojans on the way. Around them the battle roared like a wildfire. Behind the two came Hector, pressing them hard, the other Achaeans running before him and throwing away their shields and spears in panic.

Book XVIII: Antilochus found Achilles watching the Greek rout, troubled in mind, for he had a foreboding of Patroclus' death. The news brought sorrow on the warrior; he cast dust on his face and garments, and fell weeping to the ground, while the captive women beat their breasts and wailed.

Deep in the sea Thetis, his mother, heard him, and lamented, for she knew that now he would never return to her. Up through the sea she went until she came to the beach near the Myrmidonian ships. Sorrowfully she embraced her son, and asked him to lessen his troubles by telling them. Achilles replied, "What is life or the favor of Zeus to me, now that Patroclus lies dead? And Hector has stripped off the god-made armor that was mine! I do not want to live, unless I avenge Patroclus' death on Hector. A curse on the quarrel that has arisen between me and Agamemnon—it has killed my friend! But I will not give way to my anger; rather will I kill Hector, and win a glorious name, though my own life be short."

Thetis spoke: "Hector will not long boast of wearing your armor, for his death is sure. Yet do not go into the battle until tomorrow, for then I shall bring you armor made by Hephaestus, the armorer of the gods." She left him, and went to Olympus.

As they were talking, the battle surged up to the ships. Three times Hector seized the body of Patroclus, and as often Ajax and King Menelaus drove him off. And he would have succeeded had not Iris, the messenger of the gods, come to Achilles with word from Hera that he must save the body. Because he had promised his mother, he did not go out to the fighting, but stood upon the wall and shouted terribly. Hearing him, the Trojans were filled with terror and dismay. Three times he shouted, and three times the Trojans recoiled. The Achaeans went out and brought Patroclus' body to the ships; and the day's fight was ended.

Outside the walls, the Trojans gathered for a conference. Polydamas spoke first: "Let us go back into Troy. While Achilles and Agamemnon were at odds, we fought well. But now Achilles is angry—and he will not be content with fighting us, but will try to take the city. If we are there, we shall be ready for him, for he cannot take it alone."

Hector replied, "No! Why go back, when we are winning? If Achilles wants to fight, I will fight him here."

This speech pleased the Trojans, for Athene had clouded their minds, and they were moved to follow Hector's bad advice.

Behind the wall, the Achaeans mourned over Patroclus. Sitting by his friend's body, Achilles swore that he should be avenged. They washed the body, anointed it, and wrapped it in good white linen; and all night they wept for Patroclus.

Thetis, the Silver-footed, went to Olympus and sought Hephaestus. He welcomed her, and when she told her need, he made in one night magnificent new armor for Achilles.[1]

---

[1] The description of the shield is one of the famous set-pieces of the poem. It is too long to include here, and too fine to abbreviate. See any good translation.

Book XIX: Clad in her saffron mantle, Dawn brought light to gods and men. Thetis came to the ships, bearing armor so beautiful that the Argives dared not look upon it. Straightway Achilles arose, saying to his mother, "Truly this is the work of a god—no mortal could equal it. Now I will go to the battle." Then he went along the shore, calling with a great voice to the Argive leaders.

They came to the assembly, even those whose duties kept them at the ships; Odysseus and the son of Tydeus, wounded and walking with crutches, and Agamemnon, still suffering from the hurt which a Trojan had given him earlier.

Achilles stood up: "Agamemnon, son of Atreus, was it good that we should quarrel? I wish that the gods had killed Briseis when we sacked Lyrnessus! But now, let bygones be bygones: many men have died, and it is better that we meet the enemy and avenge our friends than that we still quarrel." The Achaeans shouted their applause, and Agamemnon stood up. He said, "Hear me! It is right that a chieftain should be heard. Quiet! I speak not only to Achilles, but to all of you.

"I am not to blame for the quarrel, for it was Ate, the goddess of Discord, who blinded my mind. But here, now, are the gifts I offer you, which my servants shall carry to your ships. And here too is Briseis; I swear that never has she been in my bed."

Swift-footed Achilles answered him: "As you will, King Agamemnon! Now let us no longer talk of gifts, for there is fighting to be done."

Odysseus intervened: "You are a brave man, Achilles, but think of the others! No man can fight all day long on an empty stomach. First, dismiss the soldiers, so that they may get a meal. And do you, King Agamemnon, prepare the gifts and a great banquet for Achilles. Let me advise you, too, to be more careful in your actions, and to remember that it is no disgrace for a king to correct his own mistakes."

They returned to Achilles' tent; and when Briseis saw the body of Patroclus she lamented: "O Patroclus! When Achilles killed my husband and my brothers, it was you who comforted

me, saying that Achilles would take me to Phthia as his wife!"
So she wept, and the other captive women wept with her,
seeming to weep for Patroclus, but really for their own sorrows. The other Achaeans gathered about Achilles urged him
to take some food, but he would not, for he looked upon the
body of his friend, and thought of his own home, and those
he had left there, whom he was never again to see.

But Zeus, pitying him, sent Athene; she dropped nectar and
ambrosia, the food of the gods, into his breast, that he might
not weaken.

Then he put on the flashing armor: the greaves about his
legs, the corselet on his breast, and on his head the helmet with
golden plumes. Around him he slung the bronze sword, silver-
hilted, and took up the thick shield, which shone like the
moon. Then from its rack he took the heavy spear, which only
he could wield.

Automedon and Alcimedon yoked the horses to the swift
chariot. Xanthus and Balius were their names, twin foals of
Podarge; and Xanthus was given the gift of human speech by
Hera. Achilles spoke to them, saying that they must bring him
back, and not leave him as they had left Patroclus. Xanthus
answered, "We will indeed bring you home, though you are
soon to die. It was not because of us that Patroclus died:
Apollo killed him, giving the glory of his death to Hector. And
you too will fall, killed by a god and a man." Then the Furies
struck him dumb.

Achilles answered, "Well do I know that I shall die here.
But I intend not to stop until I have made the Trojans sick
of war." And so speaking, he roared out his war-cry and set
the horses to a gallop.

Book XX: Now the gods took sides with their favorites, for
Zeus summoned them to a meeting on Olympus, and told them
that they might go into the coming battle on whichever side
they chose. To the Achaeans, drawn up by their ships, went
Hera and Athene, Poseidon of the sea, Hermes, the Messenger,
and limping Hephaestus. With the Trojans were Ares, god of

War, long-haired Phoebus Apollo, Leto, his mother, Xanthus, god of the River, and laughing Aphrodite.

When Achilles, shining in his new armor, appeared on the field, the Trojans trembled and fled before him. But when the gods came, all was changed: for Athene raised her war-cry, and was answered by terrible Ares. In the heavens, Zeus thundered, and beneath the battlefield Poseidon shook the earth, so that many-fountained Ida quaked, and even Hades, King of the Dead, feared that the Earth-shaker would reveal to men the realm of Decay that horrifies even the Immortals. Phoebus and Poseidon fought, Athene and Ares, Hera and Artemis, Leto and Hermes, mighty Hephaestus and Xanthus.

But Achilles wanted only to kill Hector. Apollo showed himself, in the form of Priam's son Lycaon, to Aeneas, and taunted him with not fulfilling his boast to fight Achilles. And Aeneas, though he feared the son of Peleus, was inspired by the god to advance, looking for Achilles in the front of the battle. Hera would have caused Poseidon and Athene to restrain him, but the Lord of Earthquakes advised that the gods should withdraw a while from the battle, and let men fight it out. The gods went aside: those favoring the Greeks sat upon the great earthwork made by gods and men for Heracles, those favoring the Trojans upon the hill of Callicolone.

On the field below, godlike Achilles and Anchises' son Aeneas rushed together, Achilles roaring like a lion fighting villagers banded together to kill him. He spoke: "Aeneas, what makes you venture against me? Have the Trojans offered a great prize for my death? Or have you forgotten the day when I drove you from Ida into the city of Lyrnessus—and then sacked the city? Had not Zeus helped you, I would have killed you then. Better for you to get back into the crowd, for Zeus cannot save you every time!"

Aeneas replied, "Why fight with words, for in that I can give as good as I get. Well do I know your descent from Peleus and sea-born Thetis; but I am son of Anchises and Aphrodite. One of these couples today will lose a son! And my lineage is as noble as yours, for I can trace it many generations back to

Dardanus. As for skill in fighting, Zeus gives that. Let us stop talking now, for the tongue is a limber weapon, and fight it out with stiff spears."

Then he hurled his massive shaft at Achilles; the point pierced two layers of the shield, but not the last three, for the work of gods is stronger than that of men. Achilles cast his ashen spear, but Aeneas dodged, and the shaft passed over his head and buried itself in the ground. Achilles rushed on him, sword in hand, but Aeneas picked up a stone such as no man now alive could lift; had he thrown it, Achilles would have come forward and killed him. But Poseidon, thinking of Aeneas' many sacrifices to the gods, rushed to the field and scattered a mist before Achilles' eyes; he drew Aeneas' spear from the shield and laid it on the ground. Then he carried Aeneas to the edge of the battle. "Aeneas," he said, "what folly brought you to fight with Achilles? He is a better fighter, and favored by the gods. If ever you meet him in battle, withdraw; and when he is dead, you may fight against the Achaeans, for none of them can stand against you."

Then he returned to the battle, and took the mist from Achilles' eyes. Achilles, though he knew that the gods were helping Hector, ran up and down the line, putting heart into the men. "Fight bravely! As for me, I am going right through the Trojan host, and I do not envy any man I reach!"

On the other side, Hector encouraged the Trojans. "Achilles is only a man! I myself will fight him, though his heart is hard as polished steel!" Then the Trojans, encouraged by Hector, went forward, but Phoebus Apollo held the hero back: "Do not fight with him, for he will kill you."

But Achilles rushed on the Trojan ranks, slaying in quick succession two Trojans, and then, young Polydorus, brother to Hector. Hector saw the killing, challenged Achilles, and threw a spear at him; but Athene blew the spear back to Hector. Achilles charged in for the kill, but Apollo hid Hector in a mist and took him away, while Achilles raged vainly. He ran amok, killing many brave Trojans—stabbing, cutting, hacking them to bits in his fury. Like a wind driving fire in the canyons of a mountain he flew through the battle, darkening the earth with his enemies' blood—the wheels and even the axletree of his chariot were splashed with it, and his hands were smeared red.

Book XXI: Driving ahead, Achilles cut the Trojans' forces in two: he drove one troop toward the city walls, and Hera shrouded them in a mist to keep them from escaping. The other band he pursued into silvery Xanthus, the river around Troy, which mortals call Scamander. They splashed through the water, whirling and eddying about like a swarm of locusts driven by fire. Achilles dashed among them with his sword, and they fled like sardines pursued by a great dolphin. Right and left he struck, reddening the water; but he kept alive twelve young men to be sacrificed at Patroclus' funeral rites. He slew Lycaon, whom he had earlier captured and sold into slavery, though the young man pled for his life: with his blade he cut through the neck; then he threw the body far into the river. Asteropaeus, son of Pelegon, threw two spears at once, grazing Achilles' elbow, and drawing blood; Achilles hurled his spear in return, but Asteropaeus avoided it, and the shaft stuck in the earth. Then Achilles drew his sword, and rushed upon his enemy, who was trying to draw the spear out of the ground. Achilles cut him open, so that his bowels lay on the ground, and Achilles exulted over him, while the fish nibbled at the body. Then he raged through the pools of Xanthus, slaying many; and indeed he would have killed more, had it not been for the anger of the River, who caused a human voice to issue from a pool, saying, "Achilles, you are more than human; but I pray you, let the slaughter be upon the plains, for you are blocking my channels with corpses." Achilles replied, "As you will, son of Zeus! But I do not intend to stop killing Trojans until I have measured myself against great Hector." And with that, he fell again upon the Trojans caught in the river. Then Scamander, whom the Immortals call Xanthus, cried aloud to Apollo. "Did not Father Zeus order you to defend the Trojans until the going-down of the sun?"

Angered at these words, Achilles flung himself upon the

River, which roared down upon him in floods. The hero seized a great tree, trying to hold himself against the torrents, but the roots tore free, and the River swept him down. Struck by terror, Achilles tried to reach the bank, but the River sent him over a great black wall of water; Achilles fled before it, the armor clanging about him. Though he was speedy, the flood was speedier, for the Immortals are greater than men, and the flood poured about him as he ran. Whenever he tried to stop, and oppose the River, an immense wave swept over him, sweeping the gravel of the stream-bed from under his feet. In his anguish he called to Zeus, "Is there no pity in Heaven? Falsely, my mother predicted that I should fall to Apollo under the walls of Troy. Why could I not die fighting Hector? Better any death than this—swept downstream like a pig-herding boy caught in a freshet!"

Poseidon and Athene heard, and encouraged him. Taking him by the hand, Poseidon spoke: "Do not be afraid, for Zeus has sent us to help you. It is not your fate to be overcome by any river; but fight on—herd the Trojans in behind their walls, and do not return to the ships until you have killed Hector. We grant you victory!"

Then the gods left them, and Achilles tried to make his way across the fields, which were still flooded. Scamander tried to keep him back, and called to his brother River, Simoïs: "Come to my aid! Fill your reedy channels with water, and rush down upon Achilles. Together let us bury him deep in the mud!" Then he rushed again upon Achilles, his waves red with bloody foam, heavy with corpses. Hera saw, and called to her son Hephaestus, "Quick! Bring up your flames! Burn the trees along the banks, the bodies, and the arms! Do not cease until you hear my word, though the River beg for mercy!" Then Hephaestus sent a great fire to the plain, burning all before it. Even within the river the fish were cooked as the reeds and trees burst into flame. Xanthus called for mercy, for his waters were bubbling like pig-fat in a caldron, and he could flow no longer. He called upon white-armed Hera for mercy, promising never again to help the Trojans; and she called to her son

Hephaestus to quench his fires; and again the river flowed quietly between its banks.

The quarrel between Xanthus and Hephaestus set off again the fight between the gods. Ares advanced, shouting taunts, upon Athene, but her aegis, which can stand against the Thunderbolt, warded off his blow. She seized a great stone, and struck the War-god to earth with a blow on his neck. Then she turned away, and Aphrodite led the groaning Ares from the field. Hera called to Athene, "See! There is that shameless one, taking her lover away! Don't let her do it!" Then Athene ran after the two, and struck Aphrodite down with a blow of her fist.

Poseidon challenged Phoebus Apollo: "Why do we stand here idle? But since you are the younger, you shall have the first blow. But why do you fight for the Trojans? Do you not remember how, after we had helped Laomedon, I by building a wall, you by tending his cattle, he sent us away without our promised reward? You should be fighting against the Trojans, not for them!" But Apollo did not take up the challenge, for he thought it wrong to fight his uncle for the sake of a troop of wretched mortals; instead, he turned to leave. But his sister Artemis taunted him, "Why carry a bow, if you never use it? Often I have heard you boast how you would defeat Poseidon if you ever came to blows—now I never want to hear that boast again!"

Apollo did not answer, but Hera was angered, and seized Artemis, taking both wrists in her left hand, and with the other knocking the bow and quiver from her shoulders. Then she slapped her heartily, until Artemis burst into tears, and ran to Zeus, who took her on his lap and comforted her.

Meanwhile, Priam climbed to the walls, and saw Achilles driving the Trojans before him into the city. "Keep the gates open," he ordered, "until the soldiers are inside the walls—then close them, and keep Achilles out, for if he makes his way into the city, there will be a slaughter."

The gates were held open by their warders, while Apollo, who had come to hold the walls against Achilles, inspired

Agenor to face the Greek hero. He thought to himself, "I could slip away, and hide on Ida until nightfall, making my way into town under cover of darkness. But Achilles would see me, and kill me. Well: there is only one thing to do, and that is to face up to him. He is only a man, as I am, and he is mortal."

Then he stood fast in front of Achilles, holding the round shield before his body. Boldly he threw his spear, striking Achilles on the shin-guard; the metal deflected the point, so that Achilles was not hurt. In turn, Achilles ran upon Agenor. But Apollo hid the Trojan in a mist, and sent him from the field. Taking Agenor's shape, he ran just ahead of Achilles across the fields and toward Scamander; Achilles ran after, sure that he could overtake the foe. And while they ran, the rest of the Trojans poured in through the gates, crowding in helter-skelter.

Book XXII: Within the city the warriors huddled together, wiping off the sweat and resting, but Hector, bound by his destiny, stood outside the Scaean Gate. Apollo, pursued by Achilles, turned and revealed himself: "Why do you chase me? I am an Immortal, and you can never catch or kill me; there in Troy are the Trojans whom you pursued."

Achilles replied, "It is well you are immortal, for I would have had my revenge on you, for this trick, if I could!" And with that he raced away over the plain to Troy.

Priam saw him first, his armor shining like the Dog Star, brightest of stars and most fateful for men. He called to his son, standing by the gate, "O Hector! Do not face Achilles alone, for he will kill you! Would that the gods liked him as little as I do—soon enough he would be meat for dogs and carrion kites!

"Two of my sons I do not see, Lycaon and Polydorus. If they are captives, I will give a great ransom; but if they are gone to the house of Hades, there is only grief for us: but not so great as the grief for you, slain by Achilles.

"Come within the walls! Save Troy and the Trojans! Think of me, an old man, dying in the pillage, my daughters torn away, my sons' wives carried off by the Greeks, the little children dashed to the ground—and I shall lie outside my own door, my own dogs licking up my blood and tearing my naked body."

And Hector's mother, baring her breast, called aloud, "O my son, remember how I gave you suck! By this breast I beg you come within, and be safe! For if he kills you, we will never lay you on a bier, and lament you, but in the camp of the Danaäns the swift dogs will devour you."

But Hector would not heed; he stood by the gate, thinking, "If I go in, Polydamas will reproach me, and rightly, for not taking his advice and leading the men back into Troy; I have trusted too much in my own strength. Better kill him here, or die in the attempt.

"Nor would it do any good to offer him the half of everything in Troy, and the return of Helen with all her wealth: for this is no time to dally. It is better to fight now."

So he thought, but when Achilles approached, Hector could not face him; he turned and ran, passing the springs of Scamander: one is boiling hot, one even in summer is cold as ice. Beside them stand the stone washing-troughs. So three times they ran around the walls of Troy, as men run for a great prize. But the prize now was no ox, or shield, but Hector's very life.

Zeus from above said, "Hector is very dear to me, for he has burned many oxen in sacrifice. Shall we then save him, or let Achilles conquer?"

Athene replied, "He is doomed! Save him if you will, but it is wrong to do so."

Zeus answered her, "No longer is he to be spared. Do as you like." And he placed the fates of the two men in his balance, lifting it by the middle: Hector's fate sank, and Apollo left him. Athene had plunged to earth at Zeus' command, and now she appeared to Hector in the shape of his brother Deïphobus. "Let us stand against Achilles now," she said; "too long has he chased you around the walls." Hector replied, "You are the best of all my brothers, for the rest are staying in the town."

Then Hector turned to Achilles and said, "Now I will run from you no longer, but turn and face you, come death or life. But let us agree that if I kill you, I will take your arms, and give your body to the Achaeans; and do you agree to do as much for me."

Achilles answered him, "Lions and men, wolves and lambs make no bargains. One of us is going to die. Fight now, and now I have my revenge for my dead companions!" Then he threw his heavy spear, but missed; Athene drew it from the earth and brought it back to him unseen. Hector threw, and hit Achilles' great shield squarely; but the spear rebounded. He had no other spear, and called to Deiphobus for one; and when no Deiphobus answered, Hector knew that he had been tricked by Athene. He cried aloud, "Well do I know now that there is no escape for me from death! Until now Zeus and Far-darting Apollo have helped me, but now my destiny is at hand. But I will not die ingloriously—I can still strike a blow to be remembered!"

He drew his sword and moved on Achilles as an eagle swoops down from the clouds on a hare. Achilles watched from behind his shield to see where it were best to strike. The armor taken from Patroclus covered Hector well, save at the spot where the collar-bone joins neck and shoulders; there Achilles struck, and the point went through the flesh. Hector toppled to the ground, and Achilles exulted over him: "There you lie, you fool who thought you could be safe from me! Now I have brought you down, to be the plaything of dogs and vultures, while Patroclus is buried and mourned!"

Hector spoke, dying, "I beg only this, that you take a ransom for my body, and let me be burned with fire, as is right."

Achilles spoke, lowering, "No ransom for you! Not even your weight in gold! Let the dogs and the birds tear your body, for I myself could cut you to bits and devour you."

And as the shadow of Death came over him, Hector spoke for the last time, "Well do I know you for what you are, iron-hearted. But remember, it may be that I can bring the anger of Zeus on you, when you are slain by Paris and Phoebus

Apollo at the Scaean Gate!" And his spirit went from him to Hades, wailing for his harsh fate, and the lost young manhood that had been his.

But Achilles said, "Lie there—and let me take whatever fate Zeus wills." Then he drew his spear from the body, and stripped off the armor. The other Greeks came to look, nor did any of them leave without beating or stabbing the body. "Ha!" they said, "Hector is easier to fight now than when he was burning our ships!"

Achilles turned and spoke to them: "Now let us see what the Trojans will do, whether they mean to come out and fight, or whether they will stay behind the walls, now that Hector lies dead. Yet let us not forget Patroclus, who lies unburied. Come with me to the ships, singing a victory song, for we have killed Hector!"

Then he stooped, and slit the tendons of Hector's ankles; he tied them together with a leather strap, and fastened them to the chariot, so that the head dragged. He threw the armor in, mounted, and drove swiftly away. Behind the chariot the head, once so beautiful, trailed in the dirt.

On the walls of Troy, Priam and Hecuba bewailed their son. But as yet no one had told Andromache, Hector's wife; she was spinning at her loom, and as she worked, she called out to the servants to heat a caldron of water, so that Hector might have a bath on his return. The noise of lamentation upon the city walls came to her, and she felt a premonition of Hector's death. Quickly she ran with her maids to the battlements; there she saw Achilles' horses dragging the body of her husband across the plain to the camp of the Achaeans. Night came upon her eyes, and she fainted, while the women clustered around her in pity.

When she revived, she cried out, "O Hector! Both of us were doomed to sorrow! And our son, still a baby, will never know a father's love, but only the harsh fate of the orphan, who must beg for everything. Poor Astyanax! Now his father is in the enemy's camp, torn by dogs, the worms eating his body!"

And so she wept, and the women wept with her.

BOOK XXIII: All Troy lamented, but Achilles, standing by the ships, spoke to his Myrmidonian troops: "We must not unspan the horses yet, but still mounted we must ride past Patroclus and mourn for him as for a dead hero. Then we may unharness, and take our food." Three times they drove their flowing-maned horses about the body, lamenting the dead, while Achilles called on the spirit of Patroclus, "I have kept my word, and dragged Hector's body for the dogs to defile; at your funeral pyre I shall cut the throats of twelve noble Trojans, to show my vengeance for your death!"

Then he flung the dead body beside that of Patroclus, and the troops unharnessed their horses and took off their armor. They sat down to a great funeral feast, oxen and sheep and swine, whose blood was poured on the ground about the body of Patroclus. The heralds invited Achilles to the funeral feast given by Agamemnon, and with much difficulty they persuaded him; but when they called for warm water that he might wash the blood from his body, he refused, swearing an oath not to let water come on his body or to cut his hair until he had buried Patroclus rightly. And he prayed Agamemnon to procure a great pile of firewood, that Patroclus' body might be utterly consumed, and his spirit be welcomed into the house of Hades.

All the Greeks feasted save Achilles; he lay by the shore of the whispering sea, and fell into a heavy sleep. In his dreams he saw Patroclus, who spoke to him, "You forget me in death, Achilles, as you never did in life. Bury me quickly, for until I am buried, the spirits keep me from passing the wide Gates of Hades. And now, your hand; for after I am burned, I shall never return. But let me not be buried apart from you; let our bodies be together, as we have been ever since your father, Peleus, received me as his guest, and brought us up together; let the bones be mingled in one urn."

Achilles replied, "Need you ask me to do these things? All shall be as you wish. But now come near, that we may embrace for the last time." But the spirit vanished, wailing, beneath the earth. Achilles arose, shouting that the spirit of

Patroclus had come to visit him, and his noise awoke the Myrmidons; until dawn they bewailed the dead.

Agamemnon had sent men to bring wood for the pyre; they laid it down by the place where Achilles meant to build his and Patroclus' burial mound. Then the Myrmidons harnessed their swift horses, and formed around the body of Patroclus. His own men carried his body, which was covered with the hair they had cut off and thrown upon it, and Achilles held up the head.

When they reached the burning-place, Achilles cut off the long lock of hair which, had he returned home, he would have cast into the river Spercheus with a great sacrifice; [1] then he asked Agamemnon to prepare the funeral feast while he and the other mourners built the funeral pyre. A great heap they made, a hundred feet long, and as broad; about it they set the flayed bodies of sheep and oxen, with jars of oil and honey. Two of Patroclus' dogs Achilles killed and threw on the pyre. And he cut the throats of twelve Trojan youths in revenge for his friend's death, and their bodies too he put on the pyre.

Then he set flame to the whole mass, but it refused to burn. Achilles stood by the pyre, and prayed to the North and the East Winds, Boreas and Zephyr, to come to his aid. Iris, messenger of the gods, heard him, and went swiftly for the winds; they came boisterously, whipping up the sea and fanning the flames. So all night long Achilles walked about the pyre, pouring out libations and weeping for his comrade.

When dawn came, Achilles sank to the ground, worn out with sorrow. But when the other Achaean chieftains gathered about him, he started up, and directed them to quench the fire with wine, and to gather Patroclus' bones that they might be put in the funeral urn. Then they were to build a mound for Patroclus, not a large one, but decent. They did as he said, laying a ring of stones about the pyre, and heaping earth within the ring.

[1] He had left home so young that he had not as yet made his formal declaration of manhood, symbolized by cutting off a long lock of hair, and throwing it into a river, with appropriate sacrifices to the river-god.

When they had finished, Achilles called to the troops, and told them to sit down in a circle that they might witness Patroclus' funeral games. From his ships he brought the prizes for the victors: pots, tripods, horses and mules, a great lump of iron, and beautiful women. First there was a chariot race, which was won by Diomedes. His squire took the prize, a bronze tripod and a beautiful woman. After Diomedes came Antilochus, who had won second place not by speed but by crafty driving, for he had forced Menelaus to one side in a narrow place, and Menelaus had had to drop back to escape a crash. Third was Menelaus, angry because of the trick played on him; but Antilochus apologized for the trick, and Menelaus gave him the prize, a fine mare, and took instead a great caldron. The last prize was given to Nestor, for Achilles thought it right that he should have something as a memento of the games, and it was not likely, at his age, that he would compete. Nestor thanked him in a graceful speech, and prayed that the gods might reward Achilles for his generosity.

Then Epeius and Euryalus bound their wrists with rawhide thongs for the boxing match. The fight was even until Euryalus looked aside, and Epeius knocked him to the ground with a blow to the jaw; and Epeius won first prize, a fine mule.

Telamonian Ajax and wily Odysseus stood up for the wrestling bout. They gripped at each other hard, and strained in their efforts to get the upper hand, but neither could throw the other. Ajax lifted Odysseus in the air, but Odysseus got his foot behind the other's knee, and threw him down, but could not pin him; then they got up, and Odysseus tried to throw Ajax, but could not. Achilles, seeing that neither could win, gave them equal prizes.

Then Ajax and Odysseus tried themselves again in a foot-race, with Antilochus, swiftest of the young men. Ajax was leading, but Odysseus prayed to Athene for victory. She heard, and caused Ajax to slip and fall, so that he was second.

Diomedes and Telamonian Ajax fought, then, with naked weapons for the prize of Sarpedon's armor, taken from him by Achilles. Three times they battered at each other, but neither drew blood. Then Diomedes struck again over the top of Ajax' shield, and cut his neck. The soldiers shouted to stop the combat; Achilles did so, and declared Diomedes the winner.

Polypoetes, Leonteus, Telamonian Ajax, and Epeius then stood out from the crowd to try throwing the discus for a prize of a great lump of iron. Epeius threw first, but his effort was laughable. Leonteus threw, and then Ajax, whose throw went far beyond those of the other two. But Polypoetes was best of all—his cast went out like a herdsman's throwing-stick over a herd of cattle.

Meriones won the archery contest. Teucer shot at the mark, a pigeon tethered to a mast set in the sand, but forgot to pray to Apollo, god of archers. His arrow struck the cord holding the pigeon, and the bird flew away; but Meriones took his bow and shot the pigeon flying. Everyone shouted that he had won first prize, and Meriones took the great axes which Achilles gave him.

The last contest was at throwing the javelin, but Achilles awarded the prize to Agamemnon, for, as he said, no one could equal the King. Then the warriors separated, for the games were over, and Patroclus' funeral had been fitly celebrated.

Book XXIV: At the end of the games, the Achaeans went to their ships to feast and then to sleep. Only Achilles could not rest; he tossed about, weeping for his friend night after night; sometimes he wandered by the seashore. In the mornings, he would drag Hector three times about Patroclus' funeral mound, trying to assuage his grief. (But the god Apollo preserved the body from further disgrace, and kept it from decay or from pollution with the earth.)

So it went for eleven days, and on the morning of the twelfth Apollo spoke to the immortal gods: "Is not this a dreadful happening? Hector also has sacrificed many a beast to you, but you help fierce Achilles who drags Hector around the tomb. This is senseless anger!"

White-handed Hera replied, "Hector is a mere man; Achilles son of a goddess and a mortal. Indeed, you came to the marriage feast, all of you, and you too, Apollo! But it is your nature to be fickle and unloyal."

Zeus intervened in order to settle the quarrel. "Hera, of course the two are unequal; still, the gods loved Hector above all men in Troy. And, while Thetis is watching, it is useless to talk of sending Hermes to steal the body, as you have been doing. The matter must be handled in this way: have Achilles take ransom from Priam, and return the body of Hector."

Iris, messenger of the gods, swept down to the bottom of the sea to bring Thetis to Olympus. She found the nymph in her sub-marine cave, weeping for Achilles who must soon die. But at Iris' command, she burst out of the sea and rose to the place of the gods. Zeus spoke to her, "Dear Thetis, you must speak to your son, and tell him of my decision: that the gods are displeased, because he will not yield the body of Hector for burial. I shall send a message to Priam that he shall go and ransom the body with great gifts."

Thetis obeyed, swooping down to the ships where Achilles sat, weeping for Patroclus. "My son," she said, "you must no longer eat your heart out in sorrow, forgetting even food and sleep! Listen to me, for I have just come from Zeus. He orders that you give Hector's body back to Priam, and take ransom." And Achilles consented.

In the meantime, Zeus had sent Iris to holy Troy. She found Priam sitting in his courtyard, his old face dirtied, his children and their wives wailing around him. She spoke to the King, "Be of good heart! I have come with a message from Zeus. You are to take a wagon, loaded with precious treasures, as a ransom for your son, to Achilles. Go alone, or with at most one man to help. And do not fear the Achaeans, for Hermes will escort you to their ships. And Achilles will not hurt you, for he loves the gods."

Priam ordered his sons to prepare a cart; then he went to his own room, where he found his wife, Hecuba, and told of the message and what he meant to do. She cried out, "How can you do such a thing? Achilles will kill you, for he does not know the name of pity! We can only stay here and wail for Hector, killed in a brave defence of the town!"

But Priam would not be stirred by her tears. He went to his treasury, and took out many beautiful garments, ten talents of gold, bright bronze tripods and caldrons, and a beautiful goblet, given him long ago by the Thracians. As he went out, he saw a great company of Trojan townfolk, and he shouted angrily at them to make way. He also gave the rough side of his tongue to his sons, those who were left, "Move along there, you ne'er-do-well sons! Once I had the finest men in Troy in my family—Hector and Mestor and Troilus. Now all that are left are cowardly boys, good at dancing and cattle-raiding, but worthless in a fight. Hasten! Bring a wagon, and quickly!"

Obediently they yoked a team to a light cart, and loaded in the presents. Hecuba came down, bearing in her hand a cup, and told Priam to make a libation to Zeus for a safe journey and a safe return. He thanked her; then, after washing his hands, he looked up to Heaven and spoke, "Father Zeus, grant that Achilles may be kind and pitiful to me; send an omen, a bird flying on the right hand, for a sign of a safe journey!"

He poured out the wine on the ground, and immediately Zeus sent a great eagle, flying on the right. Priam's heart was glad, and he set forth. As he drove through the city, his friends bewailed him as a man going to his death; but at the gate, they went back.

Zeus saw the old man and his old helper driving across the plain, and he was moved to pity. To Hermes he said, "Go down there, and take the old man to the Achaean ships in such a way that no one will see or know him." Swiftly Hermes obeyed, and appeared to Priam in the shape of a handsome young man, just as the old King had stopped to water the horses. He spoke, "Old father, where are you taking this cart in the dark night? Are you not afraid of the Achaeans, who would gladly kill you? I will not hurt you, but will help you, for you make me think of my father."

"What you say is true," answered Priam, "but surely a god

is helping me, to let me meet so well-spoken and mannerly a young man as you are."

"You speak more truly than you know. But are you trying to smuggle some treasure out of Troy, or are you leaving the town now that the greatest men of them all, your son, is dead?"

"How do you know of my son? Who are you?"

And Hermes answered, "Many a time I have seen him, driving the Achaeans back to their ships when Achilles kept us from the battle. I am one of Achilles' young men, son of Polyctor, a man of about your age. I have come out here because the Achaeans intend to assault the town in the morning."

Priam replied, "If you are one of his warriors, tell me of my son—is he still at the ships, or has Achilles thrown him to the dogs?"

"He is still there, and not a prey for dogs or ravens. And his body is not decayed or torn, though daily Achilles drags him about Patroclus' burial mound. Surely the gods must love him, for they are preserving his body."

Then Priam was happy, and said, "It is always right to pay the gods their due, as my son did! Please, sir, take this cup, and lead me safely to Achilles."

But the god would not take the cup; he jumped into the wagon and whipped up the horses, so that they came to the camp. The guards were preparing dinner, but the Good-Luck-Bringer put them all to sleep, so that Priam passed through safely. They came to Achilles' hut, erected by his men, and Hermes spoke, "O King, I am indeed a god, Hermes, sent by Zeus to lead you here. I cannot go in with you, for mortals do not entertain gods. But go in, seize Achilles' knees, and implore him in the name of his father and his goddess-mother." Then he vanished.

Priam entered the tent, where Achilles had just finished his evening meal. He walked straight to Achilles, knelt, and clasped Achilles' knees in supplication, kissing the hands which had sent so many of his sons to the house of Hades. Achilles and his men were astonished, but Priam began his prayer, "Honorable Achilles, remember your own father, who is as old as I, but not so wretched. For while you live, he can look forward to your return; but you have killed Hector, the greatest of all my sons. This great ransom which I have brought is for him. Be merciful, Achilles; think of your own father, and remember that I have done what no other living man could do: I have kissed the hands that killed my son."

Achilles was moved in his heart, thinking of his own father. He lifted the old man by the hand, and they both broke into weeping: Priam for Hector, Achilles for his father and for Patroclus. When they had recovered themselves a little, Achilles took the old man and led him to a seat. He spoke: "Truly, old man, you have suffered much, and your heart must be of iron to bring you here. But let our sorrows lie for a time in our hearts, for we cannot always lament. Men are poor creatures, whose lives the gods make short and sorrowful. Thunder-maker Zeus, you know, has two great jars of gifts which he mixes and gives to men. Sometimes a man receives only evil, so that he is an outcast on the earth; sometimes a mixture, like my father, Peleus. For he married a beautiful goddess, and had good luck and good fortune more than any other man. Yet there was evil mixed in with the good, for he begot no children to carry on his line. I am his only son, and I shall die young. And so it was for you, with your many sons and your wide-sweeping land. But since the gods brought me here, your lot has been only terror and desolation. But do not lament for your son, for you cannot bring him to life again."

"Return Hector's body, I pray you," said Priam. "Take this ransom, and may you enjoy it and return safely to Phthia for your generosity in sparing me."

Achilles replied, frowning, "Do not try my temper. I have meant to return your son ever since my mother came with a message from Zeus. And it is perfectly clear that a god brought you to me, for you could not otherwise have got past the sentries. No more! Or I shall sin against Zeus and strike you down as I struck down Hector."

Priam was frightened. Achilles rushed out of the room and directed his servants to unload the wagon. They did so, leaving, however, some beautiful garments with which to wrap the body. The women were directed to wash and anoint the body before Priam should see it, for Achilles feared that if the old man saw the body before it was prepared, he would become angry and incite Achilles to kill him, in violation of the law of Zeus. When it was ready, they laid it in the wagon; Achilles called out, "Patroclus, do not be angry that I do this. It is a great ransom, and you shall have your share."

Then Achilles returned to the room where the old man sat, and sat down opposite him. "King Priam, your son's body has been ransomed. You may see him in the morning, lying on his bier, ready to be taken away. But now, let us think of food, for even Niobe, when her six sons and six daughters were killed by Apollo and Artemis, could take food. Later, when you carry your son home, you may bewail him."

The servants prepared dinner, killing a white sheep and roasting the meat. They poured out wine, and the two ate and drank. Each looked at the other in admiration of his noble appearance and speech. When the dinner was over, Priam asked leave to retire, for he had not slept at all since the death of Hector. Achilles asked Priam to sleep outside the tent, for it was likely that, as was their custom, the chiefs of the Achaeans would come in to consult about plans. And he asked Priam, also, how long the funeral rites of Hector would last, so that he might hold the Argives back from fighting during that time.

Priam replied that while they were collecting the wood for the pyre—and that would be a hard task—they would for nine days mourn for Hector; on the tenth, they would burn the body and hold the ceremonial feast, and on the eleventh he should be buried. On the twelfth day after they would be ready to fight again. And Achilles agreed that for this time there should be no fighting. He took the old man's hand as a sign of good faith, and they went to rest: Priam outside, and Achilles beside the fair Briseis.

All the gods and men slept, save Hermes, who thought how to bring Priam away safely. He came to Priam, and stood beside his bed, cautioning him that perhaps the other Achaean chieftains would demand a ransom for his safe return. Priam was frightened, and woke his man. They harnessed the wagon and drove, guided by Hermes, safely across the plain of Troy. As rosy-fingered Dawn came to the land, they crossed the ford of Scamander.

From the walls, Cassandra was first to see them approaching. Loudly she called out, "Trojan men and women, many times have you welcomed Hector back into the city! Come and welcome him now!"

Then all the Trojans crowded to the gate, wailing for dead Hector. Priam forced his way through the crowd, and brought the body to his own house, where it was placed on a bed. Andromache sat, holding between her hands the fair head, and mourning: "O my husband, dead so young! And our son left helpless! Soon I shall be carried away in the hollow Argive ships, to a slave's life, and you, my son, will be carried with me, or perhaps killed by one of the Greeks in revenge for a friend killed by my Hector! All Troy wails for him, but I most of all, for he did not die in bed, stretching his arms to me with a last word for me to remember always."

And Hecuba lamented: "O dearest of all sons, Hector, killed by Achilles as he killed my other sons! Now you lie here, beautiful as ever, like one put to sleep by the shaft of Apollo!"

And Helen, fairest of women, mourned him, "Hector, you were kinder to me than any Trojan. Never from you, as from the others, have I had a hard word in the nineteen years since I came to Troy, and always you befriended me and shielded me from the others. Would I had died before I came here with Paris! Now there is none to be kind to me and to help me."

Then Priam gave orders that the funeral pyre should be built. On the dawn of the tenth day, the Trojans set flame to it, and it burned all day and all night. Then Priam bade them quench the flames with wine, and to take the bones of Hector from the heap. This they did, weeping, and placed the bones, wrapped in purple, in a golden vase. They lowered it into the hollow grave, and raised a great mound above it.

And this was the funeral of horse-taming Hector.

THE ODYSSEY

As one that for a weary space has lain
    Lull'd by the song of Circe and her wine
    In gardens near the pale of Proserpine,
Where that Aeaean isle forgets the main,
And only the low lutes of love complain,
   And only shadows of wan lovers pine—
   As such an one were glad to know the brine
Salt on his lips, and the large air again—
So gladly from the songs of modern speech
   Men turn, and see the stars, and feel the free
    Shrill wind beyond the close of heavy flowers,
    And through the music of the languid hours
They hear like Ocean on a western beach
   The surge and thunder of the Odyssey.
                  ——ANDREW LANG

THE ODYSSEY: THE STORY

BOOK I: I sing of the much-traveled man, very wise, very clever, who after the fall of holy Troy, wandered far through the world; he saw

> Cities, and men,
> And manners, climates, councils, governments;

many hardships he suffered in his fight to save his men's lives, and to bring them all safely home. But he failed to save them, for in their folly they ate the Sun-god's oxen, and the god took his revenge. And so I begin:

Long after the survivors of the Trojan war had returned to their homes, the nymph Calypso kept Odysseus on her island of Ogygia, for she wanted to marry him. It was the malice of the Sea-god Poseidon which pursued Odysseus, and prevented his return; but when Poseidon had gone on a journey to the Ethiopians, the gods spoke together of helping the wily one. Bright-eyed Athene said, "Father of the Gods, why is Odysseus held on the sea-girt island of Calypso? The nymph tries with all her arts to make him forget his native Ithaca, and to dwell forever with her; and you do nothing to help him. Did he not make rich sacrifices to you on the plains of Troy? Why are you angry with him?"

And Zeus answered, "My daughter, it is not I who am angry, but Poseidon; for the crafty Odysseus blinded his son, Polyphemus, the Cyclops, and it is for this that Poseidon is so enraged. Surely the Sea-god will not stand against the will of all of us; let us try to find a way to bring Odysseus home."

Athene replied, "Then if that is your will, let us send

Hermes, messenger of the gods, to Ogygia, and let him tell Calypso that she must release him. For my part, I will go to Ithaca, where I shall tell Telemachus, son of Odysseus, to call an assembly of his mother's suitors, who are slaughtering Odysseus' cattle; then I shall advise him to seek news of his father in Sparta and in Pylos." So speaking, she bound on her golden sandals, and like the wind she dropped from towering Olympus to Ithaca, where she took the form of Mentes, a leader of the Taphians. She saw the suitors playing games, while the servants prepared the hall for a feast. None of them noticed her, but Telemachus rose and greeted the visitor: "Welcome, sir! Come and dine; and then tell us what brings you here."

The young man led Athene into the hall, where he took her spear, and put it in the rack; then he conducted her to a chair, and a maid brought water for washing. The servants set bread and meat before them, and poured out wine. The suitors came in and took their places, and all ate; when they had finished, the minstrel sang. Under cover of the music, Telemachus spoke to his visitor, "I must apologize to you for speaking freely, but this gang of idlers haunts our house now that my father is dead, lost at sea. If he were here, they would sing another tune! But I pray you, tell me who you are; where is your home? How did you chance to come to Ithaca?"

Athene replied, "My name is Mentes, son of Anchialus. I stopped at Ithaca on a trading-voyage with a cargo of iron. Our families have been long acquainted, as your grandfather Laertes could tell you if he were here; I understand, however, that he lives alone in the country and does not visit you often. I will tell you why I have come—it is because I heard that your father was here. Nor do I believe that he is dead, but that the gods have hindered his return, and are keeping him in some distant place. I feel sure that what I say is true, and that soon he will be home, for he is a man who is never at a loss. And are you indeed his son? Certainly you look like him, though I have not seen him since before he left for Troy."

"My mother tells me that I am his son," answered Telemachus. "And so I believe myself to be—certainly the son of the unluckiest man in the world!"

Athene replied, her eyes flashing, "Your family is not fated to die ingloriously! But who are these men? Why is this banquet going on? Certainly these people act as if the house were their own, and as for their manners . . . !"

"Friend," said Telemachus, "once this was an honored house, when Odysseus was its master. But the gods have treated him harshly. If we knew that he had died at windy Troy, we could have built a mound to keep his name alive, and I should have taken the kingdom. But we know nothing of his fate. As for these, they are the princes of these lands around, and they are all courting my mother. She does not want to marry any of them, but she cannot put them out, though they are eating all we have."

"Surely it is time that your father dealt with this shameless crowd! Well, I know him, and well I know there would be a quick death for the lot of them. But to rid yourself of them, I advise that you summon them to an assembly, and, calling the gods to witness, tell them to leave. If your mother wishes to remarry, let her return to her father's house. For yourself, my advice is that you take a good ship and crew, and set out for Pylos, where Nestor may have news of your father; then to Sparta, where Menelaus rules; he was the last of the Achaeans to return. If they tell you that Odysseus is dead, then you may hold the funeral games, and your mother may remarry. Then it will be your work to turn this rascally crew out of your house. You must be a man now, like Orestes, who killed his father's murderer. And now I must leave; remember what I have said."

"You have spoken to me like a father, and I shall remember your words. But please stay a while; let us have something to eat, and let me give you a present to remember me by." But the goddess would not linger, and departed, flying through the hole in the roof like a bird.

Then Telemachus, knowing that his visitor had been divine, was struck with awe. He went back to the suitors, who were listening to a song of the return from Troy. His mother, Penelope, stood by a pillar, listening, her face covered by her mantle. She could not bear the song, which brought tears to her eyes, and asked the minstrel to stop. But Telemachus remonstrated, "Surely, mother, the minstrel may sing as he likes! Odysseus was not the only man who did not come home; many others also perished. It is better to work at the loom, and let men do the talking; me especially, for I am the master here." And Penelope, knowing that her son had spoken sensibly, went to her chamber, while the suitors clamored for her.

But Telemachus silenced them. "This is shameless! Let us dine quietly, for tomorrow I intend to call you to an assembly, and to let you know that you are no longer welcome here. Eat your own food! If you think it is a good plan to ruin me with your gluttony, then do as you like: but remember, the gods will grant me vengeance!"

Antinous, the chief of the suitors, replied, "You are proud of yourself, to speak in this way! Perhaps the gods are already giving you a hand! You are the heir—but may the gods keep you from being king!"

"It is not bad to be a king," answered Telemachus, "and gladly will I accept the office. There are many princes in Achaea, and one of them—perhaps myself—will succeed Odysseus. But now I am the master here, and I intend to rule this house and its servants."

Then another of the suitors spoke, "And so you shall. But who was your visitor? What news had he? Had he anything to say of your father? I should have liked to speak with him, but he left before I could do so."

Telemachus told him that his visitor had been Mentes, a Taphian; but he said nothing of the goddess' advice to him. Then they all feasted and danced, but Telemachus went to bed, where he lay all that night, thinking how he should make the journey as the goddess had directed.

BOOK II: When rosy-fingered Dawn came to the world, Telemachus arose and commanded the heralds to summon the nobles to the assembly. Quickly they gathered, and Telemachus sat in the seat of his father. The first to speak was old Aegyptius, who began, "Gentlemen, this is our first assembly since the departure of our lord Odysseus. Why are we gathered? Are our soldiers returning, or is there some other matter of importance?"

Telemachus replied, "Sir, it was I who called you together. I have heard nothing of the return of our troops, nor do I know of any important public business. My father, as you know, has been long away from us. This is bad enough; but almost as bad is this crowd of suitors for my mother. They are not men enough to ask her father for her hand, but stay at our house, eating our cattle. They are scattering my possessions as if these were their own. Nor can I restrain them, for I am one against many. I ask, then, that these men be sent away, for I have no other recourse."

No one answered, until Antinous arose and said, "Telemachus, that is a spiteful and unjust speech! For nearly four years your mother has been putting us off with false promises. And more than that—she told us that she could not marry until the winding-sheet which she was weaving for her father-in-law, Laertes, was finished. During the day she wove, but at night she unraveled her day's work. One of her women told us of the trick, and we forced her to complete the shroud. Send your mother back to her father; let the two choose a husband, for there is no woman of so great prudence or skill or wit as she, though she has used her wit to trick us. While she persists in this deceit, we shall never leave, no matter what it costs you."

Telemachus replied, "I cannot send my mother from her house; my father may still be alive; to cast her off would be a shameful deed. Then the gods would avenge my ill treatment of her, and all men would know me for a scoundrel. No—as I said before, eat my substance if you think it right to do so, but remember that I pray to the immortal gods for vengeance."

As he spoke, Zeus sent two great eagles, sailing across the town; when they reached the market-place, they fought one another fiercely, and soared off. Then Halitherses, the soothsayer, spoke, who knew all the signs and portents: "Ithacans, hear me! The sign of the eagles means that Odysseus will soon be here, and that he will work great harm for these suitors. They must no longer go on as they are doing. I know what I speak of, for it was I who told Odysseus that he would not return for nineteen years, that his comrades would all be lost, and that he would not be recognized on his return."

Eurymachus replied, "Nonsense! There are many birds, and not all are sent by Zeus. Odysseus will not return—I wish you were with him! Hear my speech: if you try to make Telemachus act against us, it will be the worse for you and for him too. Now, Telemachus, send your mother back to her father's house, and let her marry one of us, for until you do so, we shall continue to eat your cattle and there will be nothing you can do about it."

Telemachus replied quietly, "Then there is no more to say about the matter. I have presented my case before the people and the gods. Now, I shall go in a swift ship to Sparta and sandy Pylos, where I shall seek news of my father. If I hear that he lives and is returning, I shall allow one more year of this wasteful courting. If he is dead, I shall hold his funeral games, and my mother may marry again."

Mentor rose to speak, the old friend of Odysseus: "I have no quarrel with these suitors, though they have no manners, for they risk their own necks by ruining the house of Odysseus. But you Ithacans—will you say nothing to restrain them?"

Leiocritus spoke, "Fool! How could they stop us? Why, if Odysseus himself were to return, there would be little chance for him in a fight against us, one against many! We have had enough of talk. Let Telemachus go where he will—though I think he'll not go at all."

So the assembly broke up; the suitors went to the house of Odysseus, but Telemachus went to the shore of the sea, where he called upon Athene, "Hear, O Goddess! I do as you command—but see how these scoundrels treat me and my mother!"

The goddess heard, and appeared to him in the shape of

Mentor. "You are your father's son, no sluggard, no coward, and you will succeed. Forget these bullies, for their fate is decided, though they do not know it. Go home and let them see you, while I search for a strong ship and a crew in the town. While you are collecting provisions for the voyage, I will have the ship rigged and ready to sail."

Telemachus did as the goddess advised, though he was ill at ease. He returned to his house, where the suitors were killing and skinning animals for the feast. Antinous asked him to stay and eat; but Telemachus answered, "No; how can a man eat quietly with you here? While I was a boy, there was little I could do to restrain you; but now I am a man, and it is my duty to get you out of here. And I shall go to Pylos, whether you like it or not."

The suitors shouted in derision: "A fine murderous speech!" "Maybe he'll poison us." "Or just wander off like his father— then we'll agree on the man his mother's to marry!"

But Telemachus paid them no attention, and went quietly about his task of gathering the ship's stores. He called Eurycleia, his old nurse, and directed her to fill twelve goatskins with strong wine, and twenty bags with barley meal. These he meant to put on the ship, after his mother had gone to bed. The nurse did not want to help, but Telemachus reassured her, and ordered her to say nothing of his trip until his mother asked for him. Then the old woman did as he had commanded.

While Telemachus did his part of the work, Athene was not idle. In the form of Telemachus, she went about the town, selecting twenty of the best oarsmen; she borrowed a galley from Noemon, put its gear aboard, and ran it out on the sea. Then she returned to the hall, where she cast sleep on the eyes of the suitors, and when they had stumbled off to bed, she took again the shape of Mentor, and called Telemachus to her. Together they went to the ship, where Telemachus gathered the men and brought them to the house to fetch the stores aboard. Quietly they followed him, and when the ship was loaded, they stepped the mast and swung her head toward the sea. Athene

called for a following wind, and all night the ship cut through
the waves.

Book III: In the dawn the ship drew into Pylos, where the people, led by Nestor, were sacrificing to Poseidon. The crew
dropped the sail, cast anchor, and went ashore. Athene spoke
to Telemachus, "Do not be bashful, but go straight to Nestor,
for he is wise, and can tell you what you want to know."

They walked to the assembly, where Nestor sat, and the
others prepared the sacrifice with the sweet flesh of cattle.
Nestor's son offered Athene a great gold cup of wine, asking
her to make a prayer to Poseidon. This she did, praying blessings upon the land of Pylos and its people, and asking especially that Telemachus gain the knowledge he was seeking. As
she prayed, she ensured the granting of her prayers. When
they had made their libation, the men brought up the roasted
meat, and they all ate.

After the meal, old Nestor asked, "Gentlemen, who are you,
and whence do you come? Are you peaceful traders, or sea-
roving pirates?"

Telemachus replied, inspired by Athene, "Sir, we are from
Ithaca, and I come seeking news of my father, Odysseus, who
long ago fought beside you at Troy. We have heard of all the
other chieftains; the fate of Odysseus alone is still unclear. Was
he slain by the barbarians, or was he lost at sea? Tell me if you
can what has happened to him, and do not be afraid to tell the
truth, no matter how harsh it may be."

"The fight before Troy was a hard one," began Nestor, "and
it is a hard tale to tell. Achilles lies there, and Ajax, and my
son Antilochus, and many another hero. Your father was not
the least in valor, and there was no man like him for strategy.
Now that I look at you, I see the likeness, for never have I
heard any man speak so like him.

"But after the fall of Troy, Agamemnon and Menelaus quarreled, for Athene was angry with them. While the men were
still drunk with Trojan wine, the two called an assembly, and
spoke to the men. Menelaus was all for setting out homeward

immediately, but Agamemnon wanted to stay and sacrifice to Athene in the hope of appeasing her; at the last there was a general quarrel, and half the men ran out their ships with Menelaus, while the others stayed with Agamemnon. I was one of those who sailed, and so was your father.

"It was at first an easy run, and we quickly reached Tenedos, where we sacrificed. But again there was a quarrel, and Odysseus took his half of the fleet back to Troy, to meet Agamemnon. We held on for Lesbos, and so right across to Geraestus. There Diomedes separated from us, and sailed to Argos; but I kept on to Pylos. You see, then, that I know nothing of the others except what I have heard since my return. All the others returned—even Agamemnon, who was killed by his wife and her lover Aegistheus. You must have heard the story—surely it will put heart in you to go home and destroy those bullying suitors of your mother!

"This is what happened: When Agamemnon sailed off to Troy, he left his court bard to watch over Clytemnestra. But Aegistheus carried the minstrel to an island, where he left him to die, and returned to Mycenae, where Clytemnestra was an easy victim of his wiles.

"We were off Sunium, the cape of Attica, sailing easily; but Apollo struck Menelaus' steersman, and we were delayed there for his funeral rites. And again, when Menelaus had reached Malea, Zeus split the fleet with a great storm, so that one squadron was driven toward Crete, and the other, with Menelaus, to Egypt. For a long time he traded in foreign parts, so that he could not visit his brother Agamemnon. If he had done so, there would have been a quick end to Aegistheus!

"But Agamemnon returned quickly, and Clytemnestra and her lover killed him. While Orestes, her son, was in Athens, they ruled together; but when he returned, he killed them both, and as he was holding their funeral feast, Menelaus returned. I advise you, do not stay long from home, lest these suitors do an evil trick in your absence, but sail to Menelaus—or, if you like, let my horses carry you there overland. Menelaus will tell you the truth."

Then they sacrificed again, and Telemachus would have returned to the ship to sleep, but Nestor insisted that he stay. Athene, however, changed into the shape of an eagle, and flew away. Then Nestor, taking Telemachus' hand, said, "Surely you are favored by the gods! This was Athene to whom we were speaking—O Goddess, be kind to us, and you shall have a year-old heifer as a sacrifice!"

They returned to the palace, where Nestor prepared a great sacrifice of a heifer never under the yoke, and all poured libations. Then they all went to rest.

In the morning, horse-taming Nestor took his place in the place of sacrifice, surrounded by his sons and Telemachus. The heifer was led up from the fields, and her horns were gilded; then she was sacrificed, with Nestor leading in the prayers. When they had eaten the roasted flesh, Nestor called for a swift chariot, and Telemachus set out across the wide plain, with Peisistratus, son of Nestor, his driver. That night they stopped at a friendly house, and early in the morning they were on their way to Sparta.

BOOK IV: When they came to hilly Sparta, Menelaus was holding a wedding feast for his daughter. As they feasted, listening to the song of the minstrel, the herald of Menelaus saw Telemachus and Peisistratus approaching, and spoke to Menelaus, who directed him to welcome the guests, and to unyoke their horses. This he did, and then led the visitors to the bath, where they were bathed and dressed in fresh clothing for the feast. Stewards brought meat and wine, and they ate gladly. As they ate, Telemachus looked about, and said to his friend that surely the hall was as fine as that on Olympus. Menelaus overheard, and remonstrated, "No, my young friend, no one has a hall so fine as that of Zeus; but this hall is as fine as any mortal's. Seven years I toiled and traded in far countries—with the Egyptians, the Ethiopians, the Libyans, the Sidonians—to amass my treasure, and a hard task it was. It was still harder to discover that my brother had been killed by his wife, or to know that many of my friends had fallen before Troy. And hardest of all it is to wonder whether my old comrade Odysseus is alive or dead, wandering over the earth or beneath the seas. He was the best of us all!"

Menelaus' speech moved Telemachus deeply, and he hid him behind his cloak that men might not see him weep. Menelaus was troubled, for he did not know how to continue; but at that moment beautiful Helen entered the room, "My dear," she said, "have we been told the names of these gentlemen? Surely this one is the son of Odysseus, whom his father left when Telemachus was only a baby."

"Indeed, now that you say so, I see the resemblance. Look at his hands and feet, and his hair—just like his father's. And when I spoke of Odysseus, he wept."

Peisistratus entered the conversation. "Yes, you are quite correct; but he is a modest young man, and did not want to push himself forward. Nestor, my father, sent us here for news of his father, for there is no one else who can aid him in this."

"You speak well, as I should expect your father's son to do. Now let us cease our mourning, and continue our dinner; tomorrow I shall have a long story to tell this young man."

They went on with the meal; Helen brought in a drug, given her in Egypt by the wife of Thon, and poured it into their wine. It had the power of taking away grief, and causing men to forget their troubles. Then she said, "Why should we not amuse ourselves with stories? I remember one about godlike Odysseus: how he whipped himself until the scars made him look like a beaten slave, and, disguising himself in dirty rags, crept into Troy and wandered about the streets. I knew him, but he was too clever for me. It was not until I promised to keep his secret that he would let me wash him and give him decent clothing. Then he told me everything the Achaeans intended to do, and after he left me, he killed several Trojans. But I did not reveal him, for I was already weary of Troy and Trojans, and was sorry for the ill I had caused."

"That was a good story," said Menelaus, "and well do I remember Odysseus and his wisdom. When we were crouching in the Wooden Horse, I remember that you walked around it,

calling to the Argive leaders by name, and making your voice
sound like that of each man's wife. But Odysseus, who had as
much pluck as brains, held us back."

Telemachus spoke: "Sir, it makes me sad to think that not
even an iron heart can save so good a man from ruin. But now
I ask permission to sleep, for I am weary." And they all retired
to their couches.

In the morning, Menelaus rose, and went directly to Telemachus to ask him why he had come here. "Your majesty," he
answered, "I have come to hear news of my father. My present
lot is unhappy enough: my house is full of blustering scoundrels, who are eating me out of house and home, and want to
marry my mother. I beg you, tell me the truth; do not try to
spare my feelings, but tell me truly how he died."

"That is shameful!" said the King. "Surely when Odysseus
returns he will give them their due. I'd like to be there when
he meets those suitors!

"But to answer your question: I was becalmed at Pharos, an
island a good day's run from the mouth of the Nile. For twenty
days I waited for a wind, until our stores were nearly all used
up. As I wandered along the shore, I met Eidothee, daughter
of Proteus, who asked me why I was wasting my time on the
island. When I told her that I must have offended a god, so
that there was no wind, she advised me to find her father,
Proteus, who, if I could trap him, would have to tell me how
to get home, and everything that had happened while I was
away. 'About noon,' she said, 'he comes to sleep in his cave,
surrounded by seals. When he has counted all his flock, he lies
down. That is the time to seize him and hold him down. He
can change his shape as he wills, even to water or fire. But
when he comes to his own form, and lies down, then ask him
your questions.' Then she vanished into the sea, and I returned
to my ship, where I rested the night.

"On the next day, Eidothee reappeared, with four fresh sealskins to wrap me and three of my men. We lay hidden in those
sealskins until noon, when Proteus and his seals came from the
deeps. After he had counted us and lain down, the four of us

threw ourselves on him. He turned into a lion, then a snake, then a panther, then a boar, then a tree—but we held him the tighter. Finally he asked me, 'Menelaus, what is it you want?' I replied that he must tell me how to get home, and he told me that I had made the mistake of not sacrificing to Zeus before I left; that I must go back to Egypt and make the proper sacrifices. Then I asked him of the fates of my companions. He told me how Ajax had perished: after being wrecked on the coast of Gyrae, he managed to get ashore, but earned the anger of Poseidon by boasting blasphemously that he had saved himself in spite of the gods. Poseidon heard, and split the Gyraean rock with his trident, so that half remained standing and half carried Ajax to his death in the waves. He told me also all the story of the death of Agamemnon at the hands of Aegistheus and Clytemnestra. But I asked him to tell me further of the fate of Odysseus. 'I saw him in Calypso's island once,' he replied, 'weeping for his lost home. She keeps him there, and will not let him return, for it is too far for him to escape without a ship and crew. And now, Menelaus, I will tell your fortune: You will not die in Argos, but will be sent by the gods to the fields of Elysium far in the West, where falls no rain or snow, nor do storms beat, but always the soft West Wind blows.'

"Then he slipped away into the ocean, and with my companions I set out for Egypt, where I made all the necessary sacrifices to appease the wrath of the gods; and after that I made a swift voyage home.

"Now let me invite you to stay with me for a few days, and when you leave, let me give you precious gifts to remind you of me, some horses and a chariot, and a golden cup."

"Thank you, sir, but I must return home, much as your talk pleases me. As for gifts, let me have something small to carry— no horses, for in Ithaca there is no really good pasture, such as there is here. And my friends in Pylos are awaiting me in the ship, so I must leave soon."

"Indeed you shall have a gift—a cup, given me by the King of Sidon, and made by the god Hephaestus himself." As he spoke, the banquet was prepared, and all sat down to eat.

But meanwhile, in Ithaca, the suitors were playing games. Noemon came to Antinous, and asked when they expected Telemachus back from Pylos, for he needed his ship. Antinous asked, "When did he leave? Did he get a crew in town, or from the house-servants? Did he steal your boat, or talk you into letting him have her?"

"Why," said Noemon, "he came and asked for her, and of course I let him have the ship—anyone would have done as much. The crew were a fine lot, and the pilot was Mentor—or perhaps a god. For I saw Mentor in town, only yesterday, but he surely was on that ship that went to Pylos."

Antinous was furious at the news. "Here's a mess! That Telemachus got clear away from under our noses after we had sworn he'd never do it. We'll have to settle him before he makes more trouble. Let me have a ship and a crew, and I'll catch him between Ithaca and Samos on his way home. That will be the right end for him!" So they all agreed to help him.

But Medon, the herald, told Penelope what the suitors were plotting. She had not heard of Telemachus' departure, and reproved her servants for not telling her. But Eurycleia explained how she had got everything that Telemachus would need for his journey, and advised her to wash her face clean of tears. So Penelope did, and when she was quieted, went to her chamber, where she offered sacrificial grain to Athene, praying that her son might be brought safely home; and the goddess heard her prayer. But down in the courtyard the suitors gathered; then they set out for their ship.

In her apartments, Penelope lay wondering about her son, whether he could escape death at the hands of her suitors. Long she lay, until, worn with her troubles, she fell asleep. Athene made a shape in the form of Iphthime, a sister of Penelope, and sent it to her as she slept. The phantom slipped into the bedroom, and stood beside her, counseling her to be of good heart, for her son would return safely. Then Penelope, speaking in her dream, asked of Iphthime whether Odysseus were still alive; the figure would not tell her, and vanished. But Penelope, waking, was cheered with the vision.

At sea, in the strait between Ithaca and Samos, the suitors lay in wait.

Book V: High on Olympus, the gods sat down in assembly, considering the hard fate of Odysseus. Athene was the first to speak: "O Father of the Gods, a king might as well be a tyrant as a decent man, for Odysseus, who has always been a good ruler, is held by Calypso on her island in the sea. He cannot escape without a good ship and a crew, for the island is far away. And now his son has gone to Pylos and Sparta to get news of him; and the suitors are lying in wait to kill him."

Then Zeus replied, "Daughter, did you not plan this whole matter? Surely you can help Telemachus to return without harm, and send the suitors home again. Hermes, let it be your task to fly down to Ogygia, and tell Calypso that she must release Odysseus. He must sail away on a ship without a crew, built by himself, for neither gods nor men will help him. Let him sail to the land of the Phaeacians, who will give him rich gifts, and send him home in a ship."

Swiftly Hermes bound on his wingèd sandals, swooped down across the mountains to the wide sea, and sped across the long rollers until he came to Ogygia. He went up to the nymph's cave, where she sat working at the loom and singing a song. Odysseus was not there, for he was sitting on the shore, looking over the empty sea, wishing for his homeland.

The goddess greeted Hermes, and offered him ambrosia and nectar. Then he told her why he had come: Zeus had sent him the weary way across the barren sea, to order the release of Odysseus.

Calypso was angry. "You gods are all alike! You take what mortal women you want, but when a goddess finds a man, you cannot endure it. See how Zeus killed Iasion, who lay with Demeter, and how Artemis slew Orion, whom the Dawn loved! Now Zeus tells me to give up the man whom I myself saved from the wine-dark sea—whom I would have made immortal, to live here with me forever. But there is no way to fight against the will of Zeus; I will let him go. Though I have no ship or crew for him, I will give him such help as I can."

Hermes departed, and Calypso went along the shore, looking for Odysseus. When she found him, she said, "No longer need you wait here, for now I will help you on your way. Cut some trees, and build a ship; I can provide the food and clothing you will need, and will give you a good wind to speed you home."

Odysseus answered, "Unless I can trust you, I will not leave; for the way is far too long for even the best ships. Will you swear that you are not planning more trouble?"

"You are a crafty fellow; but I swear to you by the Styx, the strongest oath of the gods, that I mean no harm, hard-hearted to me as you are. If you knew how hard the voyage would be, you would stay with me and share my immortality. Always you think of your wife—though surely no woman can compete with a goddess in anything."

"I know that she is only a woman, while you are an immortal goddess. Nevertheless, I long for my home and my wife. And as for danger and difficulty, I have had my share of that already. This is only more of the same."

In the morning, Calypso gave her guest a beautiful double-bladed bronze axe and an adze, and showed him where the best trees stood. Quickly he dropped twenty great trees, and trimmed and squared them. Then with an auger he bored holes, and fastened the logs together with treenails; he put on decking, and a mast and steering-oar, and made low bulwarks of woven willow-twigs. With cloth provided by the goddess, he made a sail, and set up the rigging; and on the fourth day he ran her into the ocean and moored her fast.

On the morning of the fifth day, after he had bathed and put on fresh clothing, the nymph sent him a soft following breeze, and gladly he sailed away. Keeping the Great Bear on his left, as Calypso had told him, he held on across the dark sea, never sleeping, but sitting always at the steering-oar, for seventeen days; and on the morning of the eighteenth he sighted the land of the Phaeacians, lying low on the horizon.

But Poseidon, returning from the land of the pious Ethiopians, saw him as he floated across the sea, and was enraged. "No sooner do I go away for a while than the gods change their minds, and send Odysseus to the place where it is his fate to be rescued. But he'll have all the trouble he wants before he gets ashore!" So saying, he stirred up the sea with his trident and gathered the lowering clouds. All the winds of Heaven battered the craft, and Odysseus saw death before him. Then a tremendous sea broke over the ship, and the wind snapped off the mast; for a long time Odysseus could not get his head above water. Finally the sea passed over, and Odysseus got into the middle of what was left of his craft.

Then Leucothoë, once a woman but now a sea-nymph, appeared to him in the shape of a sea-gull. "Take off those heavy clothes," she said, "and swim for land. Wrap this veil about you, for it will keep you from drowning, and throw it back into the sea when you are safe." She gave him the veil, but he did not immediately do as she had advised him; instead, he decided to try to ride it out. But Poseidon sent a greater sea than the first, breaking up the boat; then Odysseus grasped a beam for support, and got his clothes off. Wrapping the veil about his waist, he plunged into the ocean and struck out. Poseidon looked on, grimly satisfied: "That ought to teach him respect for the gods! Let him swim until he comes to shore—I don't think he will forget this lesson." And whipping up his seahorses, he went to his palace at Aegae.

Athene, however, decided to help Odysseus, and quickly she calmed the sea. For two nights and two days he swam until he came in sight of a wooded shore, with a great surf beating on it. For a moment he had been cheered, but the sight of the rocky headlands and the reefs frightened him. He would have held on down the coast, looking for a landing-place, but a great wave dashed him into the rocks. He held on to one of them while the surf ebbed; then Athene gave him the idea of keeping just outside the rollers until he could find a smooth place. He came to the mouth of a stream which ran swiftly into the ocean and begged the stream-god to have pity on him. The god heard, and permitted him to land, crawling up the foreshore on his battered hands and knees. Quickly Odysseus took the veil from his middle and cast it into the sea, after which he looked for a place to spend the night. He found one between two thickly-twined trees, where the ground was dry and piled with dry leaves. Quickly he made a place for himself there, covering himself with the leaves, and, completely worn out, he fell into an exhausted sleep.

BOOK VI: While he lay asleep, Athene went about to help him. In a dream she appeared to Nausicaä, daughter of Alcinous, King of the Phaeacians. Taking the form of Dymas, one of Nausicaä's friends, she said, "My dear, is it not time to take the clothes to the river and wash them? Surely your mother would want you to have fine garments for your wedding, and it would please her very much to know that you are a thrifty, careful girl. Besides, think how the men will think of you when they see you in beautiful garments. So let us go to wash the clothes, early in the morning; ask your father for a cart to carry them, for they are heavy, and it is a long way to the river."

When it was dawn, Nausicaä arose and met her father just as he was leaving the house. "Could I please have a cart, father, to carry the clothes to the washing-place? You will be needing clean clothes for your meetings. My brothers, too, need clean clothes every day." She was too bashful to speak to her father of her own marriage, but he understood her, and ordered a cart.

Then Nausicaä heaped the clothes in the cart, and took a basket of food with her. At the river, she and her maidens unyoked the mules and let them graze, while they dumped the clothes into the river and washed them thoroughly. Afterward, they spread them along the ground to dry, bathed themselves, and had a picnic lunch by the stream. When they had eaten, they played a game with a ball, tossing it from hand to hand.

Athene went on with her plan: as the girls were gathering up the clothes, she made Odysseus awaken. Just at the moment, Nausicaä threw the ball to one of the maids, who missed it, and the ball dropped into the stream. All the girls screamed, and Odysseus, hearing them, wondered into what sort of place he had come—surely, he thought, these were nymphs. Taking a branch to cover himself, he stood up to see what sort of people they were. The girls, seeing the grimy, bruised man with only a branch for covering, screamed and scattered; but Nausicaä, though she was frightened, stood her ground. Odysseus thought how he should best speak to her, whether he should advance and kneel before her or speak as he was; but he decided it would be better to keep back. He spoke as gently as he could, "Madam, I am at your mercy. But are you goddess or woman? You are very like Artemis. If you are a woman, surely you are the darling of your parents and your brothers. I am afraid to approach you nearer, for I have been battling the sea for nineteen days, and now I am driven ashore here, where I know no one. I beg you, have pity on me—show me the way to the city, and lend me something to cover myself. And may the gods grant your wish, a good husband and a good home, for there is nothing better."

Nausicaä answered him, "Your speech shows that you are not a knave or a fool. I am sorry for your troubles, but these come from the gods. I am daughter of King Alcinous of the Phaeacians; you shall have the clothing you need."

Then she called her maidens back, reminding them that they must be hospitable to strangers, who are protected by Zeus, and ordered them to bring food and clothing. When they had done so, she offered Odysseus a bottle of oil, so that he might wash and anoint himself. He asked them to stand back, for he was ashamed to bathe before ladies; then he went to the stream, and cleansed the grime and the salt spray from his body, rubbed himself with oil, and dressed. When he sat down on the beach, Nausicaä looked at him with admiration, for she had never seen a man like him. Surely he must be a god, she thought, and she wished that he would stay. She called her maidens to her, and had them give him food and wine; when he had finished his meal, Nausicaä spoke to him: "Sir, you may walk with us as we go through the country, but when we approach the city, it would be better if we separated. We are a country of sailors, people rather free in their speech, and if they see us together they will ask among themselves who you are, and say that I probably picked you up somewhere. No nice girl likes to have such things said of her. So it would be more proper, when we come to the poplar wood which is sacred to Athene, that you wait until you think we have had time to get home. Then enter the city, and ask your way to Alcinous' palace. Anyone can direct you. Come in, and walk straight up to my mother, who will be sitting weaving. Go to her, and clasp her knees, asking help. She is a kindly woman, and will help you."

So they proceeded. Odysseus waited in the grove, while Nausicaä went on, driving her mules. In the grove he prayed to Athene: "Goddess, Daughter of Zeus, grant that I may have help from the Phaeacians!" Athene heard his prayer, though she did not appear before him, for she feared the anger of Poseidon.

BOOK VII: After Nausicaä had left him, Odysseus waited for a time, and then walked toward the town. Athene met him, disguised as a girl, and led him to Alcinous' palace, casting a mist of invisibility around him so that no one should mark his coming. When they arrived at the palace, she led him to the door, and told him to speak to Arete, Alcinous' queen, for she would help him on his way home. Odysseus stood before the gate, wondering how he should proceed. It was a gorgeous palace, with golden doors and silver lintels, surrounded by ever-bearing fruit trees and gardens. When he had looked at them, he stepped forward into the palace itself, where he saw the nobles of the Phaeacians dining and making libations. But they did not see him until he had approached Arete, for Athene kept him wrapped in her magic cloud. He knelt before the Queen, clasping her knees in supplication, and silence fell on everyone.

Odysseus spoke, "Arete, I appeal to you, a suffering man, and to these noblemen! Grant me, I pray, the means to return to my country, for I have endured much since I left it many years ago!" Then he sat in the ashes by the fire, while no one stirred.

The silence was broken by old Echeneus, who said, "It is not fitting, my lord Alcinous, to let a guest sit in the ashes; let him be placed in a more honorable seat, so that he may pour out a libation to Zeus; and let food be brought."

Alcinous rose, and led Odysseus to a silver throne, where a servant brought water for his hands, and food and wine. As Odysseus ate, Alcinous called for a great mixing-bowl, from which wine was poured for everyone. He spoke to the assembled Phaeacians: "Gentlemen, I think it best that we now separate, each to his own house, and gather again here in the morning to discuss how we shall set this traveler on his road. We can take him to his home; thereafter he must endure whatever fate is in store for him. I do not think him a wandering divinity. These have always appeared to us in their own shapes, because we are very close to them."

"Indeed I am no divinity," answered Odysseus, "for as you see I do not even look like one. And further, my mortal appetite shows itself in the way in which I am eating the food set before me. No matter how hard a man's sufferings may be, his mortal appetite makes him eat when he is as hungry as I am. But I shall be very grateful to you if you will help me along the road home."

So the nobles left Odysseus and the royal couple. Arete spoke first: "May I ask you, sir, who you are, and where you come from? And your clothes? For I understood you to say that you had come from far away, across the sea."

"It would be a long story to tell you everything, your Majesty, and a tale of bad luck. By some mischance I was driven ashore on the distant isle of Ogygia, the domain of Calypso, a nymph. For Zeus had struck my ship with a thunderbolt, and alone I clung to a great beam for nine days. On the tenth I landed on that unhappy island, where for seven years Calypso held me prisoner. Finally, she let me go in a boat which I had built. Poseidon wrecked my ship, and with the greatest difficulty I got ashore after two days of swimming. This afternoon I saw your lovely daughter and asked her for help. She is a sensible girl, for she gave me food and wine, and these garments."

"But she should have brought you straight to us!" said Alcinous.

"No, sir, that is not her fault, for I was afraid that you would be angry if you saw her with a strange man."

"Indeed I should not have been, for that would have been unfair to her. But you seem to me a great man in your own right; and I should like nothing better than to have you stay with me as my son-in-law. But if you prefer to go, none of us will hold you back. Tomorrow, if you like, you may go, and you will be home soon, for our ships are the swiftest in the world. But now, I think that it is time to sleep, for you are tired."

Odysseus rejoiced at these words, and prayed that the gods would always protect Alcinous and his family. Then Arete of the white arms told Odysseus that his bed was ready, and he was glad to lie down and sleep.

Book VIII: When the red-gowned Dawn had come, Alcinous and Odysseus went to the place of assembly, while Pallas Athene, in the form of a herald, went about summoning the nobles. When they had gathered together, Alcinous spoke: "My lords, this gentleman here, whose name I do not yet know, has come to us asking for help in getting home. Since it is our custom to help wayfaring men, I think it right that we should choose a ship and a crew, and make them ready for the voyage. But for now, I ask you to join with me in entertaining our friend. Come, and call the minstrel Demodocus, who sings sweetly."

While the young men went to the seaside to prepare a ship for the journey, the others went into the palace of Alcinous, where the King sacrificed sheep and boars and oxen. When the food was ready, all sat down to eat and drink, while blind Demodocus sang a lay of the quarrel between Odysseus and Achilles at a banquet. Hearing it, Odysseus raised his purple mantle to cover his face, that his hosts might not see him weeping. No one noticed save Alcinous, who spoke to his councillors, saying that now they had eaten and heard the song, it might be pleasant to go outside and see the young men at their games.

They were throwing the discus, running, wrestling, jumping, and boxing. Alcinous' son courteously challenged Odysseus to show his prowess, but Odysseus declined, being worn with toil and a stranger. Then another youth, Euryalus, spoke: "It's easy to see you are no athlete, nor a captain of a warship, but rather a tradesman or the captain of a merchantman, who has no liking for men's games."

Odysseus answered, "Sir, you have spoken very discourteously, and like a fool. Not everyone can look beautiful, but often a homely outside covers a heart and a brain. Now you are particularly good-looking, but are a numbskull. I have had a hard voyage, and suffered much; but all the same, I'll show you what I can do." So speaking, he jumped up, and without taking off his mantle, he threw the stone discus far beyond the mark set by the others. Athene, who had taken the form of a young man, called out that he had beaten everyone by a great distance. Then Odysseus, glad to find someone in the crowd who was with him, said, "Now, lads, try to beat that! And if you like to challenge me at any other sport, I'm your man— boxing, shooting, spear-throwing. I won't contend against Laodamas, son of Alcinous, for no gentleman challenges his host. Anyone else, though, is welcome to try!"

Alcinous interposed, "You have spoken well, and you have well shown this braggart what sort of man you are. And when you return to your home, remember to tell your friends that we Phaeacians are not the least in prowess. We are good at running and sailing but we take special pride in dancing, the proper accompaniment of the feast. Now, lads, come forth and show this gentleman how well you can dance, and one of you go and bring Demodocus and his lyre."

Then the young men danced, and Demodocus sang the lay of Ares and Aphrodite: how the Sun told Hephaestus that his wife and Ares, god of War, were deceiving him; how the Smith forged a cunning net of chains, and set it about the bed; how, when Ares thought Hephaestus out of the way, he went to visit Aphrodite; how the net entangled them both; how, after Hephaestus had shown them to the gods, he released them on the plea of Poseidon, and how they ran away and hid in shame, while the gods raised unquenchable laughter.

Then the dance went on, and Odysseus spoke in admiration of the dancers. Alcinous was delighted with his guest's courtesy, and suggested that the Phaeacians give Odysseus presents for his journey. This they did—swords, tripods of silver and bronze, beautiful garments, wedges of gold. Odysseus thanked them with wise and well-chosen words, and Arete prepared for him a great chest in which to keep his new wealth safe. Then she prepared him a bath, and after he was bathed and anointed, he prepared to join his hosts.

As he walked toward the hall, he met Nausicaä standing by one of the great pillars. She spoke to him shyly, "Dear friend, when you return to your home, think of me now and then, for it was I who saved your life."

Odysseus replied soberly, "My princess, I pray always to come safe home. And when I am there, never shall I forget you, but will always glorify you, for it is indeed to you I owe my life."

Then he continued to where the men were sitting over their wine. Demodocus came in, led by a squire, and Odysseus called for the ballad of the Wooden Horse. The minstrel began where the Argives sailed away, leaving the great horse standing on the plains before Troy. About it the Trojans gathered; some wanted to put a spear through it, some to throw it from the cliffs, and some to leave it as an offering to the gods. These last prevailed, for it was fated that Troy should fall. When the horse was brought into Troy, and all the Trojans were asleep, the warriors within crept out, and raged through the streets, killing all they met; and with the aid of Athene, Odysseus won his greatest fight against Deiphobus. As the bard sang, Odysseus wept, hiding his face; only Alcinous saw him.

Then he said, "Friends, this song seems to have stirred our

guest very deeply. Would it not be better to have the minstrel stop for a time, so that we can talk together, and find out why he is so moved? After all, this banquet is for him at his departure.

"And, sir," he said to Odysseus, "will you not tell us something of yourself: your name, your home? For we must plan your course thither. We have no steersmen among us, for our ships know their way across the trackless sea. And you must know, also, that Poseidon does not like our custom of helping all strangers. He threatened at one time to wreck one of our ships on her return, and to surround us with a wall of mountains. But that is for him to decide, for the gods work as they will.

"But tell us, I pray, of your wanderings. Where have you traveled? What did you see? What were your adventures? And why do you weep to hear a song of Troy? Perhaps a kinsman fell there? Tell us, for it is good to unburden your heart to a kind friend."

Book IX: Then very wily Odysseus told his story: "Prince Alcinous, there is nothing better than to sit with friends while the wine goes round, and to hear the minstrel sing. But since you wish to hear my tale, you shall, though it is a long and unhappy one.

"I am Odysseus, son of Laertes, of Ithaca, which lies far to the West. Though it is no easy land to live in, I love it, and prefer it above the soft island where Calypso reigns, or Circe's isle of Aeaea.

"After we left Troy, we sailed to the city of the Cicones, which we sacked. I divided the plunder fairly, and would have set out again quickly but my foolish sailors insisted on staying and banqueting, for we had taken many cattle and much wine. The Cicones meanwhile went and roused their friends in the back country, and in the dawn they set on us. We held them off until late afternoon, but they broke through, finally, and we barely got off with the loss of six men from each ship.

"On our way from this land, Zeus hit us with a dreadful storm. For three days we were driven through the sea, our sails torn by the wind. We got them down, and rowed as hard as we could for two days. On the third the storm broke, and we were able to set sail and run before the wind. But as we got off Cape Malea, the wind shifted to the north, and, with the current, set us out past Cythera. We were forced to run before the wind for nine days, until we got to the island of the Lotos-eaters, who eat no meat. When we went ashore for water, I sent three men inland to find out what they could about the country. In their trip, they met the Lotos-eaters, who gave them lotos, which makes a man forget his home and his people, and wish only to stay in that land. I dragged them back to the swift ships, and tied them up below-decks, for I wanted to leave no more of my crew there.

"From this land we went to the country of the Cyclopes, a fine island, with luxuriant crops, and everything a man could wish for in a good home. The soil is rich; crops and fruit grow without tilling; the hills are thick with goats and sheep. We struck the island in the night, running ashore before we knew it; but the beach was gentle, and we ran the ships up on it and slept. In the morning, we saw goats on the hills, and very soon we had plenty of meat. There was wine left from our raid on the Cicones, and we had a good meal. Then it was night again, and we slept.

"At dawn I took my own ship and crew, and went to reconnoiter the country. We headed across to the mainland, where we saw a cave by the sea. There was a great pen there, where the terrible shepherd, a one-eyed giant, kept his flocks. Like his brothers, he lived alone, a brutish savage. I took twelve men and a bottle of my strongest wine and went to see what I could see. The owner of the cave was out on the hills with his flocks, so we went in. There were great cheeses and bowls of whey, and in the pens were the young lambs. My crew wanted to drive off the lambs and take some cheeses, but I wanted to stay and see what sort of person lived there. So we killed a lamb, sacrificed, and ate; and finally the shepherd made his appearance. He threw down his load of firewood, which made such a noise as to frighten us into hiding in the back of the cave. Then he drove in the ewes, and shut the door of the cave with an immense rock; milked the ewes, curdled some of the milk for cheese, and set the rest aside for his supper. After all this, he lit his fire, and by its light he saw us.

"'Well, strangers!' he said, 'Who are you, and how did you get here? Traders or pirates?'

"I told him that we were Achaeans on our way from Troy, where we had fought for Agamemnon, and asked hospitality in the name of Zeus, who protects travelers. But he replied, 'What do we Cyclopes care for Zeus? We are stronger than he is! Now where's your ship and crew? I want to have a look at them.'

"But I told him that our ship had been wrecked by Poseidon, and that only the men he saw had escaped. Without saying anything, he leapt to his feet, caught up two of my men, knocked out their brains, and ate them. He washed them down with milk, and went to sleep. I wanted to kill him then with my sword, but realized that if I did so we could not get away, for the rock across the door was far too heavy for any mortal man to shift. So we waited for the day.

"In the morning he did his daily work, milking his ewes and lighting a fire. Then again he seized two of my men, killed, and ate them, and went out to pasture, replacing the stone at the door. I found a thing to do: from a great piece of green olive wood I cut off a fathom, and had the men trim it down. With my sword I sharpened it to a point, which I hardened in the fire; then I hid the stick. We cast lots to see which of us should share the dangerous task of blinding him while he was asleep.

"At nightfall, the Cyclops did as he had done before: after his evening tasks, he killed and ate two of my men. I filled a great wooden bowl with wine, and went up to him, saying, 'Have some of the wine with which my ship was laden. I brought it to you as a present, hoping to meet better hospitality.

Do you think that men will ever visit you after such deeds as these?'

"He took the bowl, drank it, and asked for more. Three great bowls of wine he drank, and then asked my name. By this time he was drunk, and I answered, 'My name is Nobody.' He laughed, and said, 'In exchange for this fine drink, then, I'll eat you last.' Then he rolled over, dead drunk, flat on his back.

"I made a sign to the men left me, and we pushed the pole into the fire until it was almost ready to burst into flame. Then we up-ended it, and ran it deep into his eye, twisting it as a man twists an auger. Around and around it went, while the eye bubbled and streamed blood. He awoke with a scream, and we got back from him. He stumbled about the cave shrieking; the other Cyclopes heard him and came up to see what was amiss. He called out that it was Nobody's trickery that was killing him. The others said, 'Well, if it is Nobody who is hurting you, then you must be sick. Pray to Poseidon for help.' And they went away.

"But how to escape? The Cyclops went to the door and pushed aside the rock, feeling with his hands to catch us as we passed. I had a better trick: I fastened groups of three rams together with twigs from the giant's bed, and under the middle ram I had each man lie, hanging on to the fleece. For myself I chose the biggest of the flock, and hung on. At dawn, the sheep, as their custom was, went out to graze, while he felt their backs, not knowing that my men were beneath them. I went last of all; and Polyphemus said, to the ram, 'You are usually the first! You must be sorry for the fate that has overtaken me, blinded by Nobody! I wish you could talk, and tell me where he is—I'd treat him as he deserves!" So I escaped the cave.

"When we were well outside, I released the sheep, and we drove them down the hill to the ship. The crew I had left behind were frantic with joy, for they were sure we were all killed; but their joy turned to weeping when they saw how few we were. I kept them quiet, however, and they got the sheep aboard and launched the boat.

"When we were out a little way, I shouted to Polyphemus, 'Now you have what you deserve! Perhaps you'll believe that Zeus protects travelers!'

"This angered him so that he tore the top from a cliff and threw it at us. The mass of rock landed ahead of the ship, and the wave drove us back to the shore. I set her off with a long pole, and the crew rowed like mad. When I was twice as far as before, I called to him again, though the crew would have restrained me: 'If anyone asks you how you lost your eye, tell him it was through Odysseus, son of Laertes, from Ithaca!'

"The Cyclops replied, 'The prophecy has come true! But I thought, when Telemus foretold that Odysseus would blind me, that Odysseus would be something more than a weakling who would get me drunk and put out my eye! Come back, dear Odysseus—let me give you some presents, and pray to Poseidon that he will get you home safely.'

"But I answered that I hoped to see him dead and in Hell before he got me back there. He lifted up his voice and prayed to Poseidon, 'Grant me, Father, that this trickster never gets home. But if it is his fate to do so, let him come there alone, on a foreign vessel, his crew all dead, and let him come to an unquiet house!' And Poseidon heard his wish. Again he threw, but this time the rock fell short, and the wash of it set us across the strait to the place where the other ships were grounded.

"We shared out the booty, and the men gave me the big ram, which I sacrificed to Zeus: but the Cloud-gatherer would not hear my prayers, for he was planning ill luck for me. All day we ate the flesh of the sheep and drank wine, and at night we lay down to rest. In the morning, we launched the swift ships, and sitting in order on the benches, rowed them out to sea, happy to escape, but sorrowful for the men we had left behind."

Book X: "From the land of the Cyclopes we made our way to Aeolia, a floating island, rich in all good things. The King is Aeolus, well loved by the gods. Here we stayed for a month, while I told him everything that had happened at Troy. When I asked help toward my return, he provisioned us generously, and gave us a leather bag containing all the winds, for Zeus has given him power over them. To send us on our way, he summoned a gentle following breeze, before which we sailed for nine days.

"We were so near home that we could see the fires, but I was so weary with steering that I fell asleep. Then my foolish sailors, thinking that I had something precious in the leather bag given me by Aeolus, undid the silver string which bound it—and in an instant all the winds of Heaven were loosed. The sailors wept aloud, for they were being blown out to sea, away from Ithaca; for myself, I nearly went over the side from despair. But I hung on, and lay down in the bottom of the ship, while the winds drove us back to Aeolia.

"On our return there, I went up to the palace of Aeolus, who, as you may suppose, was surprised to see me. Deeply embarrassed, I explained what had happened, and asked for further help. Aeolus, however, sent me away, for he was sure that a man so unlucky as I must have incurred the wrath of the gods.

"We set out again, rowing day and night for six days, and on the seventh we came to the country of the Laestrygonians, where we anchored. In this land, morning comes so soon after nightfall that a man who needed no sleep could work the clock round. I tied my ship a little apart from the others, to a rocky headland. There was nothing to be seen of men, except a little smoke, so I sent a patrol of two men and a messenger to look over the country.

"They followed a track until they met a girl drawing water. She was the daughter of Antiphates, the ruler of the land, and when they asked their way, she pointed out his house. When they got there, her mother, a tremendous hag, ran for her husband, who was in the market-place. He seized one of the sailors, meaning to eat him, and called the other Laestrygonians. These rushed down to the cliffs, and threw immense rocks at the ships, wrecking them, and then speared the sailors as if they had been fish. I got aboard, cut my ship free, and shouted to the crew to bend their backs and save themselves. They turned to their oars and got us free, but the others were all lost.

"Heavy-hearted, we sailed across the sea until we saw the island of Aeaea, home of the enchantress Circe. After disembarking, we stayed for two nights and two days, trying to recover from our exhaustion and the experiences we had had. On the third day, at dawn, I got up on a hill, from which I could see smoke rising through the trees. At first I thought of going on and investigating, but decided it would be wiser to send out a party. On my way back to the ship, I had a stroke of luck—a big stag crossed my path, and I killed him with my spear. I carried him down to the beach on my shoulders, and we all had a good meal.

"Next day, I told them of the smoke I had seen, and they were afraid, for they remembered the smoke of the Laestrygonian house. For safety, I divided them into two groups, one commanded by Eurylochus and one by myself. His party left first, heading inland. Before very long they came to a house in the woods, with wolves and lions playing about it. These were very friendly—indeed, they were men transformed into beasts by Circe—but the men were frightened, and got into the doorway of the house. There they called out to attract attention, and Circe admitted them. She gave them a meal, but in the food she put a drug which took away their minds; and when they had finished, she struck them with her magic wand, turned them into pigs, and drove them out to the sties. Only Eurylochus, who mistrusted her, had hung back, and when he saw what had happened to them, he returned to the ship, weeping, to tell the story.

"When I had heard it, I put on my armor, and directed Eurylochus to take me there. But he was too frightened, and begged to be left behind. Nevertheless, it was my duty to go, so I left him, and struck out.

"On the way I met the god Hermes in the shape of a young man. He asked me, 'Where are you going? I suppose you think that you can free your crew, though you cannot do so

alone. Look at this herb: it is called moly. When Circe prepares food for you, she will put her poison in it; but this will
keep you safe. When she touches you with her wand, draw
your weapon, and act as if you meant to kill her. She will be
frightened, and will invite you to be her lover. You must accept, but make her swear that she will try no further trickery.'

"I did just as he told me, and when her poison had no effect,
she screamed and dropped to her knees. 'Never has that drug
failed! You are Odysseus, I know, the man who Hermes told
me would come here, the man who is never at a loss. Please,
I beg you—sheathe your sword, and come into my arms.'

" 'How can I do such a thing,' I answered, 'knowing that
you mean to trick me again? You would make me your lover,
and turn me into a coward! Never will I do as you say until you
swear to keep me safe.'

"She swore that she meant me no ill, and I did as she wished.
She prepared a warm bath and anointed me, and gave me food
and drink. But I could not eat for thinking of my friends.
When she asked what was wrong, I told her, and she anointed
the pigs in her sty with an ointment which turned them back
into men, stronger and taller than before.

" 'Resourceful Odysseus,' she said, 'go to the sea, and bring
back the rest of your crew.' I did as she told me, and when I
reached the shore, my men were in tears because they supposed
I had been unsuccessful. But I cheered them up, and had them
bring the vessel ashore and stow our gear in a cave. All but
Eurylochus were ready to accompany me to the house of Circe;
he hung back, afraid that I would lead them into a trap. A
little more, and I would have seen his head rolling before my
feet, but the others suggested that I leave him as a guard for
the ship. However, he was afraid to stay alone, and came with
us.

"When we reached the house, Circe fed us well, for she knew
what we had endured. For a year we stayed with her, eating
and drinking and enjoying ourselves, until the men grew restless, and wanted to set out again for Ithaca. I was willing
enough to go.

"That evening, Circe told me what I must do. 'First,' she said, 'you must sail your ship to the land of Hades. You will need no pilot, for the North wind will blow you there. Your landfall will be the Grove of Persephone; go ashore there, and go on into the land of Hades, to the spot where the Burning River and the Weeping River meet. Here you must dig a small trench, and pour out libations to the dead: honey and milk, then wine, then water. After this sprinkle the sacrificial grain, and pray to the souls of the dead. Promise them that when you return to Ithaca you will offer them sacrifices. Then kill a ram and a black ewe, catching the blood in the trench, and the spirits will appear. Let none of them, however, taste the blood until Teiresias the prophet comes to tell you how you will reach your home.'

"On the next morning, I gathered my men—all except one, Elpenor. The night before he had got drunk and fallen downstairs, breaking his neck. He never had much head for drink.

"When I told them the course they must take, they wept and lamented, but to no avail. We ran the ship out, and stowed aboard the gear and the ram and the black ewe which Circe had left us. She stole away unseen, for who can see a divinity who wishes to remain hidden?"

BOOK XI: "The wind which Circe promised us held us on our course, the sail bellying out before it. We sailed across the great Stream of Ocean, past the land of the Cimmerians, who dwell at the end of the world in constant darkness, until we came ashore at the Grove of Persephone. At the appointed spot we dug a trench, as Circe had commanded, offered our sacrifices, and made our prayers. While Perimedes and Eurylochus held the sheep, I killed them—and suddenly the air was full of spirits, making a horrible whistling. The others were frightened—so was I—and quickly they skinned the animals and offered the burning flesh to Hades and Persephone. I permitted no ghost to draw near to the blood, but stood with my naked sword in my hand to keep them off.

"The first to speak to me was the ghost of Elpenor, which

had come there on his death. He told me how he had fallen, and prayed me that before I returned to Ithaca I should go to Aeaea, give him a proper burial, and raise above his mound the oar which in life he had pulled. All this I promised to do. The next was my mother, Anticleia, and though I was deeply moved, I kept her with drawn sword from drinking the blood.

"Finally the ghost of Teiresias of Thebes approached and spoke to me, asking why I had come, and telling me to let him drink of the blood. I sheathed my sword, and waited for him to speak. With the strength given him by the blood, he spoke in his living voice: 'Odysseus, your desire is to return home. It will not be easy, for Poseidon is very angry with you. But you can succeed if you will take my advice. Keep your men under strict control, especially on the island of the Sun-god, where you will land. If you do not harm his cattle, you will arrive safely, but I warn you that if you hurt them, your crew will perish, and you will wander for many years until a foreign ship brings you home alone. In your house you will find a gang of strangers trying to make love to your wife. It is fated that you will avenge yourself for their deeds. When you have done all these things, then take an oar on your shoulder and strike inland until someone asks you where you are going with that winnowing-fan. There you must plant your oar, make rich sacrifices to Poseidon, and return home, offering thanks to the gods. Your own end will be an easy one, after a long and happy life, in a peaceful and prosperous kingdom.'

"I asked Teiresias how I might speak with the ghosts of the dead, and he told me that any of them whom I allowed to drink the blood would be able to talk like living beings. The first whom I permitted to approach was my old mother, whom I told of my long and weary wanderings. Then I asked after my father and my dear wife, whether they were alive and well, and whether Penelope had remarried. She replied, 'My son, your wife waits patiently for you, though the time has been long, and your son, Telemachus, is taking your place in the nation as well as he can. But your father, Laertes, lives like a herdsman on his farm in the country, never sleeping in a decent bed, but lying whenever night catches him. He longs for your return, as I did, until the longing killed me, for it was not the shafts of Artemis that laid me low, but the ache in my heart at your absence.'

"In my eagerness to embrace her, I stretched out my arms; but three times she slipped through them. 'Why do you avoid me, mother?' I cried. 'Or are you a deceiving phantom sent by Persephone?'

"She answered, 'No, dear son; you must know that when we die we no longer have bones or flesh or sinews, but are what you see, insubstantial ghosts. Now return to your wife, and tell her what you have seen here.'

"Many another beautiful woman came before me: Tyro, who bore to the river-god Enipeus Pelias and Neleus; Antiope, mother of Amphion and Zethus, whose father was Zeus, and the beautiful Epicaste, whose son Oedipus killed his father and married his mother—a great sin! Then the gods tormented him with remorse for his unnatural act, and Epicaste cursed her son and died by her own hand. There was Leda, too, who bore Castor and Polydeuces, who live forever, though both are dead: mighty Zeus allows them to be alive and dead on alternate days. And I saw Iphimedeia, who bore twins to Poseidon, Otus and Ephialtes. Even in their youth they were giants, and when they were grown, they tried to pile Ossa on Olympus, and Pelion upon Ossa, so that they might climb into Heaven. But Apollo slew them for their presumption. Many another I saw, known in old stories—so many that I could not tell you their names. And now, for it has been a long story, it is time to sleep, whether here or on the ship."

For a long time no one spoke, until white-handed Arete began, "Gentlemen, our guest seems a wise and prudent man. Do you not think it right to be generous to such a one, since we are all wealthy?"

Alcinous answered, "Indeed it is right, and I shall see that it is done. Our friend here must remain, however, until tomorrow, so that suitable gifts can be brought."

Odysseus said, "That is a very kind thing to say. I, myself, should be glad to remain for a year on the same terms, for I should gain great respect if I returned to Ithaca loaded with wealth and honors."

Alcinous went on, "You are certainly no carrier of wild travelers' tales, but a man of sense and judgment, and you speak well. Will you not continue, and tell us whether you met any of your old companions in the land of Hades? It is not yet time to sleep, and I for one could listen to your story until dawn."

"I will continue if you wish," replied Odysseus, "though the tale will be worse than what I have told you, for it is the story of my comrades, and how they perished.

"After Persephone drove away the ghosts of the women, Agamemnon, son of Atreus, drew near to me. When he had drunk the blood, he knew me, and burst into weeping, endeavoring to stretch out his arms and clasp me. I asked him his fate, whether he had perished at sea or at the hands of the barbarians.

"He replied, 'It was none of these things, but the wiles of a treacherous woman and her lover. At the banquet to celebrate my return, they cut me down like a beast, and all my good men around me. I tried to grasp the sword in Clytemnestra's hand, but she turned her head away, and would not even close my eyes and lips in death. Be careful of women—do not trust your wife too far, for it was through one faithless wife that we sailed to Troy, and through another that I got my death. Your wife, lovely and prudent Penelope, would never do a thing like that. And your son, whom you left a baby at her breast, must be a fine tall man now. I was not allowed to see my son Orestes— tell me, where is he in the earth? For I know only that he has not come to Hades.' But I could tell him nothing of his son.

"Then appeared godlike Achilles, son of Peleus, to whom I said, 'Comrade, I came here to speak with Teiresias, to learn my way home, for I have been dogged by ill luck. But you, Achilles, honored on earth, are even here a great hero—Death could not harm you.'

"He replied, 'Odysseus, I would rather be the lowest slave in the house of a churl than a hero among the dead. But what of my son, Neoptolemus? And my father, Peleus? Are they honored in war and in the nation? If I had my living strength for only an hour, I could protect them.'

"To this I replied that I had heard nothing of Peleus, but that Neoptolemus had turned out to be one of the finest men in the Achaean forces—wise in debate and valorous in action. While we lay in the horse, waiting to be taken into Troy, there were leaders who could barely control the trembling of their knees or their frightened tears. But he sat there all on edge, his hands on his sword-hilt and the haft of his great spear, all impatience to be in the fight. When we tumbled out and fell on the Trojans, he was among the first—and though he fought in the front of the battle, he was not even scratched. Then Achilles, rejoicing that his son was worthy of his father, went with long strides back through the plains of asphodel.

"Ajax, whom I had bested in the fight for the arms of Achilles, would not speak to me, for his heart was still bitter over the defeat, though I called to him and spoke as gently as I could, using all terms of honor. I wish I had never won that prize, for my victory brought him to his death.

"I saw Tityus, also, whose liver is eternally torn by the vultures of Zeus for his crime in attacking Leto, mother of Apollo. There too was Tantalus, who for his gluttony on earth stands forever in a pool of water which, when he tries to drink it, disappears into the earth; and when he reaches for the fruits which surround him, sees them tossed up into the sky. And I saw Sisyphus, who forever and ever must roll a rock to the top of a hill—and when he is nearly there, its weight sends it crashing to the bottom. There I saw Heracles, who spoke to me, and told me of his earlier exploit in stealing away Cerberus, the guardian of the land of Hades. And then the spirits thronged about me, whistling and chirping, and I was frightened. Swiftly I got to the ship, and we cast off, helped by wind and current into the great Ocean River."

Book XII: "We returned to the isle of Aeaea, where we rested, and in the morning held the funeral sacrifices for our comrade

Elpenor, doing everything as he had asked. Circe came to greet us, followed by her servants bearing food and wine, on which we feasted.

"'Odysseus,' she said, 'there never was a braver man than you, for only you will go twice into the house of Hades. Now let me give you some advice: your next danger will be from the Sirens, who with their voices lure men into their grip, and kill them. No man who hears them can resist the desire to go to them, though their island is littered with the bones of their victims. If you want to hear them, fill the ears of your men with wax, and have the crew tie you to the mast—and if you ask to be freed, let them bind you even more tightly.

"'After the Sirens, you have a choice of two courses: one leads through the Wandering Rocks, which no man escapes; the other between two great monsters, Scylla and Charybdis. The first of these is a dreadful monster with twelve hands and six heads, with which she reaches from her cave to seize fish or men or whatever she can feed on. Charybdis, on the other side of the channel, lives below the rock, which is marked by a huge fig tree. Three times a day she sucks in the ocean, and three times a day she spits it back. If you come near her when she is in action, not even the Sea-god can save you. It would be better to glide past Scylla, for it is better to lose six of your crew than all of them. Nor can you fight her, for while you are putting on your armor, she will take another six—and she is immortal. Your best course is to put on all speed, and to call on her mother, Cratais, who will keep her from reaching out more than once.'

"'After you have passed this danger, you will come to the island of the Sun-god, where he keeps his immortal cattle. Leave them unharmed, I tell you, for if you hurt them you will be the only man to return—and in a strange ship.'

"As she ceased, dawn came; we ran the ship out, and set her on the course. I explained the danger of the Sirens to my crew, and went about to counter it. First I cut up some wax, softened it, and stopped their ears tightly. Then I had them bind me to the mast. As we approached their island, the Sirens saw us, and broke into the most beautiful song I have ever heard: 'Come to us, brave Odysseus; all who pass this way become wiser men, for we know all that is to come upon the earth.' I longed to go ashore and listen, and made signs to the crew to unbind me. But they tied me tighter until we were out of range of their voices; then they released me.

"It was not long afterward that we saw a great spray of mist, and heard the beating of the surf on rocks. I went through the ship, encouraging the men, who had dropped their oars in terror. 'Come, friends, do as I say. We got clear of the Cyclopes, and if you row your hardest, we shall get clear of Charybdis. Steersman, keep well away from that whirlpool, and hug the opposite cliff. And rowers, row as you never rowed before!'

"I said nothing to them of Scylla, for there was no way of avoiding her, and I did not want the men to worry about two dangers. Although Circe had advised me not to arm myself, I put on my armor and took some spears. So we went on, the great whirlpool to one side, at one moment showing the sea-bottom, at the next drenching the trees with spray. Just as we passed Charybdis, Scylla reached down her long necks and pulled out six of the best men in the crew, as easily as a fisherman pulls out a fish with his line. I have never known a bitterer moment than that—seeing my men stretching their arms to me and screaming my name.

"With the loss of these six we escaped the twin perils, and came to the island of the Sun. I gathered the crew, and told them that we must keep going, for both Circe and Teiresias had warned me what would happen if we harmed the god's cattle. But Eurylochus led the others in complaint: 'You are a man of iron, Odysseus, for you can sail day and night in any weather without tiring. We are ordinary people, men who need a rest now and then. And what of the weather? You know perfectly well that a squall from the south or the west could overwhelm us in an instant. No, no! Better stay here and lay up for the night.'

"I answered, 'Very well, I will not try to stand against all of you. But you must all swear that you will be satisfied with the food which Circe gave us, and promise not to touch these cattle.' They all swore the oath; we went ashore, and prepared our meal.

"Shortly after midnight, a terrible storm hit us: the sky was black with scudding clouds. As soon as it was light, we brought the ship ashore, and put our gear into a fine dry cave. I warned the men once more not to harm the god's cattle, and they seemed willing.

"We lay there for a month, the wind always foul. Finally, our food ran out, and the men had to do as best they could with what fish they could catch or game they could trap. I went inland a little way, made my ablutions, and prayed to the gods that they would show me the way home. But they put a heavy sleep on me, and down by the ship Eurylochus was acting the fool.

"'Comrades,' he said, 'every man has to die sometime, but it is foolish to die slowly by starvation. My idea is this: to kill and sacrifice some of these cattle to the gods in Heaven; and, when we return to Ithaca, to build the Sun-god a great temple, adorned with offerings. And if the Sun-god is displeased and wrecks us—well, it's one swallow of salt water, and everything is over. That's better than dying by inches!'

"They did as he advised, cutting the throats and slicing up the meat. This they offered to the gods, and then ate. Just then I awoke, and returned to the ship. As I drew near, I smelled the roast meat, and called upon Zeus: 'Father of the Gods, it is you have sent this sleep on me, so that my men have broken their oaths and destroyed themselves!'

"It was not long until the herdsmen knew of the deed and called on Hyperion for vengeance. Swiftly he went to Zeus, who promised that he would strike our ship with a thunderbolt far out on the sea, and destroy it entirely. This, by the way, I heard from Calypso later; she had the story from Hermes.

"I swore at the men, but the deed had been done. For six days they feasted on the cattle, though there were many portents: the hides crawled about, and the meat on the spits made a lowing sound. Finally, after a week, the wind shifted, and we got out to sea. When we were out of sight of land, Zeus sent a great squall which caught us flat aback—the forestays broke, and the mast went right down into the ship. Then Zeus sent a thunderbolt, which broke her up, and threw the sailors into the sea. That was the end of them, as the god had decreed.

"I got hold of the mast, which had a rope hanging from it still, and with this I lashed mast and keel together, making a small raft I could get astride of; on this I floated along. The wind shifted to the south, driving me once again between Scylla and Charybdis. I floated near the whirlpool, which threw me up on the cliff, where I got hold of the fig tree, and hung on with everything I had. In an instant, the keel and mast were sucked down into the whirlpool, leaving me stranded. It was not until evening that they reappeared; I dove into the sea, and got astride of them again. For nine days I paddled along, until I reached the island of Calypso; and after that, everything is a twice-told tale."

BOOK XIII: When Odysseus had finished his story, no one spoke, until Alcinous broke the silence, saying, "My friend, you have endured very much, but now you will soon be home. Gentlemen, it is the right thing now to give our guest his presents, and let him be on his way tomorrow." To this they all consented, and then separated for the night.

At dawn, all were at the ship with their gifts, which Alcinous loaded aboard the vessel. Thereafter, all went to Alcinous' palace, where an ox was slaughtered as a sacrifice to Zeus. All day they feasted and drank, while Odysseus watched the descending sun impatiently. When it touched the horizon, he stood up and spoke, "Now let us pour our libations, and go. The Heavens keep you safe, for you have granted my wish, to set me on my homeward way. The gods prosper you all, and bring happiness forever to you and yours!"

A great cup was brought, and all drank. Alcinous and Arete sent their servants to bring Odysseus safe aboard, carrying his clothing and his provisions. When he had entered the ship, they spread a warm blanket for him on the deck. Then the sailors bent to their oars, and like a swift race-horse the ship dashed through the foaming sea. Weariness came upon the much-enduring Odysseus, and he slept.

When the day star heralded the Dawn, the Phaeacians ran their vessel ashore in Ithaca, where they lifted Odysseus, still sleeping, out of the ship, and piled beside him all the rich gifts they had given him. They ran their ship out through the surf, and turned her head homeward.

But Poseidon was angry. "O Zeus," he cried, "why do the gods mock me? It was my will that Odysseus should suffer, though it was your desire that he should finally return safely. But these Phaeacians—they have loaded him with presents, more than he ever won at Troy, and have brought him home. What of my reputation?"

Zeus replied, "Brother, no god makes fun of you, for that would be a very evil thing. If you desire vengeance on these men, take it."

With this, Poseidon seized his trident, and made for the land of the Phaeacians. Just as the ship was rounding the cape, and running into the harbor, he struck her with his hand, and turned her into stone—the islet is still there. Ashore, everyone wondered what had happened, but Alcinous knew that the god had punished the Phaeacians for their custom of helping all travelers, and in haste they sacrificed twelve of their best bulls to Poseidon that his anger might be appeased.

Meanwhile, in Ithaca, Odysseus had awakened, and looked about him. The countryside seemed strange; he had been long away, and Pallas Athene had made it look different, for she wished time in which to help Odysseus. He mourned aloud, for though he had all his belongings, the kindly Phaeacians had left him, and he wished he were with them again, so that they could help him to return. Concealed in the form of a young shepherd, Pallas Athene appeared, and he spoke to her: "Sir, can you tell me the name of this place? Where am I? Is this an island, or a part of the mainland?"

The goddess replied, "You must be far from your home if

you do not know this land. It is a rugged country, but not
poverty-stricken, for here grow grains and grapes, and there is
good feed for beasts. Our land is known as far away as Troy,
no little distance that; the country is called Ithaca."

Odysseus concealed his joy, for he was no man to disclose
himself needlessly. "Indeed I have heard of Ithaca," he said,
"even in distant Crete. I had to leave that island quickly,
taking with me half of my goods, for I laid an ambush for the
son of Idomeneus, Orsilochus, who tried to cheat me. I killed
him, and got away on a Phoenician ship. We were bound for
Pylos, or at a pinch Elis, but the wind put us right off course.
We got here about nightfall, and rested. I slept so soundly,
being worn out, that the crew took my belongings from the
ship and put them beside me, and then made their way back
to Sidon."

The goddess smiled, and showed herself as a beautiful
woman. "Odysseus, you trickster, you would rather make up
a pretty lie than tell the truth. Even so, clever as you are, you
did not know me. I have come here to help you, to take care
of the precious gifts of the Phaeacians, and to plan a course of
action. Your troubles are not yet over. You must suffer indig-
nities before you regain your state; but bear all this in silence,
never letting anyone know you until the time is ripe."

"Goddess," replied Odysseus, "no man could recognize you
when you are disguised—and I know you of old, for you were
very kind to me at Troy. I do not remember any kindness from
you, however, when I was at sea, and wandered for years, until
I got ashore in Phaeacia. Am I indeed in Ithaca, or is this
another trick?"

"You are a clever man, Odysseus; anyone else would have
run home immediately, no matter what the danger. But you
must make sure before every step, even the one of seeing your
wife. She sits at home weeping night and day for you. As for
your return, there was never any doubt in my mind, but it was
impossible for me to stand against my uncle, the Sea-god,
after you had angered him by blinding his son Polyphemus.
Surely, though, you know this country: the Bay of Phorcys

lies before you, and there is the Temple of the Naiads, and Mount Neriton." As she spoke, she made the scene familiar again to his eyes, and Odysseus knelt, kissing the earth, and giving thanks to the gods.

Athene spoke again: "First let us hide your belongings in this cave, and then I will tell you what you must do. It is now three years that a crowd of idle rascals have infested your house, eating up your goods and courting your wife. When the time comes to take your revenge, I shall stand at your side and help you. For the time being, I am going to disguise you by changing your looks—your skin will wither, your eyes grow dull, your garments become rags. In this disguise you will be able to spy out the land. Go first of all to the hut of your old swineherd Eumaeus, where you can ask all the questions necessary for our plan. I shall go to Sparta, where I shall summon your son, Telemachus, to return home. You need have no fear for him, though these suitors have set an ambush for him; he will come through safely and will help you to get revenge." Then she touched him with her wand, and his shape changed to that of a withered old beggar-man, clad in a deer's hide, with a dirty bundle on his back. They separated, each to his own task.

Book XIV: Eumaeus was sitting in his farmstead, working on a pair of sandals, when he heard the barking of his four dogs who guarded the swine from marauders. He rushed out to find them going for an old man, who had sat down and dropped his staff; with a shower of stones he drove them off. "Lucky for you, old fellow, that they didn't tear you to bits! It's bad enough to be as I am, waiting and watching for my lost master, while others eat up his hogs; but even that is better than the homeless wanderer's lot. Come in, and have something to eat, and then tell me who you are, and where your home is."

He brought in the disguised Odysseus, and set him down on a goatskin. "Zeus reward you," said the visitor, "for your kindness in bringing me into your house."

"I couldn't let you stay outside, stranger, because such as you are protected by Zeus. And my old master, who is dead, would have wished me to do so. This new lot will do nothing for anyone; but the man who was once my master would have made my old age easy. Damn Helen and her family! She was the cause of my master's going to Troy, and he will never come back." So speaking, he went out into the sties, and slaughtered a couple of young pigs. He brought them in, cut them up, and cooked them; then he offered the food to his guest, along with a good bowl of wine.

"Eat up, stranger," he said, "even if they're small. Those suitors are going through our fat hogs like a fire. Well, one of these days they'll get their due, for the gods don't like their actions. Even a pirate has some decent feelings, but not that lot! Every day they kill beasts, and as for the amount of drinking—! When the master went away, he was one of the richest men in all Achaea, with herds here and on the mainland —cattle, pigs, sheep, and goats, with herdsmen to take care of them. Now they're vanishing—every day I send down a fat hog or two."

As the old man ran on, Odysseus sat eating and drinking, thinking how he should deal with the suitors. Then he asked, "Tell me, who was this wealthy master of yours? Have I ever heard of him?"

Eumaeus answered, "Every wandering liar who comes to Ithaca goes straight to my mistress Penelope with some story about Odysseus, and she listens with the tears rolling down her cheeks. You could probably make one up, if you wanted to; but he's dead, Zeus rest him, either on land or on sea. There's no one I'd rather have here now, for he was very good to me, and I still call him master."

Odysseus spoke, "I can tell you that he will be back before the moon is full again, I swear he will, and when he comes back, I'll ask you for payment for my news. Not until then, however, for hungry as I am, I would not lie to get a meal. And when he comes back, he will get his revenge on the men who have been bedeviling his family."

"You'll never collect that payment, old fellow, because Odysseus will never come home. Drink up, though, and let's not worry about my troubles. We all pray for his return—Penelope and his father, Laertes, and Telemachus, his son. There's a fine lad! Now, like a fool, he has left for Pylos, looking for news of his father, and those suitors are lying in ambush to kill him. Let's hope he gets clear! Tell me who you are, and since this is an island, what ship brought you here? Who are the crew?"

Odysseus replied, as he thought up a story, "I am from Crete, and of good family. My father was Castor of Hylax, and I was one of several sons; though my mother was a concubine, father treated me like the others. When he died, the legitimate sons divided the estate, leaving me with practically nothing. Since then I have led a wandering life, now up, now down, for I always loved to follow the sea. Before the Trojan War commenced, I had nine times been a ship's master, and what with raiding and what with trading, I got a good amount of money together. Well, finally, the Achaeans got me and Idomeneus to pilot their fleets to Troy, where we fought for nearly ten years. After I got home, it was only a month or so before I was on the move again. I went with my fleet of nine ships to Egypt, and when I went ashore, my men started raiding, carrying off booty and women. The countryside rose against them, and the army, led by the Egyptian King, got into the fight. The sailors were too cowardly to stand, and most of them were taken captives. I threw away my arms, and the King gave me quarter.

"For seven years I lived among the Egyptians, engaged in trade. A scurvy Phoenician talked me into a voyage to Phoenicia; there I stayed a whole year. Thence we set out to Libya; he carried me along as supercargo but he really intended to sell me as a slave. When we were off Crete, Zeus sent a great thunderstorm, and the ship was split by a lightning bolt. I got clear of the wreck, and managed to get on the mast as it floated by. After nine days of drifting, I got to the land of the Thesprotians where I heard of Odysseus, and saw some of his treasures. They told me there that Odysseus was at Dodona, consulting the sacred oak tree. They sent me off to Dulichium on a trading-vessel which was just leaving.

"The scoundrelly crew decided to sell me into slavery, and as soon as we were well off shore, they stripped off my new clothes, gave me the dirty rags I'm wearing, and tied me below decks. When we got to Ithaca, they went ashore. I managed to get free, dropped over the side, and swam ashore, where I hid. They looked for me everywhere, but I slipped past them, and found your house. It looks as if Zeus had decided I was not to die yet."

"You have had a hard time, friend," said Eumaeus, "and a long journey. But your story about Odysseus is certainly wrong, and it is wrong for you to tell such tales. No, my master did not die where men could raise a memorial to him, but far at sea. I've got tired of hearing such stuff ever since I talked to an Aetolian. I never get to town, you know, unless the lady Penelope sends for me to hear the news of these travelers. Well, this chap had a story of seeing Odysseus in Crete at the court of Idomeneus, and he swore that Odysseus would be home by autumn, bringing plenty of money. He took me in properly! So you won't get anything from me with your stories."

"Well," said Odysseus, "you don't seem to trust a soul. But let's make a bet on it—if Odysseus gets back, you give me a good mantle and pay my way to Dulichium; if he doesn't, throw me over that cliff."

"And have the gods down on me? No, thank you. But it's dinnertime—let's kill a good big hog and eat." The herdsmen brought their grunting pigs into the sty, and Eumaeus picked out the best of them, a fine fat hog; he butchered him and cooked him, with the appropriate sacrifices, and offered Odysseus the best and fattest piece. They sat down to the meal of pork and bread and good wine, and when everyone was satisfied, they thought of sleep.

Odysseus told a story, to put Eumaeus to a test. He laughed as if he were drunk, and said, "Once at Troy, I was out with Menelaus and Odysseus on a night-patrol near the city walls.

We lay down to rest. It was a terribly cold night, and like a fool I had come without my tunic. As I got colder and colder, I decided to try Odysseus' wits. I rolled over and woke him, and explained that if I didn't find a tunic soon, I would die of the cold. He thought about that for a minute, and then called for a runner to go back to Agamemnon for reinforcements. Thoas volunteered, taking off his long cloak, and running to the ships. So I wrapped myself in it, and kept warm until it was dawn."

Eumaeus said, "That sounds like the master, but your story won't have the same result here, because we have only one cloak each. When Telemachus comes home, though, he will give you decent clothing and help you on your way." Then they all went to sleep, except Eumaeus, who took his sword and a light spear, and went outside to watch over his pigs.

BOOK XV: While Odysseus slept, Pallas Athene went to Sparta, where she appeared to Telemachus. "It is time for you to go now," she said, "before those suitors eat up everything you own. Eurymachus, too, is trying hard to marry your mother, and her father wants her to. If she does go away, she will probably take much of what is left with her, for a woman likes to bring a good dowry to her new home. More than that, some of the suitors are lying off Samos, waiting to destroy you, but I don't think they'll have much luck. Sail on through the night, and when you reach Ithaca, land at the first possible place. Go up to Eumaeus' house, and send word to your mother from there that you are safely home."

Telemachus nudged his friend Peisistratus, and asked him to harness the horses and start for Pylos. But Peisistratus pointed out that it would be impossible to travel at night, as well as bad-mannered to leave without thanking their host. It was not long, however, until dawn, and when the crimson-clad goddess had come, Telemachus arose and sought Menelaus, of whom he asked permission to return.

"If you wish to return, Telemachus, by all means do so, for it is as offensive to keep a guest longer than he wishes as to send him home too soon. Please stay, however, until we can have something to eat, and let me pick out some presents for you to take with you." He ordered the servants to prepare food, while he and Helen went into the strong room where he kept his treasures. There he selected a fine wine-bowl, and Helen took from her stores of linen a beautiful wedding dress, which she gave to Telemachus, telling him it was for his bride on their wedding day. They ate their meal with thanks, and afterward they mounted the chariot. "My best regards to Nestor," said Menelaus, "and a good journey to you!"

Telemachus thanked him, and promised to convey his words. As he spoke, a great eagle flew over, bearing in its talons a white goose. It was an omen which Menelaus could not interpret, but Helen said, "This means that just as the eagle swooped down and swept up this barnyard fowl, so Odysseus will swoop down and destroy those home-fed suitors. Even now he may be at his work!"

"The gods grant that you may be right!" said Telemachus, and away they went. That night they stopped with their friend Diocles, and at dawn were again on their way, reaching Pylos in the evening. As they approached the town, Telemachus asked a favor: to be driven straight to his ship, and not asked to stay longer with Nestor. It was a hard thing for Peisistratus to decide, for the obligations of hospitality are strong; but he turned the chariot toward the beach, where Telemachus' crew were by the ship.

Quickly they loaded his gear, and ran her out through the surf. As Telemachus was making the final sacrifices, a stranger came up, a man from Argos, who had been driven from his home for killing a man. Though of good family, he had long been a wanderer, and when he heard that Telemachus was from Ithaca, he asked to go thither. To this Telemachus consented, and they all went aboard. Athene sent a good following wind, and they headed for Ithaca.

In the meantime, Odysseus was having dinner with Eumaeus and the others. He said, "Eumaeus, I think I'll go down to town and see what is there. Could you let me have a guide to show me around? I intend to give what news I have to Penelope, and perhaps the suitors will give me a job. I can light a fire and run errands for them, or help to cut up their meat or pour their wine—any kind of servant's work."

But Eumaeus said, "That's a foolish notion! Those suitors would have no use for an old fellow like you—their servants are dapper young lads. You'd better stay here—we all like you, and when Telemachus comes home, he'll give you a good outfit and send you on your way."

"Well, Eumaeus, I'll do as you say. Certainly there's nothing worse than wandering around, begging your living. Maybe, though, you can tell me about Odysseus' father and mother? Are they still alive here in Ithaca?"

Eumaeus replied, "The old man, Laertes, is still alive, but wishes that he were dead. His poor old mother, though, died some time ago of a broken heart. Ah, there was a lady! She brought me up with her daughter Ctimene, as if I had been her own son; when the girl married, she gave me a fine suit of clothes, and set me to this job. It's not too bad—I get along. But I never see Penelope, because she's pestered by those scoundrels. Once in a while I get into town, but not often enough."

Odysseus said, "You must have been here a long time! Were you captured on a raid by Laertes, or did pirates pick you up and sell you here?"

"That's a long story, but a story is always better than sleep. I'll tell you how it happened, and you can judge whether my life has been harder than yours. To begin at the beginning, my father was a king in Syrie, an island in the sea. A shipload of those scoundrelly Phoenicians visited us on a trading voyage. We had a Phoenician woman slave, and it wasn't long before one of them got on the right side of her. It was no trouble to talk her into running off with them, and she promised to bring me along, for she was my nurse. They kept their plans secret for a whole year, while they traded through the country and made up their homeward freight. Finally they were ready, and in the evening she stole some cups and dragged me down to the ship. We were about a week out, when the woman stumbled and fell into the hold, breaking her neck—a judgment of the gods! They threw her over the side, and brought me to Ithaca, where Laertes gave a good price for me. And that's my story."

"That story is one of hard luck," said Odysseus, "but some good is mixed with it—not like mine, which is all bad. Now it is time to sleep, for the night is far along." They wrapped themselves in their cloaks, and lay down to rest.

By this time Telemachus had got to Ithaca, where he ran the ship aground at the first place he saw. After his men had eaten, he told them to take the ship around to the port, while he walked inland to look over the farms. His visitor, Theoclymenus, to whom he had given a passage, he directed to the house of Eurymachus, one of the suitors. Just as he was speaking, a hawk, bearing a dove in its talons, flew by on the right; and Theoclymenus, who was descended from a prophet, interpreted that as a sign of good omen, that Telemachus was favored by the gods.

Telemachus thanked him, and said to his chief mate, "Peiraeus, will you please see after our friend here, and make sure that he has all the hospitality we can offer him?" Peiraeus willingly assented to this; they went aboard again, cast off, and headed homeward. Telemachus, however, took his spear and set off for the house of Eumaeus.

Book XVI: It was early morning when Telemachus reached the hut, and Odysseus and Eumaeus were preparing their breakfast. Odysseus heard someone approach, but since the dogs were not barking, he was sure that it must be a friend. As he spoke of this to Eumaeus, the door opened, and there was his son. Eumaeus was nearly out of his wits with joy, for he had been sure that the boy had been ambushed by the suitors. Telemachus returned his greetings warmly, and came in; Odysseus got up to give him his seat, but Telemachus said, "Don't get up; there are plenty of chairs."

Then Eumaeus set out the food which had been cooking, and

when they were finished, Telemachus asked, "Where is our guest from? He must have come on a ship, because one doesn't walk to the island of Ithaca."

Eumaeus answered, "He tells me he is from Crete, and got here on a ship from Thesprotis. I think that he is your responsibility now, because he says he wants to serve you."

Telemachus was troubled. "That will be a problem," he said, "for those suitors are too many for me, and I'm not sure I could avenge any insults they offered him. My mother, too, is trying to decide what course she should take—to marry or to stay where she is. Since he is your guest, let me send you some clothes for him, and let him stay here with you, because I simply can't defend him as I ought."

Odysseus struck in, "Sir, may I put in a word? This story of the suitors angers me. Are you going to stand them forever? Do the people of Ithaca have something against you? Have you no brothers to help you put them out? I wish I had my youth and strength again, and were Odysseus' son! I'd get them out of there, or die trying!"

"It is not so easy as that," said Telemachus. "The people are generally friendly. I have, unfortunately, no brothers. My father, Odysseus, has been gone for a long time, and as a result my mother is pestered by these suitors to remarry. They are from all the islands about here. Mother will not say what she wants to do; she does not want to marry, but there seems to be no other way to keep those suitors from ruining us with their banquets. But let the gods decide! Now, Eumaeus, please go to my mother, and tell her secretly that I am home. Don't let the suitors hear you, for they will be out to hurt me."

Eumaeus consented, and asked whether he should not go and tell Laertes also, because the old man was terribly worried about Telemachus. But Telemachus did not wish this; he told Eumaeus to have his mother send one of her women to tell the old man. Eumaeus got his sandals on, and left for town.

When he was gone, Athene appeared to Odysseus, but not to Telemachus, and motioned him to follow her outside. They went down along the wall, and Athene said, "Now is the time to reveal yourself to your son. It will not be long until the time for killing the suitors, and you can count on me to be present and to help you." So speaking, she touched him again with her wand, and his appearance changed to that which it had been before: bronzed, muscular, manly.

When he returned to the hut, his son was astonished, for he was sure that the visitor was a god. Odysseus replied, "No, indeed, I am no god—but I am the man for whose sake you have endured so much: I am your father, Odysseus." And without further words he embraced his son. Telemachus, however, would not believe him: "This is a trick, for no mortal without divine aid could change his shape as you have done."

"It is with divine aid that I have done this, with the help of Athene. Indeed I am your father, home again after nineteen years of wandering through the world. No other Odysseus will ever come here."

Then Telemachus believed, and for a long time they sat, wordless, with tears of joy rolling down their cheeks. Finally Telemachus asked his father how he had come there, and Odysseus replied, "The Phaeacians gave me rich presents, and sent me on my way in one of their ships, for as you know it is their custom to help any wayfarer. All my riches are stowed in a cave near the bay. Athene told me to come here, to plan the campaign. Now, who are they? How many? Once I know what I have to fight, we shall know whether the two of us can handle them or whether we shall need help."

Telemachus was appalled. "Father, there are too many of them for us! I know that you are brave, but you are also prudent; use your prudence! There are fifty-two from Dulichium, twenty-four from Same, twenty from Zacynthus, and at least a dozen from Ithaca—not counting their servants and hangers-on. We'd better think of what friends we can muster."

"I have thought: what do you say to Zeus and Athene?"

"There are no better; but *they* live on Olympus, and *we* are in Ithaca."

"They will be enough. Now go home, and let the suitors see you. In the morning, Eumaeus will bring me there, in the same shape as that in which you saw me. Don't pay any attention to their ill treatment of me beyond a polite remonstrance. When Athene tells me that it is time to begin, I will give you a sign. Pick up all the weapons lying around the hall, and put them away. If anybody asks what you are doing, say that they have got smoke-grimed, or that you are afraid a fight will start, and if there are weapons around, someone may get hurt. Any story will do. Leave a couple of swords and spears and shields where we can get our hands on them quickly. And one thing: keep your mouth shut about my return. Don't tell a soul, Laertes or Eumaeus or even Penelope. We can find out how the women think, and which of the men-servants are loyal."

"No," said the prudent Telemachus, "we should lose time by trying to find out how the men stood. We can easily find out about the women, but let us wait until things are over before we go around all the country investigating the men."

Meanwhile, Telemachus' ship was making port. The crew ran her in and sent a mesenger to Penelope to tell her that her son had returned. On the way he met Eumaeus, and when they reached the palace, he bawled out, "Telemachus is home!" But Eumaeus went to the Queen and told her the whole story privately.

The suitors were angered by the result of their attempt. They were about to send word to their ship to return, when they saw her in the harbor. Antinous came ashore with the word that Telemachus had somehow escaped. "We had observation posts on all the headlands, and we lay out in the strait all night waiting for him, but—Zeus knows how—he got through us. We'd better do something quickly, before he can call a meeting and accuse us. Anything could happen here; they might go so far as to outlaw all of us. It would be best to catch him alone somewhere and kill him; then let one of us marry his mother, and the rest can divide what is left of his property."

Amphinomus said, "I am not one to kill princes without the approval of the oracle; but if the oracle is favorable, I will kill him myself." They all agreed, and returned to the palace.

Penelope appeared to them where they sat in the banqueting hall, her heart full of anger. "Antinous," she said, "you are called the wisest man of your age in Ithaca, but I know you for a traitor and a scoundrel. How can you plot against the life of a prince, who is protected by Zeus? Do you not remember that it was Odysseus who saved your father's life, after he had fought against the Thesprotians, our friends? You repay him by eating up his cattle, making love to his wife, and trying to murder his son. Let there be no more of this, but cease your bloodshed, and make the others obey you."

Eurymachus answered her, "Madam, no man shall shed your son's blood while I am alive, for I will defend him with my own spear. Well I remember how, when I was a boy, Odysseus fed me, sitting on his lap. Never will we kill his son, unless it is the will of the gods that he die." But in his heart he plotted death for Telemachus.

When Eumaeus returned to the farmhouse, Athene had already changed Odysseus into his beggarly appearance, lest the swineherd be unable to contain himself and blurt out the story. Telemachus asked how his trip to town had been, and he told how he had seen a ship come into harbor, loaded with armed men, whom he had taken for the suitors.

Then they ate, and when they were satisfied, they went to sleep.

Book XVII: At dawn, Telemachus prepared to return home. He said to Eumaeus, "I am going to see my mother now, because I know she will be unhappy until I come. You had better take your friend down to town, where he can beg. It will be too much for me to be responsible for him, because I have too many things to think of. I'm sorry if he doesn't like this plan, but that's the way it will be."

Odysseus said, "A man always does better begging in town than in the country. I'm not much good at farm work; before long I will come down with him, when the day is warmer, because these rags of mine are not much protection against the morning chill."

Telemachus set off down the hill, thinking as he walked how he should deal with the suitors. When he got home, Eurycleia was the first to see him; she ran up and embraced him. Penelope appeared, weeping for happiness at her son's return. He spoke to her: "Mother dear, don't weep, or make me weep, when I have escaped death. But go and wash your face, and offer sacrifices to the gods. For myself, I have to go into town to meet a man who came home with me from Pylos."

As he went across the hall, the suitors crowded around him, full of pretty speeches and murderous thoughts. He sat down, however, with some of his old friends; as he did so, Peiraeus brought in Theoclymenus. Peiraeus asked whether he should bring up the gifts of Menelaus, but Telemachus prudently told him to keep the things on the ship, for if the suitors killed him, he wanted his friends to share the treasure. They all sat down, washed, and ate. Penelope, who had come into the hall, asked for news of his trip, whether he had heard anything of Odysseus. He told her the whole story of his visit to Nestor and Menelaus, and how Menelaus had heard from the lips of Proteus the story of Odysseus' captivity in Ogygia.

Penelope wept to hear it, and Theoclymenus broke in, "Queen, believe me, for I am skilled in reading the signs. We saw a bird of good omen from the ship, and I explained to Telemachus that it signifies the return of Odysseus—he is even now in Ithaca."

As the talk went forward, the suitors were playing their usual games. The herald Medon brought in fat beasts, which they slaughtered, and sat down to their supper.

Meanwhile, Odysseus and Eumaeus were on their way to town, Odysseus disguised as an old beggar-man. When they reached the public well beside the road, they met Melantheus, a goatherd, who abused them: "Here's a couple of fine fellows! Where are you going with that beggar, you old pig-keeper? He looks like the sort of chap who hates nothing more than work, and loves to scratch his back on people's doorposts! Wait till he gets to Odysseus' house—they'll give him a welcome with a couple of footstools in the ribs!" And he gave Odysseus a kick, but Odysseus stood up to it, though he wanted to stretch the oaf out on his back.

Eumaeus called on the gods to see the insult, and prayed that Odysseus might take care of this swaggerer. But Melantheus said, "I wish I were as sure that Telemachus was dead as I am that Odysseus will never return!" And with that, he went to the house of Odysseus, where his friends the suitors gave him plenty to eat.

Eumaeus and Odysseus went ahead more slowly, arriving while the banquet was in full swing. They smelled the roasted meat, and heard the minstrel singing to the harp. Eumaeus went in first, while Odysseus waited; but the swineherd advised him to come in shortly, before the suitors saw him and began throwing things at him for sport.

As he waited, he saw a dog stretched on the dungheap. Argus was its name, whom Odysseus had long before trained to the hunt. But, his owner gone, he lay abandoned, crawling with vermin. Argus recognized the voice of his master, and feebly wagged his tail. "Eumaeus," said Odysseus, "that was a fine dog once, and I wonder whether he could hunt."

"Indeed he could, while his master was alive. There wasn't a deer that could escape him. But now that his master is dead, there is no one to look after him. So it is with men." And so speaking, he went into the hall. But Argus, when he had seen his master's return, died.

Eumaeus, when he had entered the palace, went to sit beside Telemachus at the latter's invitation. Odysseus came in close behind him, and sat, scratching his back on the squared doorpost. Seeing him, Telemachus took a great loaf of bread and a piece of meat, and sent them to the beggar, telling him by the waiter to beg his way around the company. "May the gods grant Telemachus prosperity!" said Odysseus, in the beggar's formula, and ate. When he had finished, the minstrel's song was over, and everyone was talking at once. Athene appeared to Odysseus, urging him to beg from the suitors that he might tell the generous from the stingy ones—though she meant to kill the lot of them. As he went through the great hall, he stretched out his hand toward each, like a man born a beggar. Most of them were generous, moved by pity for his plight, but Melantheus, the goatherd, put in a word, "Gentlemen, I've seen this rascal before—he came down from the hills with Eumaeus."

Antinous said, "That's like him, to bring a tramp in here to bother us. Aren't there enough at dinner already?"

"You may be a gentleman by birth, but you don't talk like one, Antinous," said the swineherd. "Any wandering minstrel is welcome, but not many beggars. You are always most tyrannical to Odyssseus' servants, especially to me. I care little for that, so long as Penelope and Telemachus are here to take care of me."

But Telemachus struck in, "No more quarreling, Eumaeus, for Antinous likes to get people angry with his waspish tongue. And, Antinous, it is kind of you to be so concerned about my property that you want me to throw this stranger out. The gods forbid! I don't mind your giving him something, for after all it's my food, unless you would rather eat it yourself than be generous with it!"

So Odysseus continued about the hall until he came to Antinous. "An alms, gentleman!" he said. "Surely you should give most, for you are the most royal in appearance. Ah, once I was lucky like you and had servants to run when I called. But that's all over, ever since I was captured by the Egyptians and sold to the men of Cyprus as a slave."

"Who, in the name of Heaven, brought this whining scoundrel here?" said Antinous. "Get out, or I'll give you Egypt and Cyprus on the side of your head."

Odysseus drew away, saying, "Ah, if only your sense were as fine as your looks! But you're too stingy to give a man even a bit of bread from another's table." With this, Antinous picked up his footstool and flung it at Odysseus, striking him on the shoulder. But the prudent Odysseus merely withdrew to the doorstep, where he sat, shaking his head, and thinking bloody thoughts.

"A blow is not hard to take when a man is fighting off raiders and defending himself, but when a man's belly gets him a knock, he feels it. I pray the gods that Antinous sees his grave before he sees his marriage bed!"

Antinous rejoined, "Quiet, you, or get out. If you keep this up, we'll drag you outside and skin you alive." The others felt that Antinous had gone too far, but he shrugged off their objections.

When Penelope heard of this ill-mannered deed, she prayed that Apollo, the Far-darter, should strike him dead, and Eurynome, the housekeeper, said, "If wishes were arrows, there is none of them would see tomorrow." And as they talked of this, Penelope sent Eumaeus to invite the stranger in, so that they could hear his news.

Eumaeus assented, saying that the stranger had heard that Odysseus was alive in Thesprotis, and even then returning to his home. "Go and call him," said Penelope, "for while these suitors are here there is never a quiet moment. Ah, if only my Odysseus were home again! Surely he and Telemachus would have vengeance on them for all their evil deeds!" As she spoke, Telemachus sneezed loudly, and Penelope laughed. Turning to Eumaeus, she said, "Did you hear that? He sneezed, and that is a good omen that my wishes will come true. Now run and bring the stranger, and, if his story is pleasing, I will give him a good suit of clothes."

When Eumaeus brought him the message, Odysseus replied, "There is nothing I should like better than to tell her what news I have, and certainly new clothes in place of these rags would be very pleasant. But those suitors have me frightened, and no one seems inclined to take my part. If only she will wait until dark, when I can come unobserved, I shall be glad to speak to her."

When Eumaeus brought this answer to the lady, she commented, "He is a man of good sense, for there never was a lot of rogues like these."

Then Eumaeus left her, and found Telemachus, to whom he said, "I must go back to the farm and look after the pigs. Take care of yourself, for there's no telling what this lot will be up to next. May they get to Hell before they send us there!"

Telemachus thanked him, and said that he might go when he wished. After dinner he left, while the thoughtless suitors danced and drank, and night closed in on the hall.

BOOK XVIII: In the midst of the merriment, a sturdy beggar, nicknamed Irus because he ran messages for everyone, came to the hall. Seeing Odysseus, he shouted, "Get out, old fellow! Do you want me to haul you out by the leg?"

Odysseus replied, "There is alms enough for us all, and I'll not start any fight. There's room here for both. But I tell you, don't make me angry, or you'll have blood on your face."

"So you want a fight? Take off your tunic, and let's see how you do against a man!"

Antinous heard them quarreling, and called out, "Here's a show! Let's get the old boy and Irus to fight, and we'll let the winner eat with us from now on!" This seemed a good notion to the others, and they gathered around.

Wily Odysseus said, "Gentlemen, a fight between a young man and an old one is no fair match. But when hunger drives, a man can do anything. I only ask that you give me a chance, and don't join the fight on Irus' side."

Telemachus interposed, "Stranger, you do not need to fear any of us. I am the master of this house, and Antinous and Eurymachus will see fair play, along with me."

Then they stripped for action. Athene increased Odysseus' size, so that the suitors murmured that Irus would have no easy time with the old fellow, and Irus himself was ready to run, for he had no pluck at all. But Antinous dragged him to the center of the ring, threatening to ship him off as a slave if he would not fight. Odysseus looked his man over carefully, deciding whether to kill him with one blow, or to knock him down. When Irus struck at him, he slipped under the blow and countered with a right to the neck, which knocked Irus flat, rolling on the ground and groaning, while the blood poured from his mouth. The suitors laughed as hard as they could, and Odysseus dragged Irus over to the gate, where he propped him up with his stick in his hand. "Stay there, you," he growled, "and don't try to fight men after this." And he walked over to the banqueting hall, where they all congratulated him, and feasted him with a great goat-paunch, stuffed with blood and fat.

Amphinomus presented him with a couple of fine white loaves, and drank to him. Odysseus answered, "Amphinomus, you are a true son of your father, Nisus of Dulichium, for he was a very fine man. Let me tell you some things I have learned. No creature on earth is so helpless as Man. While times are good, he is happy; but when times are bad, there is nothing but to bear misfortune. Fate governs us all. Once I, for example, was a happy and prosperous man, but I brought ill luck on myself by embarking on a life of raiding and piracy. It should be a lesson to everyone not to disobey the laws of Heaven, but to accept what the gods send us in quiet. Look at these suitors here for example: eating another man's food and making love to his wife. Not much longer will he be away, and when he returns, they will wish they had never seen Ithaca. There will be blood on the floor before they get away." He poured his libation, and drank; but Amphinomus went away, his heart heavy with forebodings of evil.

Athene put it into Penelope's mind to show herself to the suitors, and she called Eurynome to help her, and to bring two maids to attend her, for it would have been immodest to appear alone in the banquet hall. While Eurynome was on her errand, Athene put a deep sleep on her, and as she drowsed, the goddess endowed her with more than mortal beauty.

When she appeared in the hall, every man of the suitors was struck with wonder. "Telemachus," she said to her son, "surely you are grown up enough to prevent such disgraceful scenes as the one we have just witnessed. Suppose our guest had been hurt? Everyone would have said that you were to blame."

"Mother," he answered, "it is true that I am no longer a child, but I cannot always do as I should like, for these gentlemen prefer riot to order. However, it was Irus who lost, not the visitor. O Gods in Heaven, when shall I see these suitors rolling like Irus, in the dust!"

Eurymachus said, "Queen Penelope, if everyone in Achaea

could see you as you are now, there would be more princes
here than the house would hold, for I swear that no woman is
your equal in beauty or wit."

"Eurymachus," she replied, "I have no beauty since my husband left. He said, as he departed, that he might never return,
for the Trojans too were good fighters; and he told me that
when my son had a man's beard, it would be time for me to
marry again. All these things have happened, though I want
to marry no man. But here is a thing I do not understand—
usually men, when they court a woman, bring her presents, and
do not eat up all her goods."

The suitors agreed that she had spoken wisely, while Odysseus smiled to himself to see how prudent she was. Each of
the nobles sent a servant to bring gifts to the house: beautiful
robes, fastened with golden pins, brooches, bracelets, and
necklaces. And Penelope took them to her chamber, where
she fastened them safely.

Then all the suitors sat down to revelry and drinking, even
past nightfall. From time to time, the maidens of the house
came in to trim the lamps, until Odysseus sent them packing,
for he wanted no immodest behavior in his house.

Eurymachus saw him, and shouted out, "Do you suppose this
is a god who is trimming the lamps? A light seems to shine
from him. No—that isn't it—it's the glow of the torches on his
bald head! Stranger, how would you like to work for me, digging ditches and tending cattle? Or is that too much work for
you?"

Odysseus replied, "Eurymachus, I'd like nothing better than
to be out beside you in the field, plowing or cutting hay. We'd
soon find out which of us is the better! Or out in the front line,
wearing our armor, and with a couple of spears. I don't think
you'd find time for jokes at my bald head. But you're only a
blowhard with no pluck—and if Odysseus were home, there'd
be little talk from your big mouth!"

At this Eurymachus lost his temper. He threw a stool at
Odysseus, who dodged it, and the missile struck a wine-server,
who dropped groaning to the floor. Immediately there was an

uproar, with the suitors all shouting at once against the beggar.

But Telemachus stood out, and said, "Gentlemen! Are you all so drunk you have lost your wits? We have all had enough, and it is time for us to go to bed. Let the waiters fill us one last bowl, and then good night."

BOOK XIX: Now that the hall was empty, Odysseus, helped by Athene, began to think how he should kill the suitors. He repeated to Telemachus the instructions he had given him earlier: to hide the weapons, using, if necessary, some story or other to cover his actions. Telemachus called Eurycleia, and asked her to keep the women away from the hall while he worked, for he was putting the weapons out of harm's way. "But," she said, "who will help you? Don't you need someone to carry a lamp?"

"No, this stranger here can earn his keep by helping me." And the old woman went off, to lock up the women while Telemachus and the stranger worked. Pallas Athene aided them, shedding divine light through the hall, and Telemachus was astonished; but Odysseus warned him to ask no questions, for the gods work as they will, unknown to men.

After the task was done, Telemachus went to his bed, while Odysseus remained in the hall, planning vengeance. While he was there, beautiful Penelope came down to sit beside the fire, surrounded by her maids. One of them, Melantho, a shameless baggage, scolded Odysseus: "You old goat! Still here, winking at the girls? Out with you, before I throw you out!"

Odysseus replied, "Why pick on me? I don't like to go around begging for my living, but it's all I can do. Once I gave alms, now I ask them. You should be careful, for Zeus does not let people stay at the top of the heap all their lives. Penelope may become angry with you or Odysseus may return, and when he does, Telemachus will tell him how you are acting, for there's little he misses."

Penelope, too, rated the girl soundly for her bad manners; then she sent Eurynome for a stool for Odysseus, that she might question him. She told him the whole sorry tale of the coming of the suitors, of her attempt to deceive them by weaving and unraveling Laertes' shroud, of their discovery, and of her incessant desire for the return of Odysseus. He told her the story he had prepared, the one he had told Eumaeus and Telemachus before, ending with the account of seeing Odysseus in Minoan Crete; and Penelope wept to hear him. She asked her visitor to describe Odysseus as he was when in Crete, and to say who were the men with him.

"It is many years since I saw him," replied Odysseus, "and it is hard to remember all the details. He had on a heavy purple tunic, fastened with a golden brooch figured with a dog holding a fawn. It was a handsome, tight-fitting cloak, too, as I remember. He had one man whose name I can call to mind, Eurybates, a tall man, rather stooped in the shoulders." Penelope wept again to hear him, for she herself had taken those garments from the storeroom and put them on Odysseus when he sailed away.

"Please do not weep so, madam," said Odysseus, "though you might have good reason to weep if Odysseus were really dead. But I tell you that he is not far off, in the land of Thesprotis, and will soon be here, though he will bring none of his old crew, nor his ship, with him. His old crew were all lost by the anger of Zeus as punishment for their slaughter of the Sun-god's cattle, though he himself was saved, and managed to get to the land of the Phaeacians. He would have been here now, except that he wanted to recoup his fortunes by trading. I have all this story on oath from the King of Thesprotis, who told me that Odysseus was even then on a voyage to Dodona, to hear the will of Zeus from the Talking Oak, and would return very soon to his home."

"God grant that your story is true! But I fear in my heart that it will not turn out so. If only Odysseus were here, you would be received fittingly. But come—maidens, prepare a bath for this gentleman, and let him have a comfortable bed. Surely it is fitting that, even in this empty house, we show proper hospitality."

"Madam," said Odysseus, "a traveler like me really prefers to

rough it. I'd rather sleep out here in the hall; and as for a bath
—well, I'd rather, if anyone washes my feet, that it be one of
the older women, for I should be embarrassed to have a young
one bathe me."

"Very well, my friend, as you choose. There is an old woman
here who has served me for a long time. Eurycleia, come and
wash this old gentleman's feet—he must be as old as your
master."

"We are indeed rather alike," said Odysseus; "others have
noticed it."

When she brought the foot-basin, Odysseus turned so that
his feet were in darkness, for he suddenly remembered an old
scar on his leg which Eurycleia would recognize. As the old
woman washed him, she passed her hand over the scar, and
knew him. As she turned to speak to Penelope, Odysseus put
his hand over her mouth, and whispered, "Yes, I am Odysseus.
But keep quiet about it—or, by Zeus, when I've finished off
these suitors, I'll finish you too."

She answered, as quietly, "You needn't talk like that, for you
know my loyalty. And when you have done your work, I can
tell you which women were faithful." Then she completed
the foot-wash, and rubbed him with oil.

Penelope went on, "Sir, let us talk a little longer, though it is
late. You know my situation: my husband gone, myself be-
seiged by these suitors. What am I to do? While my son was
a boy, there was no question that I must stay here and bring
him up. Now, however, he is a man, and he is worried about
the condition of our property, which my suitors are devouring.
And here is another thing: the other night I dreamed that a
great eagle came down on my flock of geese and killed them
all. As I stood weeping over their fate, the eagle came back,
and said, 'Penelope, noble Queen, these geese are your suitors,
and I am your husband, who will destroy them.' Then I awoke.
Tell me, what is the meaning of this?"

Odysseus replied, "Madam, surely it is to be taken at face
value: Odysseus himself spoke to you in the dream."

"Oh, one cannot always trust dreams; those sent through

the Gate of Horn are true, but not those which Zeus sends through the Gate of Ivory. And, though I should be happy to know that this was a true dream, I fear that it is not.

"But one day soon I must decide what to do. I have chosen a test: the suitor who can, like Odysseus, string his great bow and send an arrow through his twelve axes, standing in a row, shall be the one to carry me home as a bride."

"Surely," replied her husband, "that will be a good test, for the wily Odysseus will be here before any of them can meet it."

Then Penelope excused herself, and went up to her chamber with her maids, while Odysseus made ready to sleep.

BOOK XX: As he lay on his fleece, wondering how he should manage the suitors, he heard the girls coming from the suitors' bedrooms, laughing, and he growled to himself, thinking of their wantonness in his house. But he counseled himself to patience, remembering how he had out-tricked Polyphemus, when his life was in even greater peril. Tossing and turning he lay, until Athene appeared to him saying, "Why can you not sleep? Is not this your home, and are not your wife and son well?"

"Yes indeed—but how am I to deal with these rascals, who are always together? And if—with your help, and Zeus'—I kill them all, what then?"

"I cannot understand you! Remember, I am a goddess, the most powerful help there is. If they were fifty times as many, you and I together should defeat them. Now sleep, and forget your troubles." And she put sleep on him.

As he slept, his wife awoke in her chamber, and prayed to Artemis: "Grant, O Goddess, my prayer: let me die before I go with a worse man than Odysseus! For even my dreams deceive me; even now I thought that Odysseus stood beside my bed— but I awoke. Let me die thinking of Odysseus!"

Odysseus, waking at dawn, heard her moans, and prayed to Zeus: "Cloud-gatherer, now that I have safely returned, grant me a sign of success!" As he spoke these words, there was a great rumble of thunder, a sign sent by Zeus. And even better, from the lips of one of the women grinding corn, came the prayer: "A good omen from Zeus—thunder without a cloud in the sky! I wish—I wish—that today be the last day I grind corn for these worthless suitors!"

The household awoke; young Telemachus came to ask after Odysseus, and then went out to the meeting-place. Eurycleia directed the girls in the morning cleaning, while the men cut wood for the fires. Eumaeus appeared and asked Odysseus whether he got on better with the suitors; and then Melantheus swaggered in, saying, "Well, you old reprobate, are you still here? It looks as if you and I were going to have to settle this with our fists, because I don't like you one bit, and there are plenty of other places to beg!" But Odysseus did not answer him.

Then the chief herd, Philoetius, came in with some beasts for the dinner. He spoke to Odysseus: "Well, stranger, who are you and where are you from? You look like a man who has had bad luck, but you seem like a good fellow for all that! Here's hoping things change for the better! Indeed, you remind me a good deal of my old master Odysseus, the best man who ever lived. This lot here, though, are just the opposite— they keep me driving cattle in for banquets every day, and I never know what to do; if there were any profit in it, I'd run away. But one day, perhaps, Odysseus will return and send them packing."

"You talk sensibly, sir," said Odysseus, "and I have news for you: Odysseus will return, and your prayer will be granted."

Now the suitors had come in, and as they were talking over ways of killing Telemachus, an eagle appeared with a dove in his claws. Amphinomus knew this for a divine omen, and persuaded them to eat instead of plotting; they agreed, slaughtered the animals, poured out the wine, and ate heartily.

Telemachus found a place for the beggar beside the stone doorstep; he put out a small table, and served him with meat and wine. Then he said, "I will protect you from any insults.

And you, gentlemen, will oblige me by refraining from riot and disorder in my house."

They were amazed by his decisive tone. Antinous commented, "Well, this is rather offensive, but there is nothing we can do. If our little plan had not come to grief, we should not have been annoyed by that lovely voice." But Telemachus paid no heed.

Then, because it was a holy day, the animals were brought into town for the sacrifices, and the Achaeans gathered in the holy grove. But the suitors remained in the palace, drinking and feasting. Athene put it into the mind of Ctesippus, one of the wealthiest suitors, to taunt Odysseus when he saw the steward carrying him a portion of food: "Well," he said, "it looks as though our beggar friend were going to have a good meal. Let me send him something, too." And with this, he picked up a cow's hoof, and threw it at Odysseus, who dodged it, and let the missile strike the wall.

Immediately Telemachus was on Ctesippus: "It's just as well you did not hit him, because if you had, I would have put a spear through you. I know I can't stop you from eating me out of house and home, but I want no insults to my guests. Now that you are bent on my murder, I agree that it would be better than these insults to my friends."

Agelaus answered for the suitors, "There can be no objections to such a speech—let this bullying stop! But, Telemachus, so long as you persist in the hope that Odysseus will return, you can count on finding us here for our meals. Since we know he will not come back, then, let your mother choose one of us and marry him, and leave you to enjoy your property in peace."

"I have no desire to keep her from marrying one of you, but I cannot and will not say the word that sends her from her own house."

The suitors were so drunk that they laughed as if they would die to hear Telemachus' words. But their merriment faded, for it seemed to them that there was blood on their food. Theoclymenus spoke: "What has come upon you, ill-fated men? See, there is a shadow over the hall, the walls are splashed with gore, the doorway is crowded with twittering ghosts on their way to Hell."

They laughed harder to hear his speech, and Eurymachus crowed, "The traveler's mind is unhinged from his journey. Some of you show him the way out, if he finds it dark within."

But Theoclymenus, the seer, rejoined, "I can see my way well, dark as it is. On all of you I see a black cloud falling, the night of doom." And with this he made his way outside.

The suitors, however, did not abandon their fun. "Look," said one of them, "at your friends, Telemachus! The tramp eats and won't work, and the other talks and won't eat. What a prophet he is! Better tie them both up, and sell them off in Sicily—that's the only way you'll get any good out of them!" But Telemachus answered nothing; he knew that after the rich dinner there would be a richer one, made ready by the vengeance of Odysseus with the goddess' help.

Book XXI: In the storeroom, far from the banqueting hall, among the wealth of gold and bronze and iron which Odysseus had amassed, stood the great bow, gift of Iphitus to Odysseus many years before. Odysseus had not taken it to Ilium, but had left it at home. Penelope, carrying the well-wrought key, opened the doors of the storeroom, and, standing on tiptoes, lifted down the bow from its case. Laying it across her knees, she wept a little to think of the man who had owned it; then, drying her tears, she went to the banqueting hall, modestly veiling her face. On her arrival there, she called out, "Gentlemen, for a long time you have considered this house your own, saying that you were courting me. Now, since you have made my hand your prize, come and meet the test: the man who can string this bow and put an arrow through those axes is the man I will marry. Eumaeus, give this bow to these gentlemen."

Eumaeus did as she bade, weeping to see his old master's weapon. Antinous jeered at this show of feeling: "What are you whimpering about, anyhow? Sit and eat, or go and do your sniveling outdoors. Leave the bow here, for I don't think

many men can string it! I was only a boy when I last saw
Odysseus, but I've never seen a man to beat him since." So he
spoke, but in his heart he thought that he might be the winner
of the contest.

"Now, gentlemen," said Telemachus, "this is the time of decision! There never was a prize like the one you will shoot for,
the finest woman in all Ithaca! Come now, enter the contest;
and to the man who wins her I will gladly resign her." So
speaking, he dug a long trench, and set the axes in it in a
straight row. Then three times he himself tried to string the
bow, and at the fourth attempt he nearly managed the feat,
but Odysseus shook his head, and Telemachus desisted.

He took his seat, and Antinous proposed that they make their
trials in order. The first was Leodes, who could not even bend
the bow. Antinous called out, "Melantheus! Bring a fire, and
some warm wax, to soften this weapon. It has stood so long
that it has grown stiff." He did so, and the young men all tried
in turn, but Antinous and Eurymachus, who fancied themselves
the best men there, held off from the contest.

As all this was happening, Odysseus slipped outside, where
he met Eumaeus and the cowherd. He asked them, "If you had
a chance to fight for Odysseus—supposing he should appear
suddenly—whose side would you take?"

"If the gods bring him home, you'll see I'll fight for Odysseus." And Eumaeus spoke as he had. Then Odysseus took his
courage in both hands: "Well, here is your chance. I am Odysseus, returned after these weary years. If we win, you shall
have wives, and houses built near mine, and you shall be like
sons to me. Let me prove who I am: you know this scar: look
at it!"

Long and carefully they looked at the scar; then they burst
into tears of joy to know their master. But Odysseus hushed
them: "Don't let people see you weeping. Now here is what
you must do: go inside, one at a time, so that no one notices
you. The suitors will not let me try my luck, I know, but you,
Eumaeus, must manage to bring me the bow and the quiver.
Lock the women in their rooms, too, and tell them if they hear

any noise to stay where they are. Philoetius, your job is to fasten the outer gate, and see that you get it shut tight."

As they slipped back into the house, Eurymachus was trying to bend the bow, having warmed it at the fire, but he had no luck. "A curse on this thing!" he cried. "It isn't so much missing Penelope that I mind, because there are plenty of good women in Ithaca, but being shown up as weaker than Odysseus!"

Antinous, however, said, "As you know, this holy day is in honor of Apollo, god of archers. What a day to try bending a bow! But here is my advice: let us all pour libations to Apollo, and tomorrow make a great sacrifice in his honor. Then we can all try again."

At this, very wily Odysseus said, "Gentlemen, I have a favor to ask of you, particularly of Antinous, who has made such a sensible suggestion. Let me, I beg, have the bow, to see whether these old arms of mine have lost all their skill and power."

Antinous was incensed. "The devil! Where did you learn your manners? Eat and be quiet—you're drunk, that's what's the matter! You'll have the same bad luck as the drunken Centaur, who had his ears and nose slit. Keep quiet, and let the young men string this bow!"

Penelope spoke, trying to quiet them, "Surely you don't believe that this man is contending for my hand—I'm sure he didn't have any such idea. Let us all be courteous to my son's guest."

But Eurymachus retorted, "We know that he is not in the contest, but suppose he should succeed! People would say that all the best young men in Ithaca tried to string Odysseus' bow, and were beaten by some beggar or other! What would happen to our reputation?"

"As for reputation, Eurymachus, anyone who supports himself by eating another's food cannot lay claim to much. But the stranger looks like a well-setup man, and says he is of good descent. If he does manage to string it, I shall give him a good suit of clothes, some weapons to defend himself in his wanderings, and a voyage wherever he wants to go."

Telemachus put in, "As for the bow, it is mine to give or withhold as I please, for I am master here. It would be better, mother, for you to go to your room, and see to your work and the servants. This bow is for men, for me especially, not for women."

Wondering at his prudent words, Penelope went to her quarters, where she thought of Odysseus until Athene cast a sleep upon her.

During the quarrel, Eumaeus had picked up the bow and was moving down the hall. He was halted by the cries of the suitors, who shouted to him to stop, or they would throw him to the dogs. Telemachus, however, shouted from his seat at the end of the hall, "Go on, old man! You obey me, not these men." The suitors roared with laughter at Telemachus' protest, but Eumaeus carried the bow to Odysseus near the doorway. Then he spoke quietly to Eurycleia: "Go and lock yourself and the girls in the women's apartments, and pay no attention to anything you hear in the hall."

So she did, wondering; and meanwhile Philoetius, the cowherd, had slipped out and secured the outer doorway with a great ship's hawser. He returned, and sat down near his master.

Odysseus took the bow, turned it over in his hands, and examined it carefully to see whether worms had got at it in his absence. The suitors were amused: "A collector of bows, probably! See how he looks at it, as if he were going to buy it! Much good may it do him!"

While they joked, Odysseus had finished his inspection. Then with one swift movement, he strung the bow, and twanged the string as a musician twangs a lyre. The suitors turned pale: and at that moment Cloud-gathering Zeus sent a loud thunderclap. Odysseus picked up an arrow from the quiver, and drawing the string to his ear, sent the shaft through all twelve axes. Then he spoke to his son: "Your guest has not shamed you! No, I'm as strong as ever I was! Now for supper, gentlemen, and then the dancing!"

As he finished his speech, Telemachus took his sharp sword and spear, and joined his father.

Book XXII: Springing to the doorway, the fearless Odysseus threw off his rags, and drew another arrow from the quiver. "I won that match!" he cried. "Now for another!" And with that he let fly at Antinous, striking him in the throat, so that the wine-cup from which he was just drinking emptied itself on the floor, and the wine mingled with his blood.

The suitors still did not know what had happened—they thought Odysseus had killed the man by accident. They ran around the hall, looking for weapons to avenge his death, but none could they find. "You dogs!" cried Odysseus. "Did you think I would never return to Ithaca? You courted my wife and slept with my maids and ate my food—and you never thought of vengeance! Well, here it is now!"

They all turned pale as death with fear. Only Eurymachus spoke: "If you are indeed Odysseus of Ithaca, you speak the truth: we are to blame. But the man who started it all, who was the leading spirit, lies dead. It was Antinous who wanted to become King of Ithaca after he had married your wife, and killed your son. Now that you have your revenge, spare us, and we will pay you a great fine and a great tribute of gold and oxen."

Odysseus looked at him and said, "Not even if you gave me everything you own in the world. Take your choice: fight or run."

Eurymachus addressed the suitors, "He will never show mercy, and he has his bow. Well—the only thing to do is to fight. Let's go for him with our swords—if we can get him out of his corner, we have him." So speaking, he drew his sword and advanced on Odysseus, but Odysseus' second arrow was as true as the first; it caught Eurymachus just below the nipple, and went through his liver. As the others bore down on Odysseus, Telemachus whispered to his father that he would bring some spears, and some defensive armor.

"Hurry, then," said Odysseus, "I have only a few arrows left, but I can hold them off for a while." Telemachus went to the armory, where he picked up some shields and spears for his party. With them he returned to the hall, and armed Odysseus and the two servants, who took their places together. As long as the arrows held out, Odysseus shot the suitors one by one; and when his arrows were exhausted, he put on his armor and took a spear.

Beside the great outer gate Eumaeus was posted; when Agelaus wanted someone to climb up to its top and call to the people, he found the way bared. Then he sent Melantheus to find the armory, and bring spears and shields to the remaining suitors. When Odysseus saw them arming themselves, he asked Telemachus whether one of the women had betrayed them, but Telemachus confessed it was his fault for not shutting the door more securely. He sent Eumaeus to fasten it, and when Eumaeus saw Melantheus, he and Philoetius caught him, bound his arms behind his back, and hung him up in the armory, where they mocked at him.

The four of them got together beside the door, facing the angry crowd of suitors. As they stood glaring, Pallas Athene appeared in the form of Mentor, and Odysseus cheered. "Here we are! Help us! Remember our old days together, Mentor!" He felt sure that it was Athene to whom he spoke.

The suitors raged at the newcomer. "Mentor, if you let Odysseus talk you into helping him, we'll finish you off as we mean to finish him. And when you're gone, we'll lump your estate with his, and share them both among us."

Athene rebuked Odysseus: "Is this the man who fought the Trojans for nine years, and killed plenty of them? Here you are—in your own house, with your friends to help you, and you can't get up courage to cut that gang down! Let me show you how it's done!"

The suitors, meanwhile, had put their heads together, and decided to attack Odysseus six at a time, throwing their spears all together. The first cast Athene sent astray—they hit the door, the wall, everything but the four brave men. Then Odysseus gave the order: "All together, now: four spears into the thick of them!"

They aimed straight; four suitors fell, and the rest got back into a corner, while Odysseus' party drew their spears from the bodies. Again the suitors threw, and again the spears went astray. Telemachus got a scratch on his wrist, and Eumaeus one on the shoulder, but no one was badly hurt. Once more Odysseus' party cast, and again they scored hits. Philoetius exulted over Ctesippus, whom he had struck fairly in the breast: "Take that, you braggart, for the cow-heel you threw at Odysseus!" Then Odysseus and his group went forward, thrusting with their spears, driving the suitors through the hall. In the rafters, Bright-eyed Athene shook her aegis, and the fear of death came on them. Phemius, the minstrel, had so far escaped; and he thought whether to take sanctuary at the great altar or to beg mercy. He chose the latter course, and Telemachus interceded for him as well as for Medon, the herald, for neither of them had joined in the suitors' wanton debauches. Spared, they went to the altar of Zeus, and sat down, while Odysseus and Telemachus went through the hall to see whether any others were left alive. They found none.

Then Telemachus called Eurycleia, whose first impulse, when she saw the bodies, was to utter a great yell of triumph over the slain. Odysseus restrained her, for he would have no rejoicing over men who had got their just punishment. He told her to bring the women who had disgraced his house by joining in the debauches of the suitors—twelve of these there were in all. When they came, he made them carry out the dead bodies and wash the furniture clean of blood. When they had finished their task, scraping all the wood until it was clean, Telemachus herded them into the courtyard. "There will be no clean death for you, for you have dirtied my house with your actions," he said. Then he put nooses about their necks, and hanged them. For a little while they wiggled their feet, but not for long.

When this was done, Odysseus called for a fire and sulphur; and with these he cleansed the whole house. Eurycleia called the other women to greet their master, and they came, sobbing, to fling their arms about him in joy at his return. Odysseus wept too, overcome by emotion; he knew them all.

BOOK XXIII: Eurycleia hastened to her mistress' apartment, and woke Penelope, saying, "Wake up, darling! He's home—Odysseus is home—and he has avenged himself on all those suitors."

But Penelope was incredulous. "You have gone mad! Off with you now—you've waked me out of a sound sleep. If it had been one of the other girls who did this, I'd have beaten her."

"It's true—he *is* here! He was the old beggar! Telemachus knew all about it, but he wouldn't say anything. I didn't know that he had killed the suitors until Telemachus called me, and I saw the bodies in the hall. The master made me bring him fire and sulphur to purify the house—and it would have done you good to see how he avenged himself!"

"No, Eurycleia—it must have been a god who struck them down, for no one man could have managed the lot. And Odysseus is still as far from home as ever."

"You never would believe anything I told you! I swear it's Odysseus—he even has the scar on his leg. Come with me and see—if the man isn't your husband, kill me." Together they went downstairs, while Penelope thought what she should do: embrace this man, or stand apart? When they reached the hall, she sat down in a carved chair, looking at the ragged stranger, who sat alone by a pillar, wondering, himself, what she would do. For a long time no one spoke.

Then Telemachus said, "Mother, why won't you speak to your husband? Any other woman, after nineteen years apart from him, would have been sitting beside him embracing him and asking him questions."

Odysseus, however, smiled and said, "She will know me soon enough, for we have secrets that no one else shares. There is a more pressing problem: how are we to avoid blood-feuds for killing these noblemen?"

"You will have to take the lead in solving that, father," answered Telemachus. "I'll do whatever you say."

"We must play for time. Have the minstrel come in, and let us all put on our best clothes. When people hear the sounds of merrymaking, they will think that a wedding feast is going on; and that will keep them from investigating the absence of the suitors until we can, if necessary, get out to our farm holdings."

They did as he commanded, and passers-by shook their heads to think that Penelope had finally given in and married again. Odysseus, bathed and clad in his own garments, came into the hall. Athene had made him look taller and stronger and younger than ever. He sat down, and looked across the room at his wife. "I never could understand you! Any other woman would have leapt into her husband's arms, but you sit there like an icicle. Well, Eurycleia, make me up a bed downstairs."

"I just can't get used to seeing you—it's not that I'm indifferent. I remember you too well. Eurycleia, make up a bed for him upstairs—move his own bed out of the bedroom." She said this to test Odysseus, for there was a secret between them.

Odysseus retorted, "Who could move the bed? When this house was built, I made that bed, and this is how I did it: there was an olive tree in the courtyard, with a great thick trunk. I trimmed this down, and built the bedroom about it, making one of the bedposts the tree itself. This is the secret we alone know: but I don't know whether anyone has cut through the tree and moved the bed."

Then Penelope's heart melted within her, for she knew that it was her husband, and she flew into his arms. Long they sat, talking, mingling their tears. "Do not be angry with me, beloved, for doubting you so long—I have known many rascals who tried to entangle me into marriage. If Helen had known what her faithlessness would cause, she never would have gone with Paris, and caused all our woe. But now you are home, and all is well." Then Eurynome brought them to their bed; and Athene held back the swift steeds of day.

Odysseus told his wife all his adventures, and told her, also, of the task which he must accomplish before he could enjoy his kingdom in peace: to carry an oar inland until someone asked him what he was doing with a winnowing-fan, and there to plant the oar and make proper sacrifices to Poseidon. Before that, however, he planned to visit his father; and he instructed Penelope to stay within doors until he could find a way of settling the feuds which would arise from the death of the suitors. Arming himself, and accompanied by Telemachus and his two servants, he made his way quietly out of the palace.

BOOK XXIV: Deep in the land of Hades, the souls of Agamemnon and Achilles were speaking together. "Ah, Agamemnon," said Achilles, "it would have been better for you to die in battle, facing your enemies like a man, than to be struck down ignobly by a murderer!"

"Yes," answered Agamemnon, "you had a fine death, far away in Troy, with the battle swirling around your body. All day we fought, and at the end we carried you to the ships, where we mourned you for seventeen days. When your period of mourning was over, we burned your body with all the proper rites and funeral games, and even the gods wept for you. Surely that was better than my death!"

As they spoke, Hermes, the leader of the Dead, came past, leading the chirping, twittering souls of the suitors whom Odysseus had killed. Agamemnon recognized Amphimedon, whom he had visited in Ithaca. Astonished, he asked the spirit how he had met his end, and Amphimedon told him the whole sorry tale of the courtship, the insults to Telemachus and Odysseus, and finally the swift vengeance of the wronged man. "Ah, what a warrior!" said the spirit of Agamemnon. "And what a wife! People will remember her forever as the very soul of loyalty, just as they will remember Clytemnestra as the soul of faithlessness!"

In the meantime, Odysseus and his friends had made their way to the hut where Laertes lived. They went in, and put off their armor; Odysseus ordered a pig killed for dinner, while he went to meet his father. Alone, he went through the vineyard, meeting no one, until he saw the old man digging around the roots of a vine. When he saw how ragged and filthy his father was, he stopped, thinking how to approach him. Finally he went up to him and spoke: "You seem to have a very well-run farm here, old man! But I can't say much for your appearance—doesn't your master allow you any better clothing than that? Moreover, you don't look like a slave to me, but like a man of good blood. Whose farm is this? I suppose this country is Ithaca, though the only man I met didn't seem to know much. I told him I was looking for a man I met some time ago, who visited me in my house. He said his father's name was Laertes, and that he came from Ithaca."

"This is Ithaca, indeed," said Laertes, "but it's not the same since your friend left here. The place is run by a set of thieves. Tell me, though, how long it was since you met Odysseus, my son? We have given him up for dead, and have not even had the opportunity to give him a proper burial. And you, sir, what is your name and your town? Did you bring your own ship, or did someone else put you ashore here?"

"My name," said Odysseus, "is Eperitus, son of Apheidas, and I come from Alybas. It's been four years since I saw Odysseus."

Then the old man groaned in anguish, and threw dirt on his head. Odysseus could no longer contain himself, and rushed up to Laertes: "Father, don't you know me? Look, here is the scar on my leg—and you remember that when I was a little boy, you gave me thirteen pear trees, ten apple trees, and forty fig trees, and showed me the fifty rows of grapes, all ripening at a different time, that I was to have."

The old man knew his son then, and his heart nearly broke for joy. "By the gods, it is my son! And if only those suitors were out of the way, I could be entirely happy—but I'm afraid they will be sending for help."

"Don't worry about that, father—Telemachus and I took care of them. Now come on down to the farmhouse, and let's have something to eat."

They went down to the steading where Telemachus and

the others were preparing dinner. For the first time in years, Laertes bathed and anointed himself, and put on his best clothes. Athene made him look taller and stronger than before, so that even Odysseus wondered to see the old man looking so well. As they were sitting down to eat, Dolius and his sons came up, and greeted their old master with rejoicing.

Meanwhile, in the town, the rumor of the suitors' death was spreading. Weeping, the mourners gathered at Odysseus' house and carried out the corpses. Then they went to an assembly, where Eupeithes, father of Antinous, addressed them; "I demand the outlawry of Odysseus! Where is his crew that he took to Ilium? Dead, every man of them! And where are our fine sons, the best men in Ithaca? Dead! Murdered! Before he can get away to one of his foreign friends, we must have our revenge!"

But Medon stood up to speak: "Friends, Odysseus was helped by the gods. I myself saw an Immortal, in the form of Mentor, standing with Odysseus, encouraging him, and striking down the suitors in heaps."

Old Halitherses, too, spoke for Odysseus: "It is the fault of you Ithacans that all this has happened. You would not listen to me or wise Mentor, but went on with your ruinous folly—eating up Odysseus' goods and making love to his wife. I advise you not to act rashly, or some of you will regret it."

But Eupeithes' oratory carried the assembly along; they would not listen to Mentor's wise words, and rushed to arm themselves, with Eupeithes at their head.

On Olympus, Athene spoke to Zeus: "What is your plan now, Son of Cronos? Shall it be a long feud, or will you make peace?"

Zeus replied, "Daughter, did not you plan all Odysseus' actions? Solve the problem as you like. I think, on the whole, it would be better to have peace. Let Odysseus be made king, and let there be a general amnesty for the killings." Heartened by these words, Athene swooped down from Olympus to Ithaca.

As the group in the farmhouse were eating their meal, they

heard a noise of armed men approaching. Quickly putting on their own bright bronze, they drew themselves up in battle array, and Laertes rejoiced to see his son and his grandson standing together in the front. Athene spoke to the old man: "Call on the gods, and let fly with your spear!" He did so, and struck Eupeithes fair on the face; then the others, raising the war-cry, fell upon the crowd, striking right and left. There would have been a great slaughter had not Athene cried out: "Stop this bloodshed!"

The Ithacans wavered and broke, each man trying to save himself by flight, with Odysseus in hot pursuit; but Zeus flung a thunderbolt, which struck in front of Athene. Then she cried, "No more, royal Odysseus, no more! Or you will offend the Father of the Gods!"

He held his hand, and desisted from slaughter. Then Athene, still wearing the shape of Mentor, went between the two parties, and made lasting peace.

SUGGESTIONS FOR FURTHER READING

Translations:

Lattimore, R. *Iliad*. Chicago, 1951

Murray, A. T. *Iliad* and *Odyssey*, Loeb Classical Library, Harvard University

Rieu, E. V. *Iliad* and *Odyssey*, Penguin Series (1946)

Rouse, W. H. D. *Iliad* and *Odyssey*, Mentor (1950)

Shaw, T. E. *Odyssey*. London, 1933

Other Books:

Bassett, S. E. *The Poetry of Homer*, Berkeley, 1938

Bowra, C. M. *Tradition and Design in the Iliad*, Oxford, 1930

Ceram, C. W. *Gods, Graves, and Scholars*, New York, 1952

Murray, Gilbert. *The Rise of the Greek Epic*, London, 1934

Scott, J. A. *The Unity of Homer*, Berkeley, 1921

THE
AENEID

TO VIRGIL

Written at the request of Mantuans for the nineteenth centenary of Virgil's death

Roman Virgil, thou that singest
    Ilion's lofty temples robed in fire,
Ilion falling, Rome arising,
    wars, and filial faith, and Dido's pyre;

Landscape-lover, lord of language,
    more than he that sang the Works and Days,
All the chosen coin of fancy
    flashing out from many a golden phrase;

Thou that singest wheat and woodland,
    tilth and vineyard, hive and horse and herd;
All the charm of all the Muses
    often flowering in a lonely word;

Poet of the happy Tityrus
    piping underneath his beechen bowers;
Poet of the poet-satyr
    whom the laughing shepherd bound with flowers;

Chanter of the Pollio, glorying
    in the blissful years again to be,
Summers of the snakeless meadow,
    unlaborious earth and oarless sea;

Thou that seest Universal
    Nature moved by Universal Mind;
Thou majestic in thy sadness
    at the doubtful doom of human kind;

Light among the vanish'd ages;
    star that gildest yet this phantom shore;
Golden branch amid the shadows,
    kings and realms that pass to rise no more;

Now thy Forum roars no longer,
    fallen every purple Cæsar's dome—
Tho' thine ocean-roll of rhythm
    sound forever of Imperial Rome—
Now the Rome of slaves hath perish'd,
    and the Rome of freemen holds her place,
I, from out the Northern Island
    sunder'd once from all the human race,
I salute thee, Mantovano,
    I that loved thee since my day began,
Wielder of the stateliest measure
    ever moulded by the lips of man.
            —TENNYSON

THE AENEID: INTRODUCTION

Publius Vergilius Maro was born in Mantua, a city of northern Italy, on October 15, 70 B.C. His family were apparently of humble origin, but were able to provide him with a good education, first at Mantua or Cremona, then at Milan, and finally at Rome. He intended to become a lawyer, but gave up his aspirations to return to the farm and work with his father. When, in 42, Octavianus Caesar and Mark Antony rewarded their soldiers for victory at the battle of Philippi with land taken from the cities which had opposed them, Vergil lost his property, and returned to Rome. He was received into the circle of poets who lived under the protection of the great patrician Maecenas, whose name has become a synonym for the wealthy and generous patron of literature. Under these auspices, he finished first the *Eclogues,* or *Bucolics,* which he had begun while still at home; then for some years he was employed on the *Georgics,* poems celebrating the work of the farm. All these shorter works show Vergil's preoccupation with the quiet, rural life; no man wrote better on the subjects he had chosen. The *Eclogues* are in imitation of the idylls of Theocritus, a Greek poet of the third century B.C.; the *Georgics* are modeled on Hesiod's *Works and Days.*

For the last ten years of his life, Vergil was occupied in writing the *Aeneid,* his greatest single work. He was a slow and careful writer, who polished his verses until they were in the best possible form. There is a tradition that shortly before his death, he asked that the *Aeneid* be destroyed as an unfinished work; fortunately his friends disregarded his wishes.

In 19 he went to Greece, where he planned to study literature and to give the final polish to his epic; but Augustus persuaded him to return to Rome, and on the way he died at Brindisi.

The period during which he lived began as a turbulent and restless one, and ended as a time of peace and prosperity. For most of the second and first centuries B.C., the frontiers of Rome had been moving steadily outward, and, both within and without Italy, ambitious men had been scheming to take for themselves the growing power of the Empire. This expansion, and the accompanying civil strife, reached a peak during the time of Julius Caesar (102-44 B.C.). Whether we think of him as a clever demagogue or a great statesman, it was to his efforts that Rome owed her wide dominions, which at his death extended from Scotland and Spain into Asia Minor. With his death at the hands of the conspirators, led by Brutus and Cassius, there began a feverish struggle for the absolute power which he had created and bequeathed.

His first heirs were the Second Triumvirate, which emerged from the anarchy which followed Caesar's death. Its members were Octavianus Caesar (named in his will by Caesar as his heir), Lepidus, and Mark Antony. For a time Antony was the chief member of the group, which, however, was not a stable organization. For a time Antony was at odds with the Senate and in league with Octavianus; then, when he and the other two members of the Triumvirate were able to come to terms with one another, they controlled the Senate, and shared among themselves the provinces of the Empire. Antony received the East, Lepidus received Africa, and the West fell to Octavianus.

Brutus and Cassius had been defeated by the united Triumvirs at Philippi in 42, but by 40 it was clear that individual ambitions had created stresses within the Triumvirate which must inevitably destroy it. Lepidus, after his conquest of Sicily, was deprived by Octavianus of all his offices except that of Pontifex Maximus, and Octavianus became supreme in the West and in Africa. In the meantime, Antony had allied himself with Cleopatra, Queen of Egypt, and presented a threat to the Empire. At the battle of Actium (31 B.C.) Octavianus defeated him, and became the ruler of the Western civilized world. On his victory he was granted the office of Tribune by the people, and the governorship of the provinces by the Senate, as well as the title of Augustus, the name by which he is most often called.

His next problem, after taking into his hands absolute power, was to consolidate it upon a firm foundation. His policies were successful: by showing himself unexpectedly gentle to those who had followed his late enemies, he was able to avoid the civil disorders which had followed earlier assumptions of power, and in 29 B.C. he closed the doors of the temple of Janus as a sign that peace had been restored. With peace came a new era of prosperity. The Roman roads, many still in existence, bound the Empire together with rapid communications; the provincial governments were reorganized to provide greater efficiency in administration (and to ensure that no provincial governor could set himself up as an independent ruler); a postal system was introduced; and Roman ships began to plow the Mediterranean n great fleets, bearing the wealth of the world to Rome. Within the city, Augustus undertook a project of rebuilding the city so great that he could, without empty boasting, say, "I found Rome brick, and left it marble."

The Age of Augustus was especially propitious for literature. Before his time, the Romans, a practical and hard-headed people, had sought distinction through careers in the Army, the Law, or the Senate. Under an absolute monarch, however, these careers no longer led to fame. As Commander-in-chief, Augustus received credit for all victories; and the army had been reduced in size. In the courts, it was not safe to prosecute a suit against the State; and the Senate had become a mere honorary body, completely subservient to the ruler. Trade was considered to be beneath the dignity of a patrician, though the Equites, "Knights," were emerging as a powerful trading class. There remained only two careers fit for honorable men: farming and writing; and the era of Augustus saw the emergence of the great farms which are still a mark of Italian agriculture. It saw, also, the greatest period of one of the world's great literatures.

Augustus early became aware that literature, especially poetry, would be of great service to him in the consolidation of his power. The *Aeneid* may be called, then, the first and greatest propaganda poem—a poem˅ designed to influence the thoughts and actions of its readers. Earlier poets, such as Ennius, had traced the lineage of the Romans to Troy; but none of them thought, as Vergil obviously thought, of celebrating the Roman virtues, the Roman State, and the glories of the ruler. Vergil's treatment of these themes, for which his story is the vehicle, sets him apart from other Roman epic poets. It is wrong, however, to consider him a mere hack, tailoring congratulatory verses to order, for he was a great artist, who felt deeply what he wrote.

Because most of Vergil's life had been spent in the troubled period of civil wars, he and his fellow poets were thoroughly conscious of the blessings of the *pax Romana* (the peace of Rome). They rightly ascribed these blessings to the rule of Augustus, and the greatest of them, Vergil, gladly centered his work upon the national glories.

In reading the *Aeneid* we are constantly struck by the prophetic character of many of the passages. The very beginning strikes the note of the whole work: Vergil promises to sing of the man who, though driven by Fate and the anger of Juno, made his way to Latium. In Book IV, Dido's curse on Aeneas presages the Punic Wars, from which Rome was to emerge victorious. Anchises, in Book VI, goes over the long roll of Aeneas' glorious descendants; Aeneas' shield, in Book VIII, is a recapitulation of traditional Roman history. Throughout the work we are reminded that the Julian family took their descent from Iulus, whose earlier name, Ilus, recalls that of Ilium. We are never allowed to forget that Rome's glorious past is but the prologue to her glorious present under Augustus, and that, if they retain their Roman virtues, the citizens of Rome may hope for a still more glorious future.

The adjective *pius*, which Vergil regularly attaches to Aeneas, does not imply a mere religiosity. *Pietas*, to the Roman, meant a proper and deeply-felt devotion to the gods and

State of Rome, to the family, and to the concept of loyalty. Just as Jove speaks, in Book I, of the special virtues of Aeneas, Anchises, in Book VI, speaks of the special virtues of the Romans. It is no coincidence that the terms are very nearly identical; Vergil thought of Aeneas as the type of all Roman virtues. So also Achates is called *fidus*, "the faithful Achates," because Vergil knew no greater quality in a second-in-command than an unswerving loyalty and devotion to the prince. On the other hand, we have the enemies of Aeneas: Turnus, Mezentius, and Messapus. These are called reckless, or violent, or even contemptuous of the gods: qualities of the primitive tribes who were destined to be conquered by the pious Aeneas and the faithful Achates.

The book is infused, also, with religious feeling, which it is hard to distinguish from the feeling for the Roman virtues. Augustus was concerned with reviving the religious spirit of Rome, and Vergil, himself a deeply religious man, was an important assistant in this endeavor. Nothing of importance in the *Aeneid* takes place without an invocation of the gods, in the proper form, with all due ceremonies. Vergil traces many contemporary religious practices to earlier periods, showing that they are of ancient origin. This is especially true of Aeneas' visit to the Cumaean Sibyl, whose oracles played an important part in Roman history.

Any epic poem, whether its aim be the mere telling of a story or the inculcation of a moral and political attitude—as with the *Aeneid*—must inevitably be compared with the greatest epics of them all, the works of Homer. For a long time it was fashionable to make this comparison of Vergil with Homer as the "artificial" poet and the "natural" poet. Such comparisons are not, however, warranted, for all poetry is the product of art. It is true that we know much more about the life of Vergil and the genesis of his work than we do about Homer's, for about the latter we know almost nothing. It is unfair, however, to think of Homer as an illiterate bard, patching up bits of old stories and hitting upon greatness by accident, for Homer was a very great poet. It is equally unfair to think of Vergil as a plodding craftsman, whose claim to greatness rests upon the high polish which he gave his work. Both Homer and Vergil were great, but great in different ways.

Homer, of course, was always Vergil's model for the epic; and Vergil would have been the first to concede Homer's superiority. In the very first line of the *Aeneid*:

Arma virumque cano, Troiae qui primus ab oris
"Arms and the man I sing, who first from the shores of Troy . . ."

we can perhaps trace reminiscences of the first words of the *Iliad* "[the] wrath," and the *Odyssey*, "[the] man." The indebtedness can be easily traced further: the first six books of the *Aeneid* are concerned, as is the *Odyssey*, with a man's wanderings before he reaches his destined home; and the last six books (which are perhaps less successful) with battle, as is the *Iliad*. It is also possible to see more detailed parallels: like Odysseus, Aeneas passed the Cyclopes, Scylla and Charybdis, and the Isle of Circe; he penetrated the regions of the Dead; he had Dido to contend with, as Odysseus was plagued by the amorous importunities of Calypso. Like Achilles, he pursued his enemy through the thickest of the fight; like Achilles, he was successful in combat, though we have no sympathetic feeling for Turnus as we have for the doomed Hector.

The style of the *Aneid* is less simple and direct than that of the Homeric poems, probably because Vergil was very conscious of his didactic purpose, and deliberately adopted a learned and allusive manner of presentation. Besides Homer, Vergil had as models the earlier Latin poets, Ennius, who linked the Romans with Troy, and Naevius, who had written the *Bellum Punicum*, an epic on the first war against Carthage, but these poets were not of his rank, and he improved on their epic style. It is worthy of remark, in this connection, that it is somehow easier to translate Homer into simple English than to do the same for Vergil, for his style seems to demand a somewhat more artificial treatment. Tennyson, however, sums the matter up very well in his lines

> All the chosen coin of fancy
> flashing out from many a golden phrase

and

> All the charm of all the Muses
> often flowering in a lonely word.

Such lines as

> *Timeo Danaos et dona ferentis*
> "I fear the Greeks, even bearing gifts"

have lived because they say something superlatively well; and no one has ever translated

> *Sunt lachrymae rerum, et mentem mortalia tangunt,*

which is a good indication that Vergil wrote greatly.

Throughout the Middle Ages Vergil was probably the most popular Roman poet. His works were very early taken as models for the study of rhetoric and poetry, and there has never been a year when someone was not discovering for the first time the world which he opens to the reader. Dante, in his *Divina Commedia,* took Vergil for a guide to the lower regions; Tasso studied him; Camoens modeled his *Lusiads* on the *Aeneid.* Vergil's apparent prophecy of the birth of Christ in his *Fourth Eclogue* was sufficient to rank him as a heathen prophet. It is interesting, also, to note that he was often thought of as a magician. This goes back to the practice, which seems to have arisen even during the Empire, of consulting the *Aeneid* by opening the book to any page, and putting one's finger on a line, or by thrusting a knife between the pages of a closed copy (with, of course, the appropriate ceremonies!) and reading the line which it touched: the "*Sortes Vergilianiae.*" This recalls the use of the Sibylline Books. Only the works of Vergil and Homer and the Bible have been accorded this measure of veneration.

The *Aeneid* has been translated, many times, into every modern European language. One of the first books printed in

English was a translation; and every century has seen one or more renderings of the work. The passages included from time to time in the following summary are from that of John Dryden (1697) which manages to convey much of the spirit of the original, though its ten-syllabled couplets by no means echo the sonorous roll of Vergil's hexameters.

THE AENEID: THE STORY

BOOK I:

    Arms and the man I sing, who forced by fate,
    And haughty Juno's unrelenting hate,
    Expelled and exiled, left the Trojan shore.
    Long labors, both by sea and land, he bore,
    And in the doubtful war, before he won
    The Latian realm, and built the destined town;
    His banished gods restored to rites divine,
    And settled sure succession on his line,
    From whence the race of Alban fathers come,
    And the long glories of majestic Rome.

Far across the sea lay a colony of the Tyrians, called Carthage, dearest of towns to the goddess Juno. Because, long before the Trojan War, she had been slighted by Paris, who gave the golden apple to Venus, she was incensed against the son of this goddess, Aeneas. Seeing the Trojan fleet set out for Carthage from Sicily, she called up all the winds of Aeolus to batter them. Quickly the ships were scattered:

    Three ships were hurried by the sudden blast,
    And on the secret shelves with fury cast.
    Three more fierce Eurus, in his angry mood,
    Dashed on the shallows of the moving sand,
    And in mid-ocean left them moored aland.
    Orontes' bark, that bore the Lycian crew
    (A horrid sight!) even in the hero's view
    From stem to stern by waves was overborne;
    The trembling pilot, from his rudder torn,

Was headlong hurled; thrice round the ship was tossed,
Then bulged at once, and in the deep was lost;
And here and there above the waves were seen
Arms, pictures, precious goods, and floating men.

But imperial Neptune, knowing that his sister Juno was angry
with Aeneas, and knowing that it was the will of the gods that
he should come safe to Latium, interposed. He called upon
the winds to leave his domain of ocean. They obeyed, and the
seas grew calm. The Trojans made their way into a little cove,
sheltered by an island from the open sea. Seven ships, the
remainder of the fleet, met there. The crews went ashore,
and faithful Achates struck fire with his flint and steel. They
ground some meal, and ate, while Aeneas went up on a headland to see the country. There he had a stroke of luck: he
killed seven great deer, and got them back to the ships, making
a welcome addition to their meal. As they shared out the meat,
Aeneas encouraged them to be of good heart; they had passed
Scylla and the land of the Cyclopes, and, if they were strong,
the gods would surely favor them.

On Olympus, Jupiter looked down on the rescued Trojans.
Venus approached him, and asked whether he intended to
permit Aeneas to achieve his purpose, or to thwart him.

"You promised once, a progeny divine
   Of Romans, rising from the Trojan line,
   In after times should hold the world in awe,
   And to the land and ocean give the law.
   How is your doom reversed, which eased my care
   When Troy was ruined in that cruel war? . . .
   What can I hope? What worse can still succeed?
   What end of labors has your will decreed? . . .
   . . . we, descended from your sacred line,
   Entitled to your heaven and rites divine,
   Are banished earth; and, for the wrath of one,
   Removed from Latium and the promised throne.
   Are these our sceptres? these our due rewards?
   And is it thus that Jove his plighted faith regards?"

To her Jove replied, "Daughter, know that the Fates are sure, and Aeneas shall achieve his desire. I have searched the future; your son shall indeed tame the fierce barbarians, build cities, and give them laws. This shall be within the time that the sun has thrice gone through his annual course. To him shall succeed Ascanius, now called Iulus. For three hundred years his line shall reign; then twin sons, Romulus and Remus, shall found the great city which shall take the name of Rome. To this city I set no bounds of space or time; she shall rule the whole world forever. A time will come when Troy shall be the conqueror of Greece. From the line of Iulus shall come the great Caesar, whose empire shall be limited only by the circling ocean, and whose fame shall be bounded only by the stars. With his reign will come an end to war and bloodshed; the gates of Janus' temple shall be shut, and the earth shall live under universal law."

That night Aeneas lay, revolving many things in his mind; and in the dawn, having concealed his ships below the overhanging rocks, he set off with Achates through the woods along the Libyan coast. As he walked, he met his mother, Venus, in the guise of a maiden huntress. "Have you," she said, "encountered any of my sisters?"

To this her son replied, "O maiden, none have we seen; but tell us, for surely you are a goddess or a nymph, in what land are we?"

And Venus answered him, "I cannot call myself divine; the maidens of Tyria carry bows and quivers. You see about you the country of Libya, ruled by Dido. Her husband, Sychaeus, was murdered by her brother Pygmalion, King of Tyre, who was greedy for Sychaeus' great riches, and his death was long concealed from her. But it was not to remain hidden; as she slept, the ghost of her husband appeared to her in a dream, and told her the story of his destruction. He showed her where his treasure lay buried, and counseled her to escape, lest a fate as dire as his befall her. Joining together a band of those who feared the bloody tyrant, they took ship and came hither across the sea. Here they purchased land, and now you see the towers of New Carthage rising before you. But tell me, stranger, from what shore do you come, and what do you seek?"

Sighing woefully, Aeneas answered, "O goddess, to repeat my story would be a day's task, and a sad one. We are of old Troy, expelled by force—surely you have heard of us. I am Aeneas, descended from Jupiter; with twenty ships I set out, bearing my household gods, to seek a new home in Latium. Seven only are left to me; far on the seas I have been tossed, and now, expelled from Asia and Europe alike, I have landed on these barren African shores."

The goddess, moved by pity, spoke to her son, "Have courage, for the signs of Heaven are propitious. Your scattered ships are joined again; and see in the Heavens the twelve swans: pursued by an eagle, the bird of Jove, they swoop close to the ground; now, clapping their wings, they fly together again. Go forward to the city, follow this path where it leads you!" So speaking, she turned away; and her divine radiance showed that she was indeed the goddess and his mother.

> The prince pursued the parting deity
> With words like these: "Ah! whither do you fly?
> Unkind and cruel! to deceive your son
> In borrowed shapes, and his embrace to shun;
> Never to bless my sight, but thus unknown:
> And still to speak in accents not your own."

So speaking, he bent his steps toward the city, and the goddess flew off to her beloved Paphos. But she watched over him as he marched forward, casting a veil of invisibility about him so that none might do him harm.

Ascending a hill which overlooks the city, the two paused to behold it. There they saw the Carthaginians hard at their work: some were laying out streets, some building great houses where before only cottages had stood; some with great stones were raising turreted walls to enclose the city. In the center of the two was the grove sacred to Juno, for there the Carthaginians had dug up a horse's head, a sign from the goddess that the city should prosper in war and be renowned for many ages. Within the grove was the temple of the goddess, most nobly built, and endowed with rich gifts. As Aeneas beheld it, he wept, for it was adorned with carvings depicting the whole story of the Trojan War: Diomedes killing the sleeping sentries; Achilles, with the body of Hector behind his chariot, coursing around the walls of Troy: the fruitless visit of the Trojan matrons to the temple of Pallas. "O faithful Achates," said the weeping Aeneas to his friend, "see, even strangers know the harsh fate of our people."

As he spoke, Queen Dido appeared, moving through the throng with stately pace. As on the tops of Mount Cynthus Diana leads the dance of maidens, in beauty above them all, so Dido passed, with her train. She mounted her throne, where it was her custom to dispense justice; with equity she settled disputes among her subjects. Before her then were brought a great crowd of Trojans, whom Aeneas recognized: Cloanthus and Antheus and strong-armed Sergestus—captains of his ships, who had been tossed ashore by the great storm. They appealed to the Queen: "O gracious lady, spare our ships, we pray, from the fire! For we have not come here to ravage the land, or to drive away booty. Such arrogance is not for the vanquished. We are of the race of Troy, and long we have been seeking a new home, far in the West, called Italy. Our way was thither, when suddenly stormy Orion cast us upon these shores. But what race of men denies the wind-beaten traveler refuge? For what cause do you set upon us? Remember that the gods know what is right for men to do! Our leader was Aeneas; if he yet lives, and is not thrown on the rocky coast, we shall not despair. Permit us, we pray, to refit our ships and to carve new oars, and then let us be on our way to Italy."

Dido replied, "Friends, have no fear, for my own hard fate has taught me to pity the conquered. Who has not heard of the valorous Trojans? Wherever you wish to go, I will assist you with all my powers. Would that Aeneas had been driven here by the same wind, for it would please us all greatly to have you settle with us, and let Trojan and Tyrian be treated alike."

As she spoke, the cloud which veiled Aeneas and Achates cleared, and he stood forth before them all. "I whom you seek am here, rescued from the waves. O Queen, who alone have taken pity upon us, may the gods repay you well! So long as the rivers run into the sea, or the shadows of the clouds move across the hill shall we praise your name!" And with these words he clasped again the hands of his beloved comrades.

Astonished, the Queen said, "Are you indeed that Aeneas, goddess-born, but pursued even to our shores by a harsh fate? Long ago I heard from my father, Belus, the story of the Trojan War; even your foes praised your valor. Come, noble youths, and taste our hospitality." With this she led the Trojans into her great palace, rich in gorgeous furnishings, and, after a magnificent banquet, presented them with gifts. Aeneas dispatched Achates to the ships, directing him to send back his son, Ascanius, with presents saved from Troy, for the Queen.

But Venus planned otherwise. In the place of Aeneas' son she sent her own, Cupid, in the form of Ascanius, bearing gifts. The other lad she conveyed to a place sacred to herself, lest he should discover the plot.

Obedient to her commands, Cupid, bearing the presents, went to Dido's palace. Within sat Aeneas and Dido, a great banquet spread before them. Having embraced his supposed father, he went to the Queen, who took him in her lap, not knowing what god she was holding. Remembering his mother's instructions, Cupid, with all his wiles, began to erase her memories of Sychaeus, and to inflame her heart with love for Aeneas.

The viands were removed, and the wine-cups brought forth. Dido, taking a great bowl of wine, uttered a prayer that the gods be propitious to them all, and poured the libation-offering. Then the drinking-bowls went round, while the minstrel sang, and Dido, drinking not of wine but of the draughts of love, questioned Aeneas concerning the long war, and of his seven years' wandering.

Book II:

> All were attentive to the godlike man,
> When from his lofty couch he thus began:
> "Great Queen, what you command me to relate
> Renews the sad remembrance of our fate:
> An empire from its old foundations rent,
> And every woe the Trojans underwent;
> A peopled city made a desert place;
> All that I saw, and part of which I was;
> Not even the hardest of our foes could hear,
> Nor stern Ulysses tell without a tear. . . .
> I will restrain my tears, and briefly tell
> What in our last and fatal night befell.

"The Greeks, apparently disheartened at the failure to conquer Troy, pretended to sail away; but they traveled only as far as Tenedos, an island not far from the Trojan shore, where they lay hidden. Before their departure, they had built a very great horse, which they feigned to be an offering to appease Minerva, and to secure their safe return; but it was hollow within, and filled with armed men. This they left behind them; and when, confident of our victory, we sallied forth, we beheld it standing on the plain. We wondered greatly at it, and men talked of what we should do. Some were for dragging it within the walls; others were for burning it; still others for opening it to see what it contained. Laocoön, son of Priam and Hecuba, cried aloud, 'O foolish people, do you really believe that the enemy have departed? Do you think that the Greeks are without guile? Do you not remember Ulysses? Whatever this is, it is bad: I fear the Greeks even when they bring gifts.' So speaking, he hurled his spear at the figure, which rang hollow. Would that we had listened to him! But at that moment, shepherds came, leading with them a stranger. Though we knew it not then, he was ready either for death at our hands or to lead us to our own destruction.

"We gathered about him, asking him his name and nation. He replied, 'O King, I confess that I am a Greek, an unhappy creature named Sinon. While my father, Palamedes, lived, and maintained his reputation in my country, I was happy; but malicious Ulysses, ever treacherous, brought false charges of treason against him, and he was killed. Since then I have lived a miserable existence, always hounded by the enmity of Ulysses, and powerless to save myself from his persecutions. Why should I spin out my story? You know that I am a Greek; with one blow end my misery.' But, unfamiliar with Greek treachery, we urged him to continue.

" 'Weary with the war, the Greeks decided to abandon their efforts, but the winds being contrary they could not leave. The oracle declared that without a human sacrifice they could never reach their homes; and Calchas, at Ulysses' instigation, pointed me out as the victim. I was seized, and prepared with all due ceremony for the sacrifice; but in the night I made my escape, and hid in the fens near by.'

"Moved by his speech, Priam ordered that his bonds be loosened, and asked him of the horse: who made it, and why? The other, raising his freed hands to Heaven, cried out, "O Gods, now I am released from my obligations to the Greeks! Now I am free to tell their dreadful designs! And you, Trojans, I pray that, when I have told you all, you will be merciful.

" 'Pallas Athene had always been the hope of the Greeks, but when impious Diomedes and Ulysses stole away the Palladium from Troy, she averted her face from them. Even in the camp there were evil omens: the statue of the goddess glowed like fire, while salt sweat poured from its limbs. Then Calchas, terrified, declared that we must leave Troy to repeat our sacrifices at Argos if we hoped to win. This horse we prepared as an offering to atone for the theft of the Palladium. Calchas declared that if you rejected the offering, then the Greeks would be successful; if you accepted it, dragging it into the city to the temple of Minerva, then all Asia would be victorious even in the Greek mainland.'

"We believed his lies, and were about to draw the horse within the walls. Laocoön attempted to prevent us; but there came—I shudder, telling of it—two horrible serpents gliding through the sea. First they seized the bodies of his two sons; then, as he advanced to combat, they twined themselves about him, choking him so that he died. All the Trojans declared that he had suffered a proper punishment for his impiety, and, working together, we breached the walls and dragged the horse within the city. Undeterred by the laments of Cassandra, we pulled it into the temple of Minerva.

"Night came upon the city, and from the isle of Tenedos the Greeks made their stealthy way. Sinon opened the horse, and the chieftains slid down the rope. They unbarred the gates to admit their comrades, and all together fell upon the sleeping city. I dreamed that Hector stood before me, urging me to fly; then I was awakened by the roar of the burning town. Seizing my arms in haste, I rushed out, eager for battle; a few of us managed to fight for a time, but we had been overwhelmed by Greek treachery, and longer fight was useless. Through the streets we made our way to the palace of King Priam, hoping to make some stand there. The pavements were littered with the bodies of friend and foe, the bright walls grimed with blood and smoke. Arrived at the palace, we were in time to see it crumble to the earth, and old Priam slain by the cruel Pyrrhus.

"My friends had deserted me, and I was alone. Standing thus in despair, I saw Helen, for whom all this slaughter was made, hiding in the temple. Determined that she should not return with Menelaus to rule over slaves taken from Troy, I drew my sword, and would have killed her, though there is no glory in killing a woman. At that moment, however, my divine mother appeared to me, and stilled my rage. 'Seek your father Anchises, my son, your wife Creusa, and little Iulus. No longer can you defend Troy: See, there is mighty Juno at the Scaean Gate, and Pallas stands upon the walls. Even Jupiter, Father of Gods and Men, fights on the Greek side. Hasten away in flight, bringing your family with you; and I will stand beside you in every danger.' So speaking, she vanished into the gloom.

"Then it seemed to me that all Ilium stooped to its base, and perished in the flames. Swiftly I returned to the home of my father, who would not, at first, accompany me. Even the supplications of my mother and my dear wife could not move him from his determined course; but when he saw a bright and holy flame shine upon the head of little Iulus, and heard the thunder of Zeus on his left—a good omen!—he resigned himself to flight. Carrying him upon my back, we set forth, my father carrying the household gods, and Creusa and Iulus following a little to the rear. We made our way to a deserted temple of Ceres, whither our servants had gone, carrying what they could rescue. But think of my horror, when I arrived there, to find that Creusa was not with us! Filled with anguish, I returned to our house, which even then was being plundered, and went through it, calling her name. As I searched, the phantom of Creusa appeared before me, more beautiful than in life, and said, 'It is not the will of the gods that I accompany you to your fated destination; long must you roam until you come to the land where the Tiber rolls his gentle stream. There a great state and a noble wife await you. Dry your tears for Creusa, and now farewell!'

"Three times I endeavored to embrace the shade, and as often she eluded me. Then, heavy at heart, I returned to the temple. Here had come my companions, Trojans determined to follow me in exile. By this time, the morning star was rising, and, carrying my aged father, I led the way into the mountains."

Book III: "When it appeared that the gods destined the people of Troy to seek distant lands in exile, we fitted out our fleet, and early in the first summer launched into the deep, bearing our fortunes and our household gods. Not far off lies a land, cultivated by the Thracians; there we came ashore, and erected our first walls. Bent on making sacrifice to my divine mother, I tore a limb from a green myrtle which grew near by; and, dreadful to say, the tree dripped blood. Once and again I tried; at the third attempt the tree spoke, begging me to spare it, for it was Polydorus, whom Priam had sent to be reared by the King of Thrace, but who had been murdered for his gold. Struck with horror, we determined to quit that cursed land,

and, when we had pacified the shade of Polydorus with appropriate sacrifice, again we set forth.

"Far in the sea lies a lovely island, sacred to Neptune. Thither we sailed, and were received with royal courtesy by Anius its King. Going to the temple of Apollo, I prayed, 'Grant us, Father, a dwelling-place, a spot where we may build the walls of our city. Or give us a sign, that we may know where it is fated we shall dwell.' As I spoke the ground shook beneath us, and a voice was heard, 'Sons of Dardanus, you shall dwell in the land from which you are sprung; there the family of Aeneas shall reign, and his descendants after him.'

"My father, remembering our old history, said, 'Listen: in the midst of the sea lies Crete, the cradle of our family. From this land came Teucrus, our mighty ancestor. Come then, let us seek Crete, at the distance of three days' sail.'

"With eager hearts we launched our vessels, and with a following wind we came to Crete. There I erected our walls, calling the city Pergamus; and for a time we dwelt in contentment. But suddenly a great plague infected us all, sparing not even the grain which we grew. Men died swiftly, or dragged their weary bodies in sickness. My father, knowing that we were not at the end of our travels, advised consulting again the oracle of Ortygia. As I lay sleepless, I saw the ancestral gods, brought from Troy, gleaming in the bright moonlight, and they seemed to say, 'These are not the shores destined for your dwelling, but far in the West, in Hesperia, lies a land inhabited by those who call it Italy. This is your destined home; there shall we be set up again, the guardians of your hearths.'

"Astonished by the vision, I arose and offered sacrifice; and told those things to Anchises. He recognized then the double lineage of the Trojans, and knew that he had been deceived; often, he said, had Cassandra spoken of Hesperia—but who had believed her? And he counselled us to entrust ourselves again to the deeps, to sail to our destined homes.

"Soon we were at sea, and when the land had faded from view, we were engulfed by a dreadful storm, lasting for three

days. On the fourth, we saw before us the country of the Stro-
phades; there we landed. Killing some of the cattle which
grazed along the shore, we prepared the sacrifice and the banquet; but no sooner was the meal spread before us than the
Harpies were upon us, screaming, snatching the food from before us, and fouling the ground with their touch. They are obscene fowls, birds with the faces of maidens. Although when
we had prepared more food, and I had drawn up our warriors
to defend it with their swords, the Harpies seized it again, for
they are invulnerable. Celaeno, their leader, perching in a tree,
cried aloud, 'Woe to you, Trojans, for your killing of our cattle, and your attack upon us! Sail for Italy, where you shall
raise your city; but you may not succeed until for hunger you
eat your wooden platters!'

"My companions, distressed and terrified, urged me to so-
licit the favor of the gods with prayer and sacrifice. My father,
having called upon the Immortals, ordered the ships to sea,
and westward again we sailed.

"Coasting along, we passed the land of Ithaca, home of the
cruel Ulysses, and came to land at Actium. There we celebrated our games, and I hung in the temple of Apollo the arms
I had taken from the Greeks. We rounded the cape, and came
into the country of Epirus, where we were amazed to learn
that Helenus ruled and Andromache had taken refuge. As it
happened, she was even then making offering to the shade of
Hector; and beholding us she burst into tears, unable to believe that other Trojans had escaped. She told us, too, her own
sad story: how, after the burning of Troy, she had been taken
by Neoptolemus, son of Achilles, and handed over to Helenus,
who had also been made a slave by the Greeks. But Orestes,
who had been betrothed to Hermione, daughter of Menelaus
and Helen, slew Neoptolemus when he heard that Hermione
was married to him, and by this death part of the kingdom fell
to Helenus.

"Then we advanced to the city, which had been built to
resemble Troy. There I met Helenus, the prophet, and solicited

him to tell us dangers we should encounter on our voyage, and how we should surmount them.

"Having made the due sacrifices, he led me to the temple, where he prophesied: 'Goddess-born, a few things I am permitted to reveal, but not all, for Juno forbids it. Know, that you must sail a long and difficult voyage before you reach the land which you think is near. This is the sign by which you shall recognize it: a white sow, suckling thirty white pigs, shall be the place of your city. Avoid these nearer shores of Italy, for the Greeks inhabit them. And whenever you shall come to land to make sacrifice, muffle your head in a purple veil, lest the stranger, coming upon you, disturb the omens. This do forever. At the tip of Italy, between Calabria and Sicily, is a narrow strait, guarded by Scylla on the one hand and Charybdis on the other. It is safest to avoid these waters, and to coast round the island. Above all things, venerate Juno with sacrifices in Sicily, and earn her affection. Going thence, you will come to the grotto of the Cumaean Sibyl. Though your companions may chide you, saying that you lose time, consult her, that she may tell you the future of the Italian State. These are all the prophesies I may make. Go, and good fortune attend your voyage!'

"Having spoken these words, he caused a great treasure to be heaped in our ships, and provided us with oarsmen and new sails. Andromache also was ready with gifts, for, looking upon my Ascanius, she thought of her son Astyanax. And exchanging promises that our new land should be one with theirs, both sprung from Troy, we set forth.

"Past the Ceraunian mountains we coasted, directing our course to the West. Early in the morning of the second day, we spied a land ahead, and Achates cried out, 'Italy!' We poured libations, and briefly went ashore to sacrifice, as Helenus had commanded, to Juno; then quitted these lands, inhabited by Greeks. Past Tarentum we directed our course, and full ahead we could see the glowing mountain of Etna, where Enceladus lies. Then beside us was the gulf of Charybdis; bending ourselves to the oars, and tossed about by the whirlpool, we nevertheless escaped her clutches. We rowed through the night, past the land of the Cyclopes; and early in the dawn we saw upon the land a man, tattered and emaciated. Rushing to the shore, he supplicated us with outstretched arms; when we had brought him aboard, he confessed himself a Greek, left behind by Ulysses. For three years he had lived among the bloodthirsty Cyclopes, existing as best he could on berries and what he could find. We granted him succor; as we spoke, blinded Polyphemus himself strode past, guiding his steps with a great pine tree. Hearing us as we fled, he would have seized us, but, disappointed, he raised a terrible yell, at which the earth and the seas trembled. We could see his dreadful brothers, summoned by his cry. Frightened, the sailors set out to sea, but their course would have taken us again between Scylla and Charybdis, which to avoid we retraced our path over the sea.

"Now, favored by the wind, we passed the island of Ortygia, where rise the mingled waters of the river Alpheus, with those of the fountain of Arethusa, and coasting the shore, we arrived at the cheerless port of Drepanum. Here, alas! the best of fathers, Anchises, perished. His death, not foretold by Helenus, was the end of my long and unhappy voyage."

> Thus, to the listening Queen, the royal guest
> His wandering course and all his toils expressed;
> And here concluding, he retired to rest.

Book IV: But all the night no sleep came upon the eyelids of Dido, inflamed as she was by love for Aeneas. Early in the dawn she spoke to her sister, Anna: "O sister, what dreams have distracted me! What do you think of our guest; is he not manly, not heroic? And what dangers he has passed! Since the death of Sychaeus, I have vowed to live alone; only Aeneas disturbs that firm resolve. But how can I violate my pledge?"

Anna replied, "O dearest of sisters, can you think that the dead care for such vows? Why should you waste your life in solitude? What though Iarbas and the other princes of this land have not moved you to love? Think of your country, sur-

rounded by barbarians, and of the danger which may come to
you from Tyre! How prosperous, how happy would such a
union make this land! Surely it was by the favor of Juno that
Aeneas came to us. Pray to the gods that they may keep him
here, enjoying your hospitality, while the wind rages, troubling
the seas."

Inspired with hope, Dido and Anna went to the temples,
where they sacrificed and sought omens, making their greatest
offering to Juno, who watches over marriages. During the day,
Dido went through the town, showing to Aeneas the fortifica-
tions being built; at evening, the banquet was renewed, and
Dido hung upon Aeneas' every word.

Meanwhile, Juno spoke artfully to Venus, "Surely your beloved son and yourself will win great praise from the love of
these two! I know that you fear the rising power of Carthage,
but why should not there be peace? Dido burns with love for
Aeneas, and if they are married, she will convey Carthage to
him as her dowry."

Venus, perceiving the wiles of Juno, replied, "Who can reject
such terms? But I know not whether it is the will of the gods
that he should dwell here. It should be your task to consult
Jove, for he is your consort."

And Juno answered, "Let it be so. Tomorrow they plan to
hunt in the forest. I shall send a great storm of rain and hail,
driving them to shelter in a cave. There I shall be, and Hymen,
god of Marriage. Let us consecrate their vows, if it is your
will." And Venus, knowing what Juno planned, assented.

In the morning, Dido, clad in the garments of the huntress,
came to the court where the nobles waited. Aeneas, moving
with matchless grace and manly beauty, joined her for the
hunt, and the great train issued through the gates. Ascanius,
mounted on a swift horse, leaped over walls, all eager to start a
raging boar.

But now the air filled with tumult; rain, mingled with hail,
fell upon the earth, and the hunters scattered, seeking shelter
from the storm. Dido and Aeneas entered the cave, and the
Heavens witnessed their union: lightnings flashed, the nymphs

called out on the mountaintops. That day was the source of all Dido's woe, and of her death; no longer did she carry on a clandestine love, but under the name of marriage she concealed her guilt.

Through the streets of Carthage sped the goddess Rumor, whose body is filled with eyes and tongues, filling the ears of the people with mingled fact and fiction. Iarbas, King of Libya, inflamed by the reports of Dido's love for Aeneas, called upon mighty Jove for help against the wiles of the woman and her Trojan lover. And hearing him, the Father of the Gods dispatched wingèd Mercury to call back to Aeneas' mind his duty of founding imperial Rome.

Gliding to the African coast, Mercury saw Aeneas, girt with a sword given him by Dido, occupied in constructing walls and towers for the city. The god spoke, "Aeneas, is this your destined task, to raise a city here? Know that Jove has sent me to call again to your mind the duties that lie before you. If you care nothing for your own glory, think at least of your successor, Iulus, for whose line the Roman Empire is destined." And so speaking he vanished.

Awed by the divine message, Aeneas revolved in his mind whether to leave the land now so dear to him or to remain. If he should leave, how break the news to Dido? Swiftly calling to him his lieutenants, he bade them prepare the fleet for secret departure, while he himself decided how best to bring about the success of their design. Swiftly and joyfully they went to their appointed tasks.

But who can deceive a loving woman? The news reached her even before Aeneas, and wild with love and rage, she reproached him, "Cannot our plighted love restrain you from this voyage? Cruel man, will you fly from me across this wintry sea? If ever I deserved thanks from you, abandon your design, and remain here. Is it for this that I fled from Tyre, and repelled the Libyan lords? Are you my husband, or only my guest?"

Aeneas replied, "Were it only my choice, I should remain; but I cannot claim the name of husband, and the Fates have destined me for other purposes. Deeply indebted to you as I am, it is to Italy that I am called, nor may I go elsewhere. You too have known what it is to settle a foreign land—let us Trojans claim the same privilege! Jove himself has spoken to me through his messenger, and, though it is not my choice, I must obey."

Then Dido, driven to madness by Aeneas' firm resolve, swooned away. But Aeneas, strong in his purpose, made all ready for departure, and launched the ships into the sea. Looking upon him from the walls of Carthage, Dido addressed her sister, Anna: "Bear him this message: not to leave Carthage in this storm! Though he will not call himself husband, yet I have a care for him. Let him only remain until the winds have abated." She carried the message to Aeneas, but he did not relent.

Unhappy Dido, struck to the heart, longed for death; and seeing the Trojan ships depart, prepared a great pyre, saying that she intended to work magic. On it she placed the arms which Aeneas had left behind, and his other possessions. On it she poured water, like that of Avernus, and placed also on the pyre baleful herbs, cut by moonlight. Calling upon Erebus, Chaos, and Hecate, she brought down a dreadful curse upon her treacherous lover: that he might long suffer the ravages of war, and at last make a dishonorable peace; and that, on death, he should not have the rites due him. Then, lighting the immense pyre, she fell upon her sword, and died; and the flames consumed the wretched Queen.

From Olympus, Juno sent her messenger Iris, who cut from her head the lock of Proserpine:

Downward the various goddess took her flight,
And drew a thousand colors from the light;
Then stood above the dying lover's head,
And said, "Thus I devote thee to the dead.
This offering to th' infernal gods I bear."
Thus while she spoke, she cut the fatal hair:
The struggling soul was loosed, and life dissolved in air.

Book V: Meanwhile Aeneas was directing his course over the sea. Astern, he saw the fateful blaze; the sight brought dismal forebodings to the Trojans' hearts. Overhead, the sky loomed dark, and the winds increased their fury; even skillful Palinurus, the pilot, could no longer hold the ship to her course, but, calling out to Aeneas that they must not try to reach Italy in the storm, laid the vessel's head for Sicily. This Aeneas was very willing to do, for in the port of Drepanum lived his old friend and supporter, Acestes, and there his father's ashes were buried.

Acestes received them joyfully. When the next day's dawn had chased away the last stars, Aeneas summoned his companions to an assembly. "This day," he said, "is that on which, a year ago, my father perished. Though I were in the farthest parts of the earth I should remember it, and pay the sacrifices due his shade. Let us, then, hold the games, and feast. Acestes has given each ship two oxen; crown your brows with the holy myrtle, and keep a sacred watch upon your speech."

They went, led by Ascanius, to the tomb. Here, in libation, the boy poured out bowls of milk, of wine, of sacred blood, and prayed to the spirit of his grandsire. From beneath the tomb appeared a huge serpent, who, gliding over the altars, tasted the offerings, and gently retired into the tomb. Then Aeneas made a great sacrifice, both to the genius of the spot and the shade of his parent. About him, the Trojans slew the sacrificial oxen, and roasted them on spits.

After eight days of feasting, the sports were commenced, with great prizes for the victors. The first was the race of ships: eagerly the rowers, stretching their arms to the oars, awaited the signal, and sent their vessels scudding through the sea. The victor was Cloanthus, and deservedly so; for, though left behind in the beginning of the race, he called the sea-gods to his aid, and Nereids pushed him to victory. Then came the footraces: Nisus was leading, but slipped and fell, and his dear friend, Euryalus, claimed the victory. After these there were boxing with the cestus, javelin-throwing, and the chariot race

—the winners, loaded with prizes, carried them to their ships.[1]

But while they sported, Saturnian Juno, revolving in her mind many plots, dispatched swift Iris to the Trojan women. Assuming the shape of Beroe, an old Trojan wife, she cried, "Alas, unhappy women! For seven long years we have wandered, seeking refuge, and finding it only here. Why should we go further? Here is the land of our brother Eryx, and his friend Acestes—why should not we build here the walls of the town to be named after Troy? Now come with me—let us burn those accursed ships. Even the gods are propitious—see the flaming altars of Neptune!" And seizing from the altar a burning branch, she threw it at the ships. Though Pyrgo, nurse of Priam's sons, remonstrated that this was not Beroe, the other Trojan matrons followed the running figure, bearing fiery torches, and setting fire to the ships, whose pitchy calking made them an easy prey.

Now Ascanius came up, leading the other Trojans, and called out to them to desist. Suddenly aware of what they had done, the women threw away the torches, and hid themselves in the woods. But the fire continued, smoking and smouldering below the decks. Aeneas called upon Almighty Jove to aid him, and suddenly a heavy rain, with hail and thunder, drenched the ships and extinguished the fires, so that but four ships were lost.

Then Aeneas, in doubt and dread, pondered whether to continue his course to Italy or to remain in Sicily. Old Nautes, one of the wisest, advised that they should take counsel with Acestes; and as they spoke, the figure of Anchises appeared in the darkness of night, "Do as Nautes commands; I am sent hither by Jove to help you. Seek out the land of Latium with your strongest men. But first, consult the Sibyl, who will conduct you to the shades of Avernus, and will teach you there what fates are assigned to you and your race." So speaking, he vanished, for the day was close upon them.

[1] Lines 104-604 are among the best in the work, but to translate them would take too much space here. Read them in a good translation, or, better yet, learn Latin and read them in Vergil's own words.

Now Aeneas marked out with the plow a noble city, and erected a second Troy. There Acestes gave the laws, and a priest was assigned to the tomb of Anchises. The women were left to be the colonists, while the young men and the warriors prepared to sail to Cumae. Even the women, who so recently were the dupes of Juno, wept that they could not continue the voyage. But Aeneas, standing at the prow of the leading ship, cast a libation into the sea, and the oarsmen sent the fleet on its way.

In the Heavens, Venus spoke to Neptune: "Be not swayed by the will of Juno, who bears anger in her breast against my son. Remember what great storms she raised in the deep near Libya! Be propitious, I pray, and let the Trojans reach the Tiber."

And Neptune replied, "It shall be as you will; the seas shall be calm and the voyage prosperous. One life only shall be lost in the sea, one life given for many."

When the night was half over, the god of Sleep came to Palinurus, the steersman, and shook the dew of Lethe upon his head. Overcome with drowsiness he fell asleep, and the god, leaning against him, broke off part of the stern, and with it Palinurus fell into the sea, his cries unheard. Aeneas, feeling the vessel turn from her course, took the helm, weeping for the fate of his trusty companion.

Book VI: Aeneas guided his vessel to Cumae, where they moored and went ashore. The young men ranged through the woods, seeking water and game, but Aeneas, mindful of his duty, went through the groves of Apollo and Diana to the Sibyl's cave. On the bronze gates before its entrance were carved episodes of old story: of Pasiphaë, the Labyrinth of Crete, of Daedalus, first of men to fly through the air, and his ill-fated son Icarus. The priestess, seeing the Trojans, called them to her sacred temple, where, inspired by the spirit of Apollo, and speaking in a voice more than mortal, she called upon Aeneas to utter prayers. Aeneas invoked Apollo: "O thou who hast ever pitied the Trojans, and guided them in their wanderings, spare our race! And, holy prophetess, speak to me of the fate of my people, and tell whether it is destined that they shall find refuge in Latium! There I will raise a great temple, there I will deposit the oracles. But grant that these be not written, as is your wont, on oak leaves, lest they fly about in disorder."

Then, still infused by the spirit of the god, the prophetess spoke, her words echoing through the wide cave: "O thou who hast spanned the wide sea, yet more trials lie before thee! The Trojans shall indeed come to Latium, but there I see the rivers running with blood, another Achilles awaiting thee! Nor shall Juno desist from her wrath, and once again a foreign woman shall be your sorrow! But bear all these things, and though you least expect it, a Grecian city shall save the Trojans!"

When she had ceased, Aeneas replied, "All these things I have considered in my mind. Now I ask only that I be permitted to visit the realm of Avernus, and to speak, in the Elysian Fields, with that father whom I bore from Troy."

To his prayer the priestess answered, "The descent into Avernus is easy, and the return hard. But if you still desire to visit that land, first seek the tree sacred to Proserpina, Juno of the lower world, bearing a golden bough. If the fates are with you, it will come away easily, but if they are against you, not even the sword will sever it. And your friend's body also lies unburied—though you know nothing of this as yet. Bury him with due rites, and you shall have a view of the Stygian groves."

Aeneas, accompanied by faithful Achates, made his way to the shore, revolving in his mind the speech of the prophetess. As they came they encountered the body of Misenus, a great warrior, especially renowned for his power to summon warriors with the trumpet. Presumptuously he had challenged the god Triton to a trial of skill, and the enraged deity crushed him among the rocks. Then the Trojans set about preparing his obsequies, felling trees for the great pyre. They placed him upon it with the proper offerings, and burned him; then, gathering the ashes, they deposited these beneath a great mound.

Meanwhile, Aeneas went into the woods, seeking the golden bough. Before him fluttered two doves, sent by his mother; he followed them, and came to the tree, whose golden branch came off easily in his hand. This done, he quickly executed the Sibyl's orders, sacrificing four bullocks and a lamb, and calling upon Hecate; to Proserpina he sacrificed a heifer. Then the ground beneath them trembled, and the prophetess cried out, "Far hence be gone, ye unsanctified! And Aeneas, do you march boldly forward, bearing your sword." And with these words, she plunged into the cave yawning before them.

Past the places where dwell Care and Grief and Old Age and Sleep, cousin to Death, they made their way, and deeper, past the savages: Scyllas and hundred-armed Briareus, the Gorgons and the Harpies. Aeneas, struck with fear, would have defended himself with his sword; but his guide restrained him, for they were only insubstantial spirits.

At the flood of Acheron they encountered Charon, the ferryman of the dead, a grim figure, who poles his boat across the river of the dead. By the bank stood a great crowd of spirits, the souls of those buried without due rites; for a hundred years it was their fate to remain on the near side of the river, before they could cross over. There Aeneas saw many of his old comrades, debarred from entering the land of the Dead, because they had perished at sea, where the proper sacrifices could not be made, among them his steersman Palinurus, who told him how, after he had fallen from the ship, he had swum for three days to shore, and there been slain by savages. The spirit implored Aeneas either to visit the spot of his death and to erect there a funeral mound, or to carry him immediately into Avernus; but the Sibyl repelled him, saying that his slayers, to avert divine anger, would erect a memorial, and call the place of his death after his name.

Then Charon approached, and demanded of Aeneas whether he came like Pirithous to rescue any of the dead. The prophetess replied, showing him the golden branch, that Aeneas had come only to visit his parent, and that he meant no harm to the infernal deities. Then, clearing out the load of ghosts, Charon made room in his boat, which groaned under the weight of a living man, and took in much water from the river.

When they had reached the farther shore the prophetess threw into the mouth of three-headed Cerberus, guardian of the realm, a cake made with honey and poppy, which cast him into a deep sleep.

Going forward, they passed through the fields of mourning, where they saw many a shade, among them Dido. To her Aeneas spoke, weeping, and endeavoring to call forth a favorable reply; but, bending her eyes upon the ground, she retreated into a grove, where Sychaeus, her first husband, comforted her.

He saw also many a noble Trojan, and many a Greek—these fled the living hero. Deiphobus was there, and told him how he had been slain by the Greeks, who had been admitted to his house by the treacherous Helen.

As they continued their course, Aeneas saw many another, famous in story: Ixion, and Tityus, and Sisyphus; but the priestess hastened past the scenes of their torment, anxious to reach the Fields of Happiness. Arrived at the gates of these regions, Aeneas fixed in the portal his golden bough, and entered.

Here there is no gloomy darkness, but a glowing sky; here dwell the heroes who on earth assured themselves a place of happiness in death. Aeneas addressed them, asking for the abode of Anchises; but they replied that there was no fixed dwelling for any of them—each stayed where he wished. Anchises was looking upon those souls who were to inhabit the bodies of his descendants, and, beholding Aeneas, he joyfully stretched his hands in greeting. With tears of joy, Aeneas tried three times to embrace his parent, but the phantom slipped through his arms like the air.

Then Aeneas, seeing the souls fluttering around the river Lethe, asked why they filled the banks in such crowds. "These," replied Anchises, "are the souls for whom other bodies are destined by fate; they drink the water of Lethe to gain oblivion of former existence. Now I will point out to you the souls which shall inhabit your descendants.

"Men are of various natures, though they are all infused with a principle of life. It is from this that they know grief and sorrow, desire and joy. Even when the last spark of life is gone, there is yet some stain in them, and this stain must be purged away by punishments. Then we happy few are conveyed to these Elysian Fields, and after a thousand years have passed, we drink the water of Lethe, and prepare for a new life.

"See that youth, leaning on a spear: he shall be the first of your race, Sylvius of Alba. Then come others, Procas, Capys, and Numitor; and far along the line is Romulus, under whose happy guidance the city of Rome shall rise. From many of these shall lands, yet unnamed, take their names. See also great Caesar, called of the race of your son Iulus—and there stands Augustus Caesar, offspring of a god, who shall once again establish the Golden Age, and whose rule shall be acknowledged wherever the sun shines. And those others, farther off, shall bear a great name in the history of Latium, though many of them will raise war and havoc in the land, until the great ruler shall again establish peace.

"Behold warlike Marcellus, who shall shine a victor above all heroes! To him shall the rebellious Gauls bow the neck, and Carthage shall be humble. And next him that youth, bearing the same name, Marcellus—none shall excel him in piety or warlike strength, but he shall perish untimely!"

Thus, roaming through the Elysian Fields, Anchises pointed out to Aeneas the souls of many who should be great, and told him how she should succeed in winning for himself the city of Latium. As the day drew to its close, Anchises led him to the Gate of Ivory, through which come false dreams; and dismissed him.

Book VII: When Aeneas reached his ships, the sacrifices were over, and he directed the sailors to launch their vessels. Through the night they sailed, past Circe's isle, where they heard the roar of lions and other beasts whom Circe had transformed from the shapes of men. The dawn broke red, and the wind died; from his ship Aeneas beheld a grove by the mouth of the Tiber. There they landed,

> Now, Erato, thy poet's mind inspire,
> And fill his soul with thy celestial fire!
> Relate what Latium was; her ancient kings;
> Declare the past and present state of things,
> When first the Trojan fleet Ausonia sought.
> And how the rivals loved, and how they fought.
> These are my theme, and how the war began,
> And how concluded by the godlike man:
> For I shall sing of battles, blood, and rage,
> Which princes and their peoples did engage;
> And haughty souls, that, moved with mutual hate,
> In fighting fields pursued and found their fate;
> That roused the Tyrrhen realm with loud alarms,
> And peaceful Italy involved in arms.

Old Latinus, son of Faunus and Marica, was King of Latium. His one son had died in youth, leaving him only his daughter, Lavinia. The princes of the countries about sought her hand, especially Turnus, King of the Rutuli. Her parent was eager to join them in marriage, but the omens forbade. Within the precincts of the palace stood a sacred laurel. Here came a great swarm of bees, clinging to the branches; and the prophet interpreted the sign as an omen of a great hero coming to the land, and ruling in the lofty palace. Again, when Lavinia kindled the holy altars, she seemed to be all in a blaze, and to spread the light of the fire through the palace. This too the soothsayer interpreted to mean that Lavinia would be great in fame and fortune, but would bring to her people a terrible war.

Deeply concerned with these signs, King Latinus went to the sacred grove near Albunea, that he might consult the oracles. Lying on the fleeces of a hundred ewes sacrificed to the gods, he beheld many visions, and heard from deep within the grove a voice saying, "My son, do not seek to join Lavinia with Turnus in marriage, for your future son-in-law is even now arriving, a foreigner, who shall exalt the name of Latium to the skies, and to whose descendants the whole world shall be subject." This answer Latinus kept within his breast, but Fame carried it through the land.

Meanwhile the Trojans were consuming the last of their provisions by the ships. The meat had been placed upon thin cakes of bread; and Iulus, being hungry, ate his cake, saying, "Well, are we eating the platters too?" Aeneas recognized the omen; for he remembered that Celaeno had prophesied that when the Trojans reached a spot where they should eat their platters, they should hope there to found their first city. And rejoicing at the knowledge, he bade them join with him in a sacrifice venerating the genius of the place and the gods. Upon this, Almighty Jove thundered thrice, and displayed a cloud gleaming with light.

On the next day, the Trojans explored the country which was to be their homeland, and sent envoys to King Latinus. While Aeneas was laying out their first city, in the form of a camp, these approached the city, where they were received by Latinus in the great central palace, which was also their chief temple. He addressed them graciously, asking whether they had been driven ashore, or had selected the landing place; and Ilioneus, spokesman for the Trojans, replied, "O King, we were driven here by no storm save that which broke over Troy from Mycenae, driving Jove-born Aeneas to seek shelter far from his native land. We ask only a small settlement on your shores; we shall be no disgrace to you, but will enhance your fame among the nations. Many peoples have asked us to dwell with them, but it is the will of the gods that Dardanus, our ancestor, should be venerated again in his native land. Nor do we come empty-handed; Aeneas presents you with gifts and with treasures preserved from flaming Troy."

As Ilioneus spoke, Latinus kept his eyes fixed impassively upon the ground, thinking less of the history of the Trojan race than of his daughter's marriage. Concluding that Aeneas was the man destined to marry his daughter, he said, "What you desire, Trojans, shall be granted you. Only let Aeneas come in person to visit me, for I have a daughter whom the oracles do not permit me to join to a husband of our nation; they say that a husband shall come to her from foreign shores. If it be he who is ordained by the Fates, I too desire him to come." And so speaking, he chose from his stable a hundred fine steeds, all armed, to be led forth and presented to the Trojan envoys, who mounted them, and returned.

But unrelenting Juno, perceiving that the Trojans had begun their city, and had abandoned their ships, thought within her heart, "Ah, see how these have escaped the flames of Troy and foreign captivity! Is it in vain that I pursued them with storms, or drove them past Scylla and Charybdis? Though my own divinity be not powerful enough to destroy Aeneas, yet I can call upon the infernal gods! And though I be not permitted to debar him from winning the Latin kingdom, and the hand of Lavinia, yet I may spin out his sufferings, paying the maiden's dowry in Trojan and Rutulian blood, and making the goddess of War her bridesmaid!"

With these dreadful words, she plunged to earth, and, summoning the Fury Alecto, inspired her to fling from her dark locks one of her snakes into the heart of Amata, mother of Lavinia. Infected with its subtle poison, she spoke to her husband, "Is Lavinia to be given to a Trojan exile? Have you no pity on your daughter? Was it not a Trojan who led off Helen? And what of your solemnly-given oath, to marry her to Turnus? If truly it is destined that you have a foreign son-in-law, then every land save our own is foreign; and Turnus no less foreign, for he traces his ancestors to Acrisius of Mycenae."

Unable to move Latinus' resolute mind, Amata departed from the palace, taking with her Lavinia, and followed by the matrons of Latium. Like a votary of Bacchus, she whirled through the forest, waving above her head a blazing torch, and singing the wedding song for her daughter and Turnus, while Alecto goaded her on.

Then the fury, assuming the form of an old hag, went to Ardea, where Turnus lay asleep in his palace. There she spoke to him, "Turnus, will you sit idly by while King Latinus breaks off the match you have purchased with your blood? Go, defeat those foreign armies; protect the Latins. The majesty of Queen Juno commands that you arm your soldiers, and consume both the invaders and their ships with fire. Let Latinus know the terror of facing Turnus in arms!"

But Turnus derided her: "All this has been spread abroad by Fame, that a fleet has arrived at the Tiber's mouth. But old women often pretend themselves prophets. It is your task to watch over the statues and temples of the gods; leave war to men."

Enraged, Alecto assumed her proper form, crowned with serpents, and cracking her whip: "Old woman, am I? Do I deceive you with false signs? Look upon me, and know me for one of the Dreadful Sisters." And so speaking, she hurled a firebrand into his breast, which inflamed him with martial rage. Then, calling out his armies, he prepared to march against the Latins.

But Alecto prepared further woe for Trojans and Latians. Seeing Iulus hunting along the shore, she put his hounds on the trail of a great stag, raised by Tyrrhus, warden of the royal forest from a fawn, and a pet of the household. Seeing the great beast, Ascanius shot an arrow, piercing him, and the stag with difficulty returned to his stall. There Tyrrhus, seeing it, snatched up his arms, and calling his shepherd-companions to his aid, encountered the Trojans. These were not slow to defend themselves, and in a brief time they had killed many of the natives.

Then Juno, glad of the war, sent Alecto back to her dreadful mansion of Cocytus, while she herself accompanied the Latians, bearing the bodies of their dead, to meet Turnus. The Rutulian King called upon Latinus to make war upon the invaders, but the aged monarch, knowing the impiety of this action, retired into his palace.

There was a custom, since religiously observed among the Latin cities, that the beginning of war should be signalized by the opening of the temple of Janus. This Latinus was urged to do; and when he refused, Saturnian Juno herself swung wide the gates.

Now all Ausonia, before so peaceful, is on fire with war. All arm themselves; here men rub their leather bucklers and bright spears with fat; there they forge their fathers' swords anew. Swiftly they prepare the brazen corselets and the smooth greaves, and lead forth the swift steeds to the war-chariots.

Now there enter on the scene many of the allies, warriors from whose loins are sprung many of the noble families of Italy: Clausus, father of the Claudian race, Umbro, and the valiant maiden Camilla.[1]

Book VIII:

> When Turnus had assembled all his powers,
> His standard planted on Laurentium's towers;
> When now the sprightly trumpet, from afar,
> Had given the signal of approaching war,
> Had roused the neighboring steeds to scour the fields,
> While the fierce riders clattered on their shields;
> Trembling with rage, the Latian youth prepare
> To join th' allies, and headlong rush to war.

Led by Messapus and Ufens, and that contemner of the gods Mezentius, they drew their allies together, sending as far as the city of Diomede for help.

Aeneas, perceiving all these things, considered with anxiety his future course. When it was night, he lay down to sleep; and he slept, Father Tiber appeared to him, saying, "Aeneas, be not dismayed by these warlike threats, for this is your destined land. That you may know this is not a false vision, you will find tomorrow a white sow, with thirty pigs; where she lies, you will found your city. Go to the land of the Arcadians, who perpetually war with the Latin nation; admit them as members of your confederation, join with them as allies. I myself will show the way along my stream. With the first light of day, offer sacrifices to Juno, and set forth."

---

[1] Lines 647 to the end of Book VII contain a complete catalogue of the names of Turnus' allies. They are omitted here.

Day dispelled both night and the vision, and Aeneas, offering thanks to the river-god, selected two galleys, which he launched on the Tiber. Swiftly they rowed, when lo! they beheld the promised omen, a white sow; Aeneas sacrificed her to Juno. All that night they rowed, and until noon of the next day, protected from hostile observation by the trees on the banks; and when they beheld the city of Evander, they turned their prows to shore.

It chanced that on that day the King was offering sacrifice to Hercules, and when Pallas, his son, perceived the approaching Trojans, he snatched up a spear, and forbade them to interrupt the rites. Aeneas, holding before him a branch of peaceful olive, said, "We are sons of Troy, driven from our destined land by the Latins; we have come to Evander, asking his help in arms."

Pallas immediately asked them to come ashore; they proceeded to the sacred grove. Courteously Aeneas spoke, "Worthiest of the sons of the Greeks, we, though Trojans, have no apprehension of danger from you, for we are both sprung from the line of Atlas. Relying upon our kinship, I saw no need of formal embassies, but present myself a suppliant on your threshold. The same nation which oppresses you is in arms against us; let us take and give pledges of friendship."

Evander replied that he well remembered old Anchises, and had received from him many presents. Promising to render any aid in his power, he led the Trojans to the banquet, where they feasted. Then Evander explained the occasion of the sacrifice to Hercules: many years before, the cruel giant Cacus had inhabited the crags, and from them had conducted raids upon the persons and the property of the inhabitants of the region. Fresh from the slaying of Geryon, Hercules came, driving before him his booty of cattle. Cacus, maddened by the Furies, stole four of the heifers, dragging them to his cave by the tails, that their footprints might not betray their course. But one of them answered the lowing of the others; and Hercules, seizing a great rock, burst open the doors of the cave, entered, and slew the giant. For this deliverance, the Arcadians offer annual thanks; and he prayed Aeneas to join with them in the sacrifices. Then the rites were renewed; the altars smoked with offerings, while the minstrels sang the Labors of Hercules.

As they walked back to the city, Evander told Aeneas the stories of the various spots which they passed. First, he said, the land was inhabited by fauns and nymphs, and a rude nation of men, who knew no laws. Then Saturn, fleeing from Jove, formed them into a nation; this was their Golden Age, of undisturbed tranquility. Following this came the races of men now inhabiting the land, and a succession of kings, from whom the places take their names. He showed the Tarpeian Rock, and Argiletum, the hills Janiculum and Saturnia, and his humble palace, where now stands the golden Forum.[1]

The night came on swiftly, and Aeneas retired to slumber. Meanwhile his mother, Venus, spoke to her husband, Vulcan, and prayed him to forge for her son a suit of divine armor. Vulcan, well-pleased with his wife, assented, and plunged to his workshop in the caves of Etna. There the grim Cyclopes were forging great thunderbolts for Jove, and fashioning a war-chariot for Mars; but at his call, they laid aside their work, and set to making Aeneas' armor.

On earth, Evander and his son, Pallas, rose, and joined Aeneas and Achates in the great courtyard. The King of the Arcadians said, "Small indeed is our power, for we are hemmed in on the one side by the Tiber, on the other by the warlike Rutulians. But there is a city, Argylla, once conquered, and ruled tyrannically by Mezentius. His people rose against and expelled him; he fled to his accomplice Turnus, and now his city demands that he be returned for punishment. Those troops I assign to your command, for the soothsayer has restrained them until now with the prophesy that under a foreign king the nation shall have its vengeance. Even now they are encamped, and are sending envoys to ask our aid. My own son, having a Sabine mother, derives from this land; but I place

---

[1] Vergil is obviously here pointing out spots which every Roman would recognize as parts of the city.

him under your leadership, that the oracle may be fulfilled."

As he finished speaking, Venus sent a flash of lightning and a resounding peal of thunder; the rest were amazed, but Aeneas recognized the divine omen. Joyfully he explained that his mother had promised him this token of victory, and he called upon Evander to join him in the war.

Having made sacrifice, Aeneas went to his ships, where he selected the bravest to accompany him, and dispatched the others to return to the Trojan camp. Then, accompanied by Pallas, he set forth through the opened gates, watched from the walls by the Arcadian matrons.

Near Argylla there is a grove, sacred to Sylvanus. Here they took their way and rested. Meanwhile the goddess Venus had brought the gleaming armor made by Vulcan, and here she delivered it to her son. On the shield the wondrous artificer had represented the glories of Rome which were to be: there one might see Horatius Cocles, single-handed repelling the advance of proud Tarquin's men; Manlius, defending the Capitol against the Gauls; Catiline, trembling before the Furies; and all the story of the grim wars with Egypt, and the heroes who saved Rome.[1]

BOOK IX: But meanwhile, Juno sent her messenger Iris to Turnus with the message that Aeneas was even then allying himself with the enemies of the Rutulians, and that the time was propitious for an attack on the Trojan camp. He knew the goddess, and, stretching out his hands to Heaven, vowed to obey the commands given him.

They drew up their army in array: Messapus commanded the vanguard, the sons of Tyrrhus marched in the rear; in the center was the proud chariot of Turnus. From their walls the Trojans saw a great cloud of dust rolling across the plains, and, summoning their warriors, they barricaded the camp.

Turnus, reconnoitering his enemy, saw that the walls were well defended, and that it would not be easy to force the

---

[1] Another set-piece, too long to give here in its entirety, and full of events recognizable by every Roman.

Trojans to accept battle in the open. But beside the river lay the Trojan fleet, and, calling upon his followers, he fell upon the ships with blazing firebrands.

But long before, when Aeneas had built these ships on Mount Ida, Cybele had asked of Jove that they be made immortal, for they were built from groves sacred to her. The god replied that no god could give immortality to vessels built by mortal hands, but granted that those which escaped the perils of the journey and reached Latium might become goddesses of the ocean, like the Nereids. Now, when Turnus attacked them, the promised day had come; and they slipped from their moorings to plunge into the deep and reappear as goddesses.

But Turnus interpreted the omen to mean that the last hope of escape was cut off from the Trojans, and exhorted his companions to storm the town—not with a wooden horse, but with their own strong arms. Fourteen hundred warriors were selected to keep watch upon the besieged, while the others prepared a camp. From the walls the Trojans, led by Mnestheus and Sergestus, watched the hostile preparations.

Among them were Nisus and Euryalus, swift-footed youths. Nisus proposed to his friend that they volunteer as messengers to summon Aeneas back to the camp, and, when Euryalus eagerly consented, they sought the council of the chiefs, before whom they laid their plans: to make their way through the camp of the Rutulians, who were deep in drunken slumber, and, traveling along the ways which they had learned while hunting, to reach Aeneas with the news of the fight. Deeply touched by the young men's bravery, Iulus assented, and the other leaders promised precious gifts. They stole out across the walls, and their circling trenches; passing through the enemy camps, Nisus struck down Rhamnes and his three servants, and Euryalus made no less slaughter. As they advanced toward the camp of Messapus, Nisus perceived that they were losing sight of their chief objective, and persuaded Euryalus to cease his killing. As they quit the camp, Volscens, at the head of a troop of horsemen, saw the moonlight gleam on Euryalus' helmet, which he had taken from Messapus, and called upon them to stop and give an account of themselves. They crept into a wood, where they became separated in the dark, and when Nisus perceived that Euryalus had been captured, he rushed upon Volscens, killing him as he himself was slain. The Rutulians took their heads to the camp, but had little joy in the trophies, for they carried also the lifeless body of Volscens, and in the camp they saw the corpses of those slain by the two youths.

Bearing the two heads as battle-standards, the Rutulians advanced to the fray. Then Rumor, coursing swiftly through the town, brought the sad news to the mother of Euryalus, who, from the walls, bewailed her dead son.

And now the shrill trumpet summoned the warriors to battle. The Volscians advanced in close ranks, protected by a covering shield, and prepared to fill the trenches and break down the ramparts. From the walls the Trojans poured down arrows and heavy stones, and at last, with a great pile of rock, they broke through the wooden shield, and the enemy retired in defeat.

On a great tower, built of wood, the Trojans fought with valor, though the Rutulians poured in darts through the loopholes. Turnus, seizing a firebrand, threw it with great force into the tower, where the flames spread, forcing the Trojans to retreat. The tower fell with a resounding crash into the plains, and its two defenders, Helenor and Lycus, fell to the enemies' swords. Then the battle was joined along the wall; great was the slaughter, and great the valor of the Trojans. Ascanius, fighting his first battle, staunchly exhorted the Trojans to fight bravely, and set them a glorious example.

From above, Apollo inspired Iulus; then, assuming the form of old Butes, Anchises' trusted guard, appeared in the battle, and restrained the boy from further combat. Pandarus and Bitias sallied forth, and Pandarus single-handed ventured to fight against Turnus; but Juno turned aside his lance, and the Rutulian King transfixed him with a dart. Then the enraged Trojans, gathering their strength together, slowly forced Turnus to retreat toward the river, pressing him hard on every side.

Nor could Saturnian Juno assist them, for Jove had decreed that Turnus should quit the high walls of the Trojans. Battered and bruised, Turnus flung his sweating body into the river, and was borne across it to his friends.

Book X: Meanwhile the Father of Gods and Men summoned the divinities to a council, where he demanded of them, "Why have you contended so fiercely with one another? You know it was my purpose that there should be no war between Trojans and Italians—why, then, have you transgressed my commands? The time for fight shall come when fierce Carthage shall attack Rome: then you may fight and plunder." Thus he spoke, briefly; but Venus replied at length, "Sire, do you not see how Turnus assaults the Trojans, how the fight is carried on even on the battlements of the town? Will you not suffer them to be relieved, and do you permit new enemies to arise against Aeneas? If it is without your permission that the Trojans have come to Italy, let them suffer; but if it is by your will, why should any god pervert your commands? Need I recall the trials of Aeneas, the malice of your spouse against him? If indeed you plan that Juno shall succeed, at least grant me that I may save Ascanius alive, and carry him to an ignoble existence in one of my shrines. Let Carthage then rule Rome! What has Aeneas gained from all his tribulations, if it be not granted to him to dwell in Latium? Better to let him return to Troy, and to make a new city where it once stood."

To this Juno, hot at heart, retorted that all the Trojans' woes had come from their own misgovernment: for had not Paris fled with Helen, there would have been no Trojan War, nor was it wrong that Turnus should defend his native land against the invader. The gods listened, and the sound of their whispers was like the wind in the groves.

Then Jupiter spoke, and all remained silent. "These are my commands: since it is not permitted that the Trojans should be allied with the Ausonians, let each strike out his own fortune by battle. His own valor shall secure disaster or success; let

the Fates take their course." And he confirmed his words with
the awful oath of Styx, the greatest oath of the gods.

On earth, the Trojans were closely surrounded by the Rutulians, who raged around them with fire and slaughter. From
the walls, the bands of heroes defended their city, hurling
down darts and great rocks upon the besiegers.

Aeneas at midnight was returning to his galley, having made
an alliance with Evander and Tarchon, and added their forces
to his. At dawn the thirty vessels were plowing the river on
their return; and to Aeneas, seated at the helm, appeared the
white-armed nymphs who had been formed of the vessels burnt
by Turnus. They told him of their fate, and how Cybele had
created them. Then they told also how Turnus was endeavoring to intercept the Tuscan and Arcadian cavalry, and promised that the morrow should see a great slaughter of Rutulians.
Then the goddesses pushed the ships through the water with
the speed of a flying javelin; and Aeneas, heartened, raised
the spirits of his men with the good omen.

As he came into view of the beleaguered town, the Trojans
raised a cry of joy, and redoubled their efforts. To Turnus and
the other Rutulian princes this seemed incredible, until they
looked back and saw the river full of vessels, all gliding to the
shore. The sight did not dismay the reckless one; he cheered
on his men, encouraging them to attack the Trojans while they
were attempting to land—for Fortune favors the brave. Meanwhile Aeneas had come to shore, and, leaping from his vessel,
attacked the rustic and undisciplined Latins, laying low Theron,
their chief. But Turnus undaunted hurried his troops to the
battle. With Mezentius and Lausus he flew toward the Trojans,
and made great havoc in their ranks.

On the other side, Aeneas, Iulus, and Pallas strove mightily,
Pallas rallying the Arcadians when the Latin foot-soldiers
pressed them too hard. Many a brave duel was fought that
day! Then Turnus commanded his troops to retreat, that he
might fight in single combat with Pallas, and, leaping from his
chariot, engaged the youth on foot. Pallas grazed his foe with
a spear, but the dart of Turnus found its mark—and exulting,

he stripped off Pallas' armor. Then Aeneas, cutting his way through the opposing army, strove to wreak vengeance on Turnus for his friend's death; but Juno, appealing to her spouse, intervened. Dropping from the sky, she created a phantom in the shape of Aeneas, which advanced before the troops, and challenged the Rutulian to combat. When Turnus hurled his spear, the phantom retreated; and, imagining that he had put the Trojan to flight, Turnus pressed after him, his sword uplifted to strike.

It chanced that one of the ships was moored to a steep rock near by; the image of Aeneas sped aboard, and seemed to hide itself. Turnus threw himself upon this vessel, and Juno suddenly cast it adrift; as it sped down the stream, the deceiving shape vanished into the clouds. Then Turnus, knowing that he had been deceived, three times tried to slay himself either by the sword or by casting himself into the sea; and as often Juno restrained him, while the ship was carried by wind and tide to the city of Daunus.

On the shore, the true Aeneas had been seeking his foe, that he might avenge Pallas, and on the other side Mezentius performed prodigies of valor. The two encountered; Mezentius' dart slipped from Aeneas' shield, and killed Antores; Aeneas' spear pierced the armor of Mezentius, but its force was spent, and the wound was not mortal. Aeneas, seeing the blood flow, pressed in with his sword, but Lausus, stepping between the two, took the force of the blow and was killed. Then Mezentius, lamenting the death of his son, advanced upon Aeneas, casting darts from his chariot. Aeneas warded them off with his shield, leapt upon Mezentius, and plunged his sword into his throat.

Book XI: Though Aeneas was sorrowful for the death of Pallas, he paid to the gods due reverence for his victory over Mezentius, erecting a great oaken pole in the middle of the camp, and hanging on it the armor of the defeated warrior. Then he prepared to send the body of Pallas to Evander, accompanied by great piles of armor taken from the Rutulians.

From the city of Latinus came envoys, bearing olive branches, and praying that he grant them a respite that they might gather up their dead. To this Aeneas consented, making a truce of twelve days' time.

Then they built upon the shore great funeral pyres for the slain, and offered sacrifices. Three times they rode about the burning piles, lamenting the dead. On the other side, the Latins in their fashion burned their slain; and for three days and nights the sky was red with flames.

To complete the distress of the Latins, their envoys returned from the city of Diomede with the news that he could offer them no help; either they must obtain other allies, or sue for peace. Deeply troubled in his heart, the aged Latinus called an assembly of his nobles, to whom the emissaries repeated their tidings.

When the minds of the assembly were calmed, Latinus spoke: "It is wrong to wage war with the favorites of the gods. Hear then my proposal: as you know, I possess a tract of land to the West; let this be given now to the Trojans, and there let them build their cities, and be friends with us. If, on the other hand, they choose to settle elsewhere, let us offer them help in building and provisioning their ships, and send them on their way. And I propose, also, that a hundred envoys be sent to Aeneas with these offers."

Drances, good in debate, but a weakling in war, arose to speak: "All these things, gracious King, it is right to do. Nor should that man who has brought upon us all this slaughter with his defiance of the gods be allowed to prevent us. I add that it is right that, being her father, you offer the hand of Lavinia to Aeneas. Let this war no longer strew our fields with our dead!"

Then Turnus: "Drances, it is well known that you have a wealth of words; yet why will you not put your valor to the test? Have I been put to flight? Is the war lost with a single indecisive battle? Have we no courage? Though Diomede will not support us, we are rich in allies, Messapus, and Tolumnius, and the redoubtable Camilla. And if the Trojans consent, gladly will I put all to the test in a single combat against Aeneas."

As they debated their plans, a messenger arrived with the news that the Trojans were approaching in battle array. Quickly taking command, Turnus dispatched his warriors, some to the walls, others to scour the plain on horseback, and others to follow him to the combat. Camilla, Queen of the Volscians, asked to be given the post of honor, and to encounter the Trojans; but Turnus sent her to lay an ambush for the Trojan cavalry; he would reinforce her horsemen with his own foot troops.

Camilla was especially dear to the goddess Diana, for her father, Metabus, had many years before devoted her as a babe to the goddess' service. It happened in this way: having been expelled from his city of Privernum for tyrannous deeds, he had retreated with the child to the hills; and here he was hard pressed by the Volscians. Unable to carry her by swimming across the flooded river, he bound her to a spear, and, with a prayer to Diana, hurled her across. Then, escaping his foes by swimming, he retrieved the infant, and brought her up in the thickets of the forest, where, even as a child, she proved her warlike bent.

The Trojans approached across the plain, their front screened by light-armed horsemen, and the Rutulians poured forth to meet them. When the armies were within a javelin's throw, they rushed upon one another; first to turn were the Latins, who were pressed back to the walls. Pursued by the Trojans, they wheeled about and charged, sending their enemies back; twice they fled, and twice they faced about. But on the third onset, the battle mingled in close fight, so that a man struck his enemy as he could; a furious combat ensued.

Amid the heaps of slain Camilla rushed through the combat, dealing death to all she encountered, even to the valiant Trojans and Tuscans. Arruns, a Trojan, watching for an opportunity to encounter her, saw the maiden warrior intent upon taking the arms of Chloreus; and with a prayer to Apollo, hurled his great spear, wounding the maiden to death. Then

Diana's messenger, Opis, drew her great bow, and with the whizzing arrow slew Arruns.

Now the Rutulians and Latins, losing heart with her death, retreated, making their way to the city walls; many were slaughtered in this movement, for those within, seeing their armies fleeing, shut the gates and left the warriors to their destruction. Turnus, lying in wait in the grove, heard the evil tidings, and moved toward the plain. He and Aeneas saw one another, but the end of the day approached, and they left their combat.

Book XII: When Turnus saw that the Latin ranks had broken, he became the more determined to offer single combat to Aeneas. He asked Latinus to make the treaty at once; either he should dispatch the invader to Tartarus, or let him reign in Latium, the husband of Lavinia. Latinus replied, "There are many other maidens in Ausonia, fitted to be your bride; let me lay before you the truth, unhappy as it may be. It is destined by the gods that I should wed my daughter to a foreign prince; but overpowered by friendship for you, I broke their commandments and took up arms against the warrior destined to rule here. You see what calamities and disasters have followed this impious course of action. Defeated twice, our streams red with our warriors' blood! And what will those of all Latium say if I send you to your death? Consider the chances of war, I beg you, and retire to your native Ardea."

But Turnus, inflamed with anger, would not hear the wise words of Latinus. Then Amata joined her prayers with those of her husband, imploring Turnus, always dear to her, to avoid combat with Aeneas. But the Rutulian prince replied, "O mother, do not send me from you with the inauspicious omen of tears, for no man can delay his death-day! And Idmon, my herald: bear this message to Aeneas: Let the Trojans and the Rutulians no longer engage in combat, but let Lavinia be won as a bride by the decision of our own arms."

When the dawn was clear on the morrow, Turnus armed himself and went to the plain before the town. Aeneas, in the

armor given him by his goddess-mother, came also to the place
of combat, which was prepared for the sacrifices. Beneath the
walls of Latinus' city the Ausonian legions sat, and opposite
them sat the Trojan and Tuscan forces, not in battle-array,
while the priests made ready to pour the libations.

Juno, beholding the scene, and knowing that in the fight
Turnus should be defeated, called upon Juturna, his sister, a
goddess presiding over pools and streams: "O nymph, while
the fates permitted, I protected Turnus and Latium; but today
he engages in an unequal fight. If you dare, help your brother,
kindle the war anew, or dissolve the truce, for it may be that
by this attempt, which I permit, a better fortune will attend
the unhappy Latins."

Now the kings moved to the space between the armies, followed by the sacrificial beasts. Turning their eyes to the sun,
they broke the salt-cakes, and rehearsed the treaty. Aeneas
spoke, raising his unsheathed sword, and invoking the gods,
"If the victory fall to Turnus, it is agreed that the Trojans shall
retire to the city of Evander, nor shall the children of Aeneas
visit these realms with invading armies. But if victory fall to
me, then never shall I compel the Italians to be subject to the
Trojans, for I aim at no empire of my own; rather, let the two
nations dwell together in peace, and let my father-in-law,
Latinus, bear rule in his lands. The Trojans shall build a city,
to which Lavinia shall give the name."

Latinus, laying his hands upon the altar, confirmed the words
of Aeneas; then over the flames they sacrificed the animals, and
loaded the altars with their flesh. But to the Rutulians these
seemed unequal terms; and when they beheld Turnus approach
the altars, pale and silent, their fears were aggravated. Then
Juturna, taking the form of Camertus, went through their
ranks, inflaming them to battle: "Rutulians, are you not
ashamed to let one life stand between you and victory? If we
engage, we shall hardly have one enemy for two of us—but if
we sit idle here, we may be ruled by a foreign lord!" These
words she reinforced with a sign from Heaven: the bird of
Jove, pursuing a flock of screaming water-fowl carried off in

his talons a great swan. The other birds, turning upon the attacker, forced him to drop his prey into the river; and To- lumnius, the soothsayer, interpreted the omen to mean that the invader would be driven off by the concerted attacks of the besieged.

Then Tolumnius hurled a dart across the place of sacrifice into the thick of the Trojans, killing the son of Gyllipus, and Messapus rode down Aulestes. Aeneas, perceiving the conflict break out, cried to his troops to hold their places, and not to violate their sacred oaths. But as he spoke, an arrow pierced his thigh, and he was forced to retire from the field. Turnus, paying no heed to the truce, roared through the troops in his great chariot, slaying right and left.

While he made such havoc in the field, Aeneas, with his trusty Achates, was trying to wrench the shaft of the arrow from his thigh, so that he might return to the fight. Iapyx, the skilled physician, tried to withdraw it, but in vain; then Venus conveyed into the water with which Iapyx was cleaning the wound a stalk of dittany; and suddenly the blood was staunched, the arrow-head dropped out of itself, and all pain left the hero. Quickly rearming himself, he issued forth and rejoined his troops.

When the Rutulians saw Aeneas again in the fight, their hearts failed them, and they turned back. Mounted in his chariot, Aeneas disdained to strike down lesser warriors, but sought only Turnus. Juturna, fearing for her brother, struck down his charioteer, Metiscus, and assuming his shape and voice, guided Turnus' chariot through the battle, evading the revenge of Aeneas. As often as the Trojan hero drew near to his chosen foe, his charioteer turned aside; then Aeneas, crying out for vengeance, struck right and left against the flee- ing Rutulians, while Turnus, avoiding him, slew many a brave Trojan.

Then Aeneas' divine mother put it into his heart to lead the armies against the now-undefended cities. Rallying his strongest about him, they rushed to the walls, bearing scaling- ladders and torches. The Latins, dismayed at this new attack, rushed aimlessly through the streets, not knowing what to do; and Amata, in despair, slew herself.

Meanwhile Turnus, weary with slaughter, and pursuing a few scattered Trojans, heard the cries from the town, and endeavored to turn his chariot; but his charioteer tried to dissuade him. Then Turnus spoke, "Sister, whom I long ago recognized, are you content to be the cause of an ignoble death for me, your brother? Shall I let the city be razed? Shall I turn my back on death? Is it so evil to die? O Infernal Powers, befriend me, since the gods are my enemies! Let me descend to you, unspotted with the name of coward!"

A messenger came up, to tell the Rutulian chieftain of the changed state of the battle. Rushing to the walls of the city, he shouted to his men to hold their hands, and to leave the issue of the contest to him and Aeneas alone. Hearing the shout, Aeneas hastened from the burning walls to meet his enemy; the combatants desisted from strife, and watched the encounter.

Like two bulls they rushed upon one another, stroke falling upon stroke. Rising upon his toes, Turnus delivered a mighty blow; but the blade shivered into a thousand pieces. (Some report that in haste Turnus had seized Metiscus' sword—but what steel can penetrate divinely created arms?) Turnus fled through the ranks, calling for his sword, but Aeneas promised instant destruction to any who should venture to help. Five times they circled the field, and for no slight prize: it was the life of Turnus which was at stake.

From a wild olive tree Turnus endeavored to disengage the spear of Aeneas, which had become fixed in its tough roots, but he failed. Juturna, again in the shape of Metiscus, ran up, and gave her brother his sword; Venus, indignant at the intervention, twisted the spear from the tree, and gave it to Aeneas.

Jove and Juno looked down from above at the combat, and the Father of the Gods spoke: "When shall this strife be at an end? You yourself know that Aeneas is destined to become a god—is it right that such a one should be wounded by a mortal? Desist now from your anger; for though you have been permitted to harass the Trojans by sea and land, and to bring sorrow with the joys of Aeneas' wedding, I forbid you to attempt more." She replied submissively, "I confess my part in the attempt of Juturna to assist her brother, and because it is your will I withdraw from further combat. Yet I implore that you do not force the people of Latium to change their ancient name, their language, or their dress. Let Latium live, and the kings of Alba reign forever; let Troy perish with its name."

To this Jove gladly assented; then turned his mind to the dismissal of Juturna. Summoning a Fury, he sent her to the battlefield, where, in the shape of an owl, she flew before Turnus. Beholding the omen, Juturna cried out, and plunged into the river.

Aeneas pushed the attack with all his fury; though he missed his cast with a huge stone, he struck Turnus with his spear, and the Rutulian sank to his knee, wounded. He called for mercy, and Aeneas held his hand; but seeing the belt of Pallas whom Turnus had slain, he cried

"Traitor, dost thou, dost thou to grace pretend,
    Clad, as thou art, in trophies of my friend?
    To his sad soul a grateful offering go!
    'Tis Pallas, Pallas, gives this deadly blow."
    He raised his arm aloft, and, at the word,
    Deep in his bosom drove the shining sword.
    The streaming blood distained his arms around,
    And the disdainful soul came rushing through the wound.

SUGGESTIONS FOR FURTHER READING

Translations:

Dryden, John, in *The Complete Poetical Works*, Boston, 1909
Fairclough, H. R., in Loeb Classical Library
Lewis, C. Day. *The Aeneid*, London, 1952

Other Books:

Mackail, J. W. *Vergil and His Meaning to the World Today*, London, 1923

Encyclopaedia Britannica, "Virgil"

BEOWULF

BEOWULF: INTRODUCTION

For centuries before the Normans broke into England, bringing with them a new speech and culture which were to redirect
English life and language, the English had cultivated their own
kind of poetry. Easily the greatest example of this poetry is
the *Beowulf,* the story of a mighty warrior who twice defeated
monsters in single combat, and who was slain in a fight with a
dragon, which he had wounded to the death. Beowulf, the
hero of the poem, is the epitome of the native English hero:
strong, brave, gentle, loyal to his lord and to the warriors serving under him; straightforward, needing no Odyssean tricks
to accomplish his purposes; fond of fighting, and thirsty for
the honor which can be gained only in battle. Beowulf would
have despised Achilles for hiding among the women or for
sulking in his tent; as for the very wily Odysseus, he would
have thought him one of those foreigners who need to employ
trickery to get things done. But Achilles' vengeance for
Patroclus, or Odysseus' great seamanship, he would have re-
spected; and in all this he is truly English.

The society which produced such a hero was not greatly dis-
similar to that of the Homeric poems. The great mass of the
Germanic people were free peasants, who, though not despised,
seldom appear in the literature, for, as in early Greece, this
concerned itself with the warrior class. The core of this ruling
class was the band of warriors, who centered their loyalty upon
their leader. This leader was often a king; but the poetry displays little national feeling, for the social structure was still
rather tribal than national. The bond which held this heroic
society together was that of personal and family loyalty: the

warrior was loyal to his kin, his leader, and his companions; the leader was loyal to his followers, rewarding them for their services with gold and land.

The obligation of loyalty continued to death, and beyond, for a warrior was bound to avenge the death of his kinsman or his leader, or to die trying. The *Beowulf* is full of references to this duty to be loyal, and to the unhappy plight of those who were caught in the conflict of loyalties. What shall King Hrethel do when his son Herebeald, accidentally kills another son, Haethcyn? The slaying must be avenged, but father cannot kill son. Or what shall the Danish followers of Hnaef do, when he is killed in an attack by their hosts, the Frisians, and both sides fight until they can fight no longer? Winter is on them; they cannot go home; vengeance is physically impossible. We hear that a truce was patched up between Danes and Frisians; that the Danes took service with Finn, the Frisian leader; that no Frisian, on pain of death, should taunt the Danes with their shameful action. The winter passes, the ice breaks up—and the followers of Hnaef fall swiftly upon the Frisians and avenge their lord. That they won the battle was no doubt pleasant to the Germanic audience; but, in a way, unimportant. What mattered was that they chose the possibility of death rather than be known as followers of their lord's slayer.

From a society which thoroughly enjoyed hearing such stories we might perhaps expect nothing more elaborate than a series of heroic lays, short poems of battle and vengeance. Such lays, of course, exist, and there were probably more of them than we now possess. But by the eighth century of our era, when the *Beowulf* was composed, Northern England was a center of European culture, and was to remain so until it was overrun by the Scandinavian invaders. Although the heroic values persisted, and loyalty between leader and follower was still the strongest strand in the social fabric, the society had grown more aristocratic, even courtly. Such a society could— and did—produce a work of genuine literary art, not merely a set of folk-songs loosely strung together. It is possible, of course, to discern in the underlying material a great deal of folk-story, but the man who wrote the *Beowulf* was not interested in a mere heaping-up of wonders; his design was to produce a genuine epic which would appeal to cultivated hearers. As a result, we have in a simple but by no means primitive society a subtle and complex epic. Without knowing Homer, the *Beowulf*-poet did what Homer had done some fifteen hundred years earlier.

Like Homer, also, the *Beowulf*-poet was writing of a nation not his own, though closely allied to it. The story of the *Beowulf* is set in Scandinavia, not England. And though many of the speeches show a strong Christian influence, it is certain that the people who composed the first stories about Beowulf were Northern pagans. But, like Homer, the *Beowulf*-poet was able to fit stories of a far-off and heroic time into a framework of contemporary society and belief.

In telling his story, the poet had at his command all the resources of Germanic verse. This is different from the verse with which most of us are familiar in that the lines are divided into two parts, which are held together, with (usually) two alliterating words in the first half-line and one in the second. To illustrate, here are some lines from an early passage in the poem:

> Oft *Sc*yld *Sc*efing   *sc*eathena threatum
> *m*onegum *m*aegthum   *m*eodosetla ofteah
> *e*gsode *e*orlas . . . . .

Such lines are capable of many variations in rhythm; they are quite flexible, though they were apparently governed by strict rules.

The stylistic devices, of which the poet knew and used many, are also different from those employed by Homer or Vergil, or by modern poets. They are of two sorts: those which govern the choice of words, and those used in the construction of sentences. Of the first group, a common one is the kenning, a sort of metaphor or periphrasis, which is found in all Germanic poetry. An example of the kenning is the "war-friends," for swords; of the periphrasis "whale's wallow," for the sea. Another figure is litotes, the statement of a positive by the negative of its opposite: "He was not last at the sword-play"—that is, he was the first in battle. Allied to this is the use of understatement: "Queen Hildeburh," sings the bard, "had little reason to praise the good faith of the Jutes"; in other words, she had every reason to deplore their bad faith.

Within the sentence, the poet very commonly employs the devices of variation and parenthetical remarks. In variations, the statement is repeated in different words, or a slightly different facet of the subject is presented:

> "They inhabit a secret land, wolf-cliffs, windy headlands;
>   A fearful fen-path, where the mountain stream
>   Runs down under the cover of the cliffs,
>   A flood under the earth."

In parentheses, the poet comments upon the action or the people of the story, or upon the wise conduct of life. For example, in his introductory story of Scyld Scefing, he bursts out with, "That was a good king!" Or, in speaking of the miserly wife of King Offa, he points out that "That is no queenly way for a lady to act, beautiful though she be." Or again, in the short gnomic sentences, "Fate goes ever as it must," and "Fate often helps a warrior, if his spirit is brave."

The use of these devices gives the modern reader a feeling of jerky and sidelong movement. But we must remember that the *Beowulf*-poet was composing for an aristocratic audience who knew not only the story of Beowulf and his monster-combats but also, in all their ramifications, the stories at which the writer glanced. Furthermore, they had a courtly appreciation of good literary technique and good verse; the poet's exploration of Germanic verse-patterns as well as his comments upon the grim business of living were to them sources of aesthetic enjoyment.

They seem also to have taken pleasure in things which we should call rather gloomy. Although many of the set-pieces, the purple passages, are perceptive and eloquent, they seem rather dark to us. Nature, for example, is never presented in terms of a bright spring morning; rather, it appears in the clouds lowering over the moors, in the hard-driven spindrift of the wintry North Sea. One of the best-known descriptive passages is that describing Grendel's lair; let it stand as an example of the poet's way of looking at his background:

"They inhabit a hidden land, wolf-cliffs, windy headlands, a fearful fen-path, where the mountain-stream runs down under the cover of the cliffs, a flood under the earth. It is not far hence, in mile-measure, that the mere lies; over it hang rimy groves, fast-rooted woods droop over the water. There every night one may see a fearful wonder: a fire in the flood. None lives of the sons of men so wise as to know its bottom. Though the heath-stepper, wearied by hounds, the hart of strong horns, enter the wood, put to flight from afar, he will give up his life on the shore sooner than go in to hide his head—that is no canny place! Thence the wave-mingling rises up, wan under the welkin, when the wind stirs wild storms, until the sky darkens, the heavens weep."

Coupled with this gloomy view of nature is a gloomy view of man's life in the world. The *Beowulf*-poet felt it necessary to point out whenever he could that life was real and earnest, and that a man's only duty was to live and die a hero, however hard the way to heroism. The inevitable tensions of such an existence, under the strains of shifting loyalties imposed by a tribal society, were, to the poet and his hearers, the true stuff of literature. They knew what happened to Hnaef and Finn; but how did Hnaef's followers feel about their impossible situation? What thoughts had they about themselves, men who had taken service with the slayer of their lord? (But what else could they have done?) What incidents, in themselves slight, but pregnant with an evil meaning for everyone, led to the final onslaught on the Frisians, the hoarse battle-cries, the burning hall? The probing of these questions, not merely getting on with the story, was the poet's task. And he liked doing it, pointing out, as he did so, that over all the actors in the drama brooded a fate which sometimes even a man's utmost valor could not avoid. Nothing then was left but to fulfil a warrior's last duty by a heroic death.

The picture is grim, but in its very grimness there is something fine. Although it is hard for us, now, to project ourselves imaginatively into Germanic heroic society, we can admire the men who chose for themselves as the highest good this sort of dedicated life, who were willing, if fate so ruled, to die without reluctance for the causes they thought good. Therein lies a principal value of the *Beowulf:* it draws for us a picture of Germanic life of the early Middle Ages, and tells us a good deal of what we know about the history of these peoples: but beyond this, in its exploration of this life and its problems, it tells us what our Germanic ancestors thought the good life should be.

The *Beowulf* is preserved in only one manuscript, Cotton Vitellius A xv, now in the British Museum. Its preservation is almost miraculous, for when Henry VIII dissolved the monasteries, many thousands of books were scattered and destroyed; and in 1731 the library of Sir Robert Cotton was partially burned. The manuscript of the poem was considerably injured, mostly at the front and back; and when it was rebound further damage was done. Fortunately, in 1787, Thorkelin, a Danish scholar born in Iceland, made a copy of the manuscript as it then stood, as well as a translation into Danish. In 1807, the English fleet bombarded Copenhagen, and his translation and notes were destroyed; the copy, however, was preserved. Had it not been saved, we should know much less of the text than we do, for until the end of the nineteenth century, when the manuscript was carefully rebound, bits of pages crumbled away where they had been scorched.

This manuscript copy dates from about the year 1000 A.D., some three hundred years after the poem was first written. It is in the West-Saxon dialect, but shows traces of earlier and Northern forms which indicate that it was written in the North of England.

BEOWULF: THE STORY

The poet commences with the story of Scyld Scefing (Shield, son of Sheaf) who as a child drifted to the shores of Denmark in an unmanned boat. He grew up, to become in turn a king of great splendor and renown. He terrified his enemies; he got gold and land; he made his country great; he rewarded his followers generously—that was a good king! When, full of years, he died, his warriors prepared for him a great ship, and loaded it with gold and armor. They set it adrift, and he returned whence he had come many years before.

Generations later, his descendant Hrothgar built a great hall called Heorot. In it he feasted his warriors, and they heard the sweet song of the minstrel, as he sang of the earth's creation. But Grendel, an evil spirit who lived in darkness, one of the brood of Cain, heard with envy the joy in the hall. When the singing and drinking were done, and men had sought their benches about the great room, this evil spirit came; in their sleep he took thirty thanes, and carried them to his own dark dwelling. In the morning the King was told of the murder; nor was that the last time Grendel came; the next night he stole in and took others—he did not mourn about that!—and for twelve years he continued his raids, until the building stood empty.

Then at his home in Geatland Beowulf, the friendly follower and neighbor of King Hygelac, heard men sing of these evil tidings. With fourteen followers he set out in his ship for Hrothgar's land. On being challenged by the coast-guard, Beowulf told why he had come, and was courteously passed into the country. Hrothgar welcomed Beowulf, and generously entertained him and his companions. Wealhtheow, Hrothgar's queen, also welcomed him, but Unferth, the King's counselor, a waspish fellow, tried to discredit Beowulf by twitting him with the loss of a swimming-contest. Beowulf showed the sort of man he was by a courteous but firm reply, in which he told the story of the match with his friend Breca: how for five days they swam, bearing naked swords to defend themselves from monsters, until the seas drove them apart. Then the waves carried Beowulf to the land of the Finns; on the way, he slew nine monsters.

The feast was resumed, and Beowulf made his formal boast of what he intended to do: to fight Grendel without weapons, to defeat him by the strength of his hands alone. Then all went to bed: the Danes to their own sleeping-quarters, the Geats within the hall.

"Then came from the moor under the misty slopes Grendel moving; God's anger was on him. The ill-scather intended to entrap one of the men in the high hall.

"He went under the sky to where he most clearly knew the wine-hall, adorned with gold. That was not the first time he had sought the hall of Hrothgar; but never in his life, before or since, did he find worse luck! He came to the hall, this joyless warrior; the doors quickly sprang open, though fast with forged bands, when he struck them with his hands. The evil plotter, swollen with rage, entered the hall; quickly the fiend trod the fair floor; from his eyes there stood out a loathsome light, likest to a flame. Within the hall he saw many a warrior, the band of kinsmen sleeping, a company of heroes together. Then his mind rejoiced; he meant, ere day, to divide the life from the body of each of them, since there had come to him the hope of a plenteous feast. But it was not fated that he should partake of men after that night.

"The strong kinsman of Hygelac looked to see how the evil hurter would make his attack. Nor did the wretch think to delay—quickly he seized at the first snatch a sleeping warrior, tore him without hindrance, bit the bone-locks, drank the blood from his veins, swallowed him in huge morsels; quickly he finished the dead one, feet and hands and all."

Then he approached Beowulf; never had Grendel encountered such a hand-grip! Strongly Beowulf held him; Grendel wanted to escape, to seek his devilish companions. Beowulf stood up and held him back; their fingers cracked with the strain. Grendel made for the door; Beowulf was pulled along. The hall resounded; it was a wonder that it did not fall, but it was fast bound with iron. Many a mead-bench was torn from its fastenings when those two strove together. Beowulf would not use his sword, for he had sworn not to do so; but even if he had used it, the good iron would not have bitten Grendel, for he had put a spell upon swords. The evil warrior found that his body would not withstand the strong grip of Beowulf: the sinews tore, the bone-locks burst, quickly his arm was torn from the shoulder. Grendel escaped, sought the fen-paths, his joyless dwelling, sick to death; well he knew that his end was come! Beowulf rejoiced in the night's work; he had carried out his boast to the Danes, that weaponless he would slay the monster.

Then in the morning there was many a good warrior about the hall to see the token of victory, Grendel's arm and shoulder hung under the spacious roof. No one there was sorry about his death! Many came riding to see the wonder; they said that nowhere was Beowulf's equal in valor. To celebrate the victory, they held games: some raced their horses, some heard the minstrel sing of Sigmund's wanderings and battles.

Hrothgar rejoiced, for never had he thought again to enjoy the fair hall; but Beowulf, with the help of God, had cleansed it for him. Hrothgar decreed a great feast within it. There he gave Beowulf a golden banner as a reward for his victory, and a sword, golden-hilted, a mail-coat and a helmet; never was there a more lordly gift in a meadhall. To each of Beowulf's companions, also, Hrothgar made noble presents, and for the man slain by Grendel he paid the full price of a man.

Then was song and joy together; the minstrel sang of the fight at Finnsburh, how Hildeburh, Finn's queen, had little reason to praise the good faith of the Jutes. Blameless, she was deprived by war of her loved ones; battle took all of Finn's thanes save a few, and his guest, Hengest, could in no way offer battle. A truce was made; the Danes swore an oath of allegiance to Finn, their lord's slayer. The Frisians might not, on pain of death, twit them with this deed. Then the funeral pyres were built; Hildeburh lit that of her son; the flame swallowed all. The winter wore on; Hengest might not sail the wintry seas, for storms blocked his way. But he thought of vengeance, and in the spring Hunlafing laid on his lap the sword, whose edge was well known to the Frisians. Then he rose, and his men with him, and fell on the Frisians; they burnt the hall, carried off Hildeburh, and went home to Denmark, glad of their vengeance! So sang the minstrel.

Then came Wealhtheow, queen of Hrothgar, and laid about Beowulf's neck a magnificent necklace and gave him a ring of twisted gold, and bade him enjoy them forever, and to be a friend to her sons. Then the warriors drank; and at last Hrothgar went home, leaving the hall to Beowulf and his companions.

They set their shields beneath their heads, for it was their custom to sleep ready for battle. But as they slept, Grendel's dam came, determined on vengeance for her evil son's death. The warriors slept; Beowulf did not know of her coming. She took with her the arm of Grendel, her son, and Aeschere, a counselor of King Hrothgar. That was no good exchange!

In the morning Beowulf was brought to Hrothgar's hall, where Hrothgar told him of the night's evil work, and of the place where the monsters dwelt: a grim and secret land, deep in the fens, where even the deer, hard-pressed by dogs, would turn and fight rather than go forward to a more terrible death. Beowulf answered that he would avenge Aeschere:

"All of us must abide our ending day; let him who can do something glorious before death, for that is best for the warrior."

A man who knew the way led them into the fens; they passed steep cliffs, dreary woods, homes of monsters. On the cliff by the water-side they found Aeschere's head. Then they came to the pool where Grendel's mother dwelt. Beowulf dressed himself in his armor, that swords might not hurt him, and put on the sword which Unferth lent him, Hrunting; never had it failed to battle. Then Beowulf directed Hrothgar, should he not return, to send news of the battle to Hygelac, together with the precious gifts he had received, and to make a present of his own sword to Unferth; and he leaped into the pool.

For the space of a day he sank through the waters, defending himself against the monsters which dwelt there, until he saw a light shining under the pool. There he found Grendel's mother, a fearsome hag, who dragged him into her lair. He attacked her with Hrunting—but the iron would not bite on her charmed hide. He gripped her then strongly around the body, and she as eagerly gripped him. Had it not been for his mailcoat, the son of Ecgtheow would have died there, but the strong rings saved his life. Then Beowulf saw among the weapons a sword, the old work of giants, the finest of weapons, so great that no one save Beowulf could wield it. He seized it and with one blow cut her head from her shoulders. She crashed to the floor—the warrior rejoiced in his work.

Then Beowulf looked about the cave; he saw many treasures. There too was the body of Grendel. From it he cut the head, and the body leaped under the blow.

The warriors sitting about the brim of the pool saw the blood and flesh floating upward through the water, and said among themselves that Beowulf was dead. Hrothgar and his men went home, but Beowulf's men stayed, little as they thought to see their lord again. Sick in mind, they stared at the pool. Up through the water swam Beowulf, carrying Grendel's head and the sword; but the hot blood of the monster had melted the blade, so that only the gold-adorned hilt was left. They returned to the hall, bearing Grendel's head, which was so heavy that four men must carry it. At Heorot, Beowulf gave Hrothgar the hilt of the sword and the head of Grendel; and he promised that thenceforward men should sleep without care in the hall.

In a stately speech, Hrothgar praised Beowulf, and prophesied that in the future he would be a great man among his people. Not at all would he be like Heremod, who, though a prosperous king, alienated his friends and warrior-companions, and ended wretchedly.

Then at night they rested; and in the morning Beowulf thanked Hrothgar, and promised him that if Hrothgar needed help again, he should have it; and Hygelac, Beowulf's lord, would be ready at need. Hrothgar thanked him, and they said farewell. Beowulf returned to his homeland, where he told Hygelac how all had gone, and gave him many gifts.

After the death of Hygelac, and when the reign of his son, Heardred, whom Beowulf placed on the throne and defended, was done, Beowulf was chosen king; and for fifty years he ruled well and prudently. But the quiet of his reign was broken by a dragon, whose hoard had been robbed. The dragon woke; he sniffed along the stones, and tracked the robber. Spewing fire, he swept over the countryside, laying all waste. That was the heaviest of sorrows to Beowulf, that his land should be swallowed in flame. Angered at heart, he clothed himself again in his old armor, and with eleven warriors he went to seek the dragon. No longer was Beowulf the mighty warrior of his youth; but as King he could not suffer any other to bear the danger of the dragon-fight.

He went into the dragon's lair on the headland; the dragon approached, and Beowulf drew his sword. But the iron would not pierce the hide; and the heat of the dragon's breath overcame the hero. The others, terrified, fled away; only Wiglaf, son of Wihstan, remained. He taunted his companions: "Well do I remember how we boasted at the beer-drinking that we should never desert our lord at need! Now is the time to make good the boast; as for me, the best thing is that the flame embrace my body and his. Well do I know that he shall not suffer this peril alone; together, with sword and shield, shall we carry on the fight!"

Again the dragon came on, and Beowulf struck; but the sword broke with the violence of the blow. The dragon reared up, and Wiglaf wounded it in the belly; then Beowulf cut it in two with his battle-knife. The flames gushed out, and the dragon died.

Then Beowulf spoke to his faithful retainer, and thanked him for the help he had given at need. He told of the deeds of his youth, and of the glory in his life, for well he knew that the count of his days was done.

"For fifty years I held this people, nor was there a king who dared offer me battle. I held it well; never did I swear an evil oath. Wounded to the death, I may well rejoice, for never will the Creator accuse me of the murder of kinsmen when life goes from my body. Now do you, dear Wiglaf, go under the stone, and bring out the dragon's hoard, that I may see it."

They brought forth the great hoard—gold and gems, the work of men of old, and Beowulf was glad. He gave to Wiglaf a golden ring from his neck, and entrusted the kingdom to him.

The warriors of Beowulf built a great burial place on the headland, and placed within it all of the gold. Then they built a great fire, and on it they placed the body of their lord. About it rode the fighters; they sang their woe: so shall men bewail their King, and tell of his noble deeds; it is right that a warrior shall mourn his king with words when the soul must go forth from the body. So the Geats mourned their lord; they said that he was the mildest of kings, and the gentlest; most friendly to the people, and of honor most desirous.

SUGGESTIONS FOR FURTHER READING

Translations:

Hall, J. R. C. London, 1911

R. K. Gordon. Everyman's Library, London, 1927

Kennedy, C. W. New York, 1940 (in alliterative verse)

Other Books:

Lawrence, W. W. *Beowulf and Epic Tradition*, Cambridge, Mass., 1930

Chambers, R. W. *Beowulf: An Introduction to the Study of the Poem*, Cambridge, Mass., 1921

See also the notes to Klaeber's edition of the poem, New York, 1936

THE SONG OF
ROLAND

THE SONG OF ROLAND: INTRODUCTION

The *Song of Roland (Chanson de Roland)* is representative of a type of French poetry which was written in the eleventh and twelfth centuries, and which is termed *chanson de geste*. The name itself, which means a "song of deeds," emphasizes a fundamental way in which the *Song of Roland* differs from such a work as *Paradise Lost*. While the Miltonic epic is introspective in approach, the *Roland* is a poem of action, written for men of action.

In Wace's *Geste des Normanz*, the famous *jongleur* Taillefer is mentioned as singing before William at Hastings a song "of Charlemagne and Roland, and of Oliver and the vassals who perished at Rencevals." It is possible, then, that at least part of the *Roland* existed in 1066, although there is no proof that Wace refers to the poem as we know it. Authorities believe that the present version is the work of more than one author; the earlier portion is probably that dealing with Marsile. There is evidence that the last revision and the completion of the poem with the "Baligant" episode, bearing the signature of "Turoldus," took place during the period of the first armed expeditions into Palestine, about the first decade of the twelfth century, during the reign of Philip I. Annexations to the Christian domains, in spite of growing feudal resistance, had left the Crusaders in possession of Jerusalem; but their hold was precarious. The refusal by the Caliph of Egypt of Christian offers of alliance against the Turks at the close of the First Crusade, and his sending of expeditions against them in Syria and Palestine, as well as the defeat of the Emir El-Afdhal by Robert of Normandy several years later, suggest the situation in the

"Baligant" episode of the *Roland*. The greater economic security resulting from the strengthening of domestic feudalism was giving rise to a trend toward the growth of towns and the increasing power of the bourgeoisie. Among the ecclesiastical and military aristocracy, the shifting of interest away from Christian strongholds in the Holy Land was a source of great concern. The twelfth century poet of the *Roland*, addressing primarily the secular-minded clergy, military and political leaders of his time, recalls the ideal of militant Christianity under Charlemagne, in support of the movement for a new Holy War in Spain and the Orient. The story of Roncesvalles appeals to its audience through their basic ideals: loyalty to their ruler, religious duty, and chivalric codes of conduct.

Count Roland represents the perfect chivalric warrior of his time. He is young, nobly born, wealthy, and handsome. The most famous of Charlemagne's Peers, he is entrusted with the guardianship of a March, or border; he is Charlemagne's nephew and "right arm." Roland's favorite pastimes are hunting, jousting, and war, his highest ambition to bring new glory to his ruler and new laurels to his own name, and to spread the Christian faith throughout the world by force of arms. Loyalty is Roland's very core of existence—loyalty to King, family, country, and religion. He possesses also the Christian virtues of generosity, gentleness, and unquestioning obedience. His unusual fortitude and skill in deeds of arms have a moral meaning in a society which believed implicitly in the validity of trial by combat and ordeal. Roland is sensitive about his honor to the point of vanity, fearing more than anything else the tarnishing of his magnificent reputation as a warrior and the satirical songs which the soldiers might make about him if he failed in courage. His exaggerated bravery and pride cause him to fail to consider his duty, as a commander of men, to protect those under his command. The hopeless situation resulting from this imbalance calls forth Roland's more mature qualities of character. As he faces certain death, his courage is refined through suffering. He realizes too late what he has done in his refusal to summon Charlemagne and the main army, and he feels deep compassion for the men whom he has failed to save. His acceptance of guilt and his development and atonement through suffering and death are treated with epic high seriousness. As he dies, he offers his right glove to God, as a vassal relinquishing a fief to his lord, in token of atonement and submission.

Oliver, son of Regnier, Duke of Genoa, is brother-in-arms to Roland, equal to him in power, lineage, and knightly virtues. He is the brother of Aude, Roland's betrothed. Oliver, however like Roland in other respects, is less volatile in temperament, combining prudence with bravery. He advises Roland to call for aid before the battle begins. However, once committed to the struggle, and realizing that help summoned later will probably arrive too late to save many of the rear guard, Oliver prefers to die unvanquished in spirit; and Roland's later intention to blow Olifant, his trumpet, is the cause of their famous quarrel. The relationship of Oliver and Roland resembles that of Hector and Aeneas. At first, during the more hopeful stage of the conflict, their comradeship is lightened by touches of gaiety; but it must soon be dominated by tragedy. To Oliver is given the naming of Roland's tragic flaw: pride in his own powers. The situation gives rise to several very moving scenes between the two. When Oliver, mortally wounded and blinded by his own blood, strikes Roland by mistake, Roland's pathetically ready forgiveness foreshadows his future suffering, when he sees Oliver die. The character of Oliver perhaps reflects the demands of military and political leaders of the twelfth century for a leader who would combine the heroic qualities of a soldier like Bohémond I, leader of the First Crusade, with the balance of a more modern leader of men.

Turpin, Archbishop of Rheims, the most important churchman in the poem, is in many respects a personification of that unity of religious and secular elements which characterize medieval society and art. Like other ecclesiastics of the period, he receives his benefice and his worldly powers in fief from the King, under the same conditions of service and fealty which govern secular nobles. Although he speaks formally for the

Church in his speeches to the troops, he is also a formidable warrior, and he accompanies Roland as a companion and an equal, like the famous soldier-bishop Adhémar of Le Puy, who led a division at Dorylaeum under Bohémond. Before he is mortally wounded, he slays four hundred pagan enemies; his heroism as a fighter is not weakened by any clerical scruples concerning the shedding of blood—at least, not when the blood is Mohammedan. Among those who fall before him is the sorcerer Sigorel; this triumph is most significant, representing perhaps the only piece of conscious allegory in the entire work. Turpin's prowess in arms is derived from the same Deity Who, later in the poem, demonstrates His judgment against the treacherous Ganelon by awarding miraculous victory to young Thierry of Anjou. Virtue in a man of God need not be conjoined with meekness and pacifism. Turpin mediates the quarrel between Roland and Oliver. He gives absolution and blessing to the dead Peers, when he is himself pierced by four lances. His death is truly Christian; he perishes in a compassionate effort to bring water in the Olifant for the dying Roland.

The final triumph of Christian doctrine over pagan heresy is, however, given to Charlemagne the King, who, with supernatural aid, defeats the Emir Baligant of Cairo in single combat. The figure of Charlemagne dominates the action, opening and closing the poem; many authorities believe that the piece should be titled the *Song of Charlemagne and Roland*. Charlemagne combines the chivalric virtues of bravery, nobility, skill in arms, and personal piety with wisdom and venerable age. Most of the supernatural element in the poem is introduced in connection with his character; his visions and aid from Heaven emphasize the divine nature of his right to rule. The leader of Christian peoples against the pagan, he personifies social and religious order; he rules wisely, serving the good of his people; he plunges his nation into war only for the best of all possible reasons—the extension of the boundaries of Christendom and the conversion of the pagans.

Ganelon, the traitor, is a most interesting figure. He possesses many of the qualities of a chivalric hero; his character is often rather sympathetic. He is faithful, according to his own definitions of fealty. Indeed, the question of his punishment for the fatal conspiracy with Marsile raises a difficult problem in definition. Feudal loyalty, being centered in the ideal of personal fealty, differs radically from more modern definitions of the term, which bring in national or idealistic obligations. Ganelon does not have as his primary purpose harm to his liege lord, Charlemagne; he aims his treachery at the rear guard, rather than at the main army where Charlemagne rides. His motive, as he explains in his brilliant self-defense, is private revenge, to which a feudal warrior has a right, provided that he gives formal defiance to his enemy. This Ganelon has done, in the presence of the King, to Roland, Oliver, and the Peers. Ganelon is, as he explains, jealous of Roland's wealth, and Roland's nomination of Ganelon for the dangerous mission to King Marsile convinces him that Roland seeks his life, fanning his long-standing sense of injustice into active hate. Even in his conferences with Marsile and Blancandrin, Ganelon had uttered nothing but praise of Charlemagne; he delivers the King's message, although he adds insulting terms of his own to stir Marsile to rage. His plot is against Roland only, who, he tells Marsile, is the author of the Spanish war, and without whom there will be no further invasions of Spain. Although his action cost France twenty thousand men, including the flower of its chivalry, Ganelon is not technically guilty of treason. Charlemagne is groping for a more inclusive definition of the term, and God seems to bear him out in his decision. But the case requires divine intervention in the trial by combat, before Ganelon may be condemned.

Characterization in the *Song of Roland* attains a high degree of dramatic objectivity. The chief emphasis is upon the stirring action, which progresses in an orderly manner, without digression, achieving almost perfect unity. The language is strictly disciplined and the chain of action carefully forged. In the resultant atmosphere of seriousness and urgency, we learn of the characters almost entirely through their own words and actions. This simplicity of treatment has led several critics to

remark that the *Roland* is rather narrow in its proportions;
J. W. Machail, in fact, terms it "an epic lay, rather than an epic
in the full sense." However, current opinion seems to agree on
both its epic nature and its technical excellence. The simplicity
and directness of the work are the result of mature artistry.
The development of character within the poem reveals excep-
tionally profound insight into human behavior; but its effec-
tiveness depends largely upon the absence of self-conscious
"psychological" description. The author is almost completely
absent from his work, at least insofar as such a thing is possible.
Wilmotte points out that the most important devices for attaining vividness of portraiture are speeches, dialogues, and mono-
logues. He observes that approximately 655 out of a thousand
lines in the *Roland* are of this type, a much higher percentage
of speech than is found in the Homeric or Vergilian epics.
While such technique sacrifices a certain amount of grace and
variety, it avoids entirely the facility and diffuseness of exposition which prevent the later *chansons de geste* from achieving
epic status. The *Roland* bears none of the conventional ornaments of these later poems. But there are indications of a
developing "courtly love" treatment of behavior, in Roland's extreme sensibility and in the love-death of Aude.

A considerable degree of epic breadth is attained in the
Roland by having the conflict of earthly armies reflect a conflict of divine forces, as in the third book of the *Aeneid*. The
slow, logical progression-within-unity of the action also widens
the scope of the work by suggesting a certain inevitability in
the result of the struggle. The importance of the crisis in the
universal plan of history is made convincing by the vitality of
the language and the elevation and seriousness of tone. Other
devices for attaining epic breadth are the use of large numbers
of human beings and the brilliant employment of suggestion in
depicting scenes briefly and powerfully.

The *Song of Roland* is composed in epic strophes, or *laisses*.
The longest are thirty-four to thirty-five lines long, and the
shortest has only five lines. There are about three hundred
laisses in the poem. The *laisse* is unified by the terminal asso-

nance—similar vowel-sounds—of its lines, which are never quite
the same for two successive *laisses,* although there will often
be a tendency toward rhyme. The *laisse* is generally a self-
contained unit, although on one or two occasions a speech will
continue over more than one. Usually there is a separate incident for each *laisse,* changes of assonance marking steps forward in the action. The Oxford edition was apparently a
jongleur's copy; the word *Aoi,* which terminates the *laisse* and
is sometimes found in the middle of the *laisse* also, has been
interpreted as either a refrain or exclamation to end the line
or a note indicating a *crescendo* in the music to which the
poem was sung or chanted. The last line of the *laisse* is nearly
always summarizing or climactic in nature. The *laisses simi-
laires,* in which one event is repeated several times with change
of assonance, are used as an emotional relief in crises, or as a
method of lingering upon an especially effective incident. A
sufficient sense of continuity is achieved by frequent repetition
from one *laisse* to the next or by alliterative linkage, as well
as by the urgency and tension of the action itself. The meter is
decasyllabic, and the cesura occurs usually after the fourth
accented syllable. Alliteration is frequent and musical, and the
meter is easily and masterfully handled, with interesting use
of elision and pause and accent variation.

The *Song of Roland* was, in the later Middle Ages, the best
known poem in Europe not written in Latin. Under Charlemagne (742-814) France became the first empire of Europe,
and in the train of his conquering armies came an awareness
of French culture which gave a new impetus and a new direction to all the vernacular literatures. As writing in these vernaculars—the spoken languages of the people—became more
and more popular, the story of Roland and Oliver grew into
one of the three principal subjects—"matters," they were called
—of romance. French writers—and, after the Norman Conquest,
those of England—from the twelfth to the fifteenth centuries
composed many poems, either for the court or the market-place,
celebrating sometimes the adventures of Charlemagne, but

more often those of the Twelve Peers under the leadership of Roland and Oliver. We still have many of these, for they were immensely popular, were widely copied and, later, printed.

The story of Roland and Oliver was quite as popular in Italy (which Charlemagne had invaded) as in France, and two of the best poems on the subject, apart from the *Song of Roland* itself, were composed there. The first of these was the *Orlando Innamorato (Roland in Love)*, by Matteo Maria Boiardo, composed in 1482 and first printed in 1484. It deals with the story of Roland's falling in love with a pagan princess and the adventures he went through in his pursuit of her. Boiardo left his poem unfinished, but in 1502 or 1503 Ludovico Ariosto completed it with his poem, the *Orlando Furioso (Roland Run Mad)*. In this work, Roland's infatuation with the pagan maid is explained by the fact that he had, literally, lost his senses. They were restored to him—after he had insanely devastated most of the world with a tree-root—by his friend Astolfo, who rode to the Earthly Paradise on a hippogriff, found the vial containing the lost senses, and brought them back to Roland. Both poems are infused with the romantic chivalry which imbued much of the popular literature of the later Middle Ages and the Renaissance, and both also are full of wonderful happenings. They were immensely popular in their day and later, and because they are not without merit, they had a good deal of literary influence, both in Italy and abroad. The picture of Roland and Oliver which they offer is, however, widely at variance with the heroic picture found in the *Song of Roland*. We have omitted them, therefore, because they add nothing to our knowledge of the Paladins who gave up their lives for Charlemagne and sweet France.

THE SONG OF ROLAND: THE STORY

Charles, the great monarch, lord of Frankish lands, had for seven years fought beyond the mountains, had to the country's end led forth his host of conquerors. In all of Spain, there was but one city unshattered—stern Saragossa, grim mountain fortress, held by King Marsile, a king who loved not God, but served Mahound and offered up his prayers to Apollo. Evil must be his end. In Saragossa, King Marsile, within an olive orchard, held court upon a bench of blue marble; around him were more than twenty thousand men.

"Listen well, my lords," said he, "see what misfortune overcomes us! Charles, the great king, has come from sweet France, to our confusion and overthrow. Nor have I any force to offer resistance; against such men as his no warriors of mine can stand in battle. I pray for guidance, that you may save me from dishonor and death."

No man was there among Marsile's counselors wise enough to answer. At last Blancandrin arose, that sage and subtle man of Valfunde; there was a man knightly in valor, worthy to aid his lord!

"Be not at all dismayed by this, lord," said he. "Send to Charles the Proud vows of service and of friendship. Send to him bears and lions and hounds for the chase, seven hundred camels and a thousand moulted falcons, three hundred mules bearing gold and silver, fifty wagons to cart it away. With it he may satisfy his mercenaries. Tell him that too long he has scourged this land with war, that it is time for him to return to Aix, that at Michaelmas season you yourself will follow him there, to receive baptism and to own yourself his liegeman in all things. If he should require hostages, give him men—ten or twenty—that he may be secure in his thoughts. My own son shall be one of them; send the sons of our wives, even at peril of their heads. Rather let them lose their lives than we our land and our honor!"

Thus, said Blancandrin, should the French army be dispersed. But when, at Michaelmas, Charles should hold high festival at Aix, his expected guests should neither arrive nor send word. True, the young men must die; yet Spain, the bright, the beautiful, should be saved.

The Pagans agreed. The council being ended, Marsile summoned from among the nobles ten of the wiliest, Blancandrin among them, and sent them to Charlemagne, bearing olive branches and gifts, to carry the fraudulent message, promising that success would be rewarded with lands and treasures for each.

The Emperor, meanwhile, after long siege, had captured Córdoba; fallen were the high walls, and with his catapults he had razed the towers. Great was the booty when his knights sacked the city, and no Pagan remained, unless he were a corpse or a convert. Charles sat in a great orchard, upon a throne of pure gold. White were his beard and hair; noble his stature, proud his countenance. Around him sat his knights, upon white carpets.

As the King of fair France sat rejoicing, the Saracen messengers came before him. They greeted him with show of love and good faith. Bland and courtly was Blancandrin's speech, and great was the King's hope that Marsile, though once a bitter enemy to France and to the True Faith, might yet be saved. But he was not hasty in his reply; it was his custom to speak at his leisure. A tent was pitched, and the ambassadors were entertained that night with honor.

Charles, rising early, when daylight came once more, heard Mass and Matins, and summoned his Peers, that he might take counsel. Duke Ogier, Archbishop Turpin, Richard the Old, Henry, his nephew, Acelin of Gascony, Thibaud of Rheims and his cousin Milon were there. There were present also Gerier and Gerin, and with them came Count Roland and Oliver, the brave and noble. A thousand Franks attended. Ganelon came, he who would perform the act of treachery. And thus began the council of which much evil must arise.

Charles told his Peers of the Saracen offer, but they were reluctant to advise him. Then Count Roland, who disagreed with the King, rose from his place to speak against the agreement.

"Woe be upon that day when you give Marsile your trust!", he cried. "For during the seven years that we have warred with Spain, I have conquered for you Noples and Commibles. Valterre too have I taken, and the country of Pine; Balaguer and Tudela and Sexilie have fallen to me. Then King Marsile did blackest treason; he dispatched fifteen men, each bearing an olive branch, and each Pagan spoke to you words like these. You asked your Franks for advice, who were rather irresponsible in their counsel. You sent the Pagan two of your counts. One was Basan, and the other, Basile. On the hills below Haltilie he ordered their heads struck off. Continue the war as you have begun it! Lead your fighting retainers before Saragossa. Besiege the city, even if it takes all your earthly days. Avenge those two noble men slain by the traitor!"

The Emperor was silent, his head bowed in thought. Ganelon spoke, opposing Roland. "Whoever advises you to reject this offer cares not what sort of death we die," he declared. He stressed the practical advantages of the treaty, and mocked at Roland with veiled insult.

After Ganelon, Naimes addressed the King; no better vassal was there in the court. "King Marsile has been vanquished in this war," he said; "and when he sends to you asking for mercy, it would be sin to injure him further." The Peers agreed with Ganelon and Naimes, and the King's next question concerned the appointment of a messenger to send to Saragossa. Naimes, although a hoary and venerable man, was the first to volunteer, but was refused. Roland, although he had opposed the treaty, was the next to speak; but Count Oliver answered emphatically,

"Of course not. Your temper is short, and you are proud

of heart. I should be afraid that you might get into trouble. If the King wishes, he might well send me."

When the great Charlemagne replied that neither they nor any of his Peers should bear the message, Archbishop Turpin of Rheims rose from the assembly and begged for the staff and glove of ambassadorship.

"Go and seat yourself on your rug of white silk!" ordered Charles. "Speak not unless I so command you!"

It was evident that Charles would send none of his dear companions upon so cherished a mission; yet someone had to go, and once again he placed his question before the assembled nobles.

Roland spoke with pride and wisdom. "Send Ganelon, my stepfather," he said. And all the Franks agreed.

Count Ganelon was in great distress. From his mighty shoulders he flung the sable scarves, and he stood there in his silken tunic. Bright were his eyes, and haughty his countenance. So nobly handsome was he that all the peers could not forebear to look at him. Ganelon, although unwilling, accepted the general choice, when sealed with the command of the King, promising, nonetheless, to indulge his fancy in avenging himself. Roland's laughter fanned the flames of his wrath.

"Sire," cried Ganelon, "Roland is the cause of all this! Never, while I live, shall I love him; nor Oliver, since he is Roland's comrade; nor the Twelve Peers, because they are friends of his. In your presence, Lord, I defy all of them!"

The glove and staff were proffered to Ganelon; as he moved to receive it, the glove fell to the ground—a very ill omen to all present. Alone, he took his way to the Saracens, for he refused all companionship that was offered him.

Ganelon, riding beneath the lofty olives, fell into company with the wily Blancandrin. They understood each other after very little speech had passed between them; and they rode together until they had pledged each other their faith that Roland should die.

In Saragossa, beneath the spreading yew tree, stood a throne draped in silk where Marsile held audience with the ambassador. Behold there Blancandrin and Ganelon! Ganelon delivered to the Saracen King the words of Charlemagne, but so distorted were they by guile that Marsile became enraged. Pretending to calm the King, he said,

"In your anger you are very wrong; for Charles, lord of France, the sender of this message, says: Receive the Christian Faith, and he will give to you in fief half of Spain. His nephew Roland shall have the other half, and in him you must find a very proud fellow-vassal, I fear. If you fail to agree to these terms, the Emperor will come to besiege Saragossa. You will be taken by force and brought in chains to Aix, where shameful death must be your lot."

Blinded by wrath, the Saracen King saw little of the letter from Charlemagne, but misinterpreted it to suit his own mood.

The son of Marsile cried, "Ganelon, the speaker of folly, deserves life no longer. Deliver him to me, that I may do justice upon him!"

When Ganelon heard this, he drew his sword; beneath the pine tree, he stood defiant. But Blancandrin, who had told the King of the pledge of brotherhood between him and Ganelon, drew him softly forth before the throne. Marsile, confessing that he had treated Ganelon too lightly, offered him a pledge of five hundred sables for amends, telling his wish for amity between the Saracens and the Franks. Ganelon answered that never, while Roland, Oliver, or the Peers were alive, could this wish be accomplished, for "with this guard, Charles is safe, and need fear no man." And thus was born the treachery that was to compass Roland's death, the infamous rear-guard attack that was to rob France of her finest warriors. On the relics in his sword Murgleis Ganelon swore to the treason, and therein he did great sin. The Saracens swore friendship with Ganelon, and many gifts of price were his reward. To Charles, Marsile sent the gifts required, and twenty hostages of noble birth.

The Emperor, as was his custom, had risen early to hear Mass and Matins. As he stood on the green with his best-loved warriors, Ganelon came once again before him, and with great guile did he speak.

"God save all present," said he, "for here I bring the keys to Saragossa, and I have brought enormous wealth for you, with twenty hostages. Have them well guarded." He described the magnificence of the Saracen court, and assured him of Marsile's good wishes in all things. "Before the first month shall pass, Sire," he said, "you shall see him follow you to fair France, where he will receive your professed Faith, and with joined hands will own your lordship over himself and all his lands."

"May God be praised," answered Charles, "for you have done well, and you shall never lose by this act."

A thousand trumpets were blown before the host. The French broke camp, and took their way toward sweet France. To Count Roland fell the command of the rear guard, by the clever maneuvering of Count Ganelon. Through the wide valleys rode the Pagans, full armed, lances ready; what a pity that the French knew not of it!

That night, Charles dreamed that his ashen spear was snatched by Ganelon, and that it was broken into many splinters, while he stood powerless to prevent the deed.

Oliver and the Twelve Peers joined Roland in the leadership of the rear guard. "Never shall Charles lose hereby palfrey or charger, mule or riding-ass, steed or sumpter, unless it be purchased by the sword," said Roland.

"Well do I know that you speak truth," answered Ganelon.

Much yet did Charles fear that France might in some way be harmed by Ganelon; he forgot not his angelic vision of the spear.

Marsile summoned all his barons, and in Saragossa he ordered them to beat the great drums. The image of Mahound was placed in the greatest tower, and no Pagan was there but worshiped it. Then they rode, pennons flying in the wind, until they saw the flag of France. The rear guard of the Twelve Peers would not fail in fight. Marsile's nephew received as boon the right to strike the first blow against Roland, and twelve of the Saracen King's greatest barons were chosen to meet the Twelve Peers. They feared not, for they were good vassals, and not one was there but believed Mahound mightier than all the saints in Christendom. Marsile's twelve peers went into the pine wood to arm themselves. With them were no fewer than a hundred thousand Saracens, thirsting for battle.

The Pagans, armed with triple-thick coats of mail, bore Saragossa helmets—renowned in battle—and swords of Vienne steel; fair were their painted shields, their lances of Valencia, their pennons white and azure and crimson in the sun. In serried ranks they rode, their armor all afire. A thousand trumpets blared, to make it fairer still; so loud their sound that the French heard it, from far away.

Said Oliver, "Sir Friend, I think that we may have to fight the Saracens!"

"God grant that that may be the case," replied Roland, "for a man should suffer hardship, endure extremes of weather, and even lose his skin for his lord! Let every man be sure that he deals his heaviest blows, that the song sung of us be not ill! The Pagans are wrong; the Christians are right. As for me, I mean to give no bad example!"

Oliver, climbing upon a hill, saw the Saracen horde, gathered to bring sorrow to all good Christians. "Ganelon knew of this," he cried, "the blackguard, the traitor, when before our lord he singled us out!" Oliver could not count the divisions of the enemy; he was filled with dismay. Thrice he begged Roland to blow his horn, summoning Charlemagne's main body of men before all help should be past.

"God forbid," Roland replied in scorn, "that my kinsmen should be disgraced through me, or that through me sweet France should be disparaged! Nay, I shall strike, with my good Durendal, and you shall see my blade all dripping with blood!"

Again did Oliver the wise urge his request. "I see no blame in what I ask," he said, "for mighty are the Saracen hosts— our army tiny indeed!"

"The greater, then, my ardor and our glory!" cried Roland. Roland was bold, and Oliver was clever, but both were of courage beyond that of ordinary men. Never, when both were mounted and armed, did either shun combat for fear of death. Worthy the counts, and lofty their words. But the Pagans rode with fury. Prepared to die for their lord, the chosen twenty thousand dismounted, and Turpin blessed them all. They were absolved from sin, and the Archbishop blessed them with the Cross, in the name of the Almighty. Armed, in knightly fashion, they awaited their last battle. Count Roland, too late, realized Ganelon's unspeakable treason; yet, for Marsile, his bargain must be gained at sword's point.

On his swift steed, Veillantif, Roland crossed the plain. Full armed was he, his face laughing in scorn. Near him rode his comrade Oliver. The armies prepared to fight.

"I have nothing to say," said Oliver. "You did not condescend to wind your horn, and now you have no Charles to stand beside you. Nothing does he know of this; nor has he therefore blame, nor do those that ride with him. Ride hard, noble lords, and stand your ground! Give all your thoughts to the exchange of blows! As you receive them, so return them, and forget not the battle-cry of Charlemagne!"

At these words burst there from the Franks the mighty battle-cry. Nor might any who heard them forget that cry, "Montjoie!" Whoever hears the word cannot but remember mighty deeds. Then forward they rode— Ah, God, how proudly! Nor did the Pagans lag in receiving them. See the combat joined!

Marsile's nephew, he that begged for the first blow with Roland, was the first to fall, his helmet riven, his shield bent, his breast cut open, and all his bones burst. Before Oliver fell Falsaron, Marsile's brother. And before Archbishop Turpin lay Corsablix, great king of Barbary; Satan flew away with his accursed soul. Nor could the Emir of Balaguer, though a noble warrior, stand before Gerier.

Said Oliver, "Most pleasing do I find our battle!"

Great was the combat; no laggards were there. Count Roland, taking no thought for his safety, thrust with his spear as long as even the shaft remained. And with his naked sword he slew the valiant Saracen Chernuble. Oliver, his lance in splinters, passed Roland in the battle.

"Where is your sword Hauteclaire, with its hilt of gold and its crystal pommel?"

"I have not drawn him," answered Oliver, "for I have been much too busy dealing death-buffets!"

But with Hauteclaire he slew Val-Ferree, cleaving through helmet, body, and saddle and breaking the back of the horse he rode. "In that blow," cried Roland, "I own you for my brother! It is for such strokes that the King loves us!"

It was a battle wondrous in its grimness. The Pagans died by hundreds and thousands, and there the Franks lost their best defenders. In France, there were storms; buildings crumbled, and darkness fell at noon. Many feared the end of the world. They knew not that the very elements mourned the death of Roland.

The second battle came upon the French while they were gathering their dead. Turpin slew the wicked Abisme, traitor and murderer; and no one among the Franks thereafter doubted that the crosier was safe with that Archbishop. Often did the warriors pray Roland to protect them. But the Archbishop then spoke his inmost thoughts:

"Noble lords, lay aside unworthy thoughts!" he said. "Flee not, in God's name! Let no brave man have reason to make for you a song of shame. Far better is death in combat. We must soon die—of that we are sure. We cannot live beyond this day, but of one thing I can make you certain: Paradise is yours!"

So filled with joy were the Franks that there was not one who failed to take up the battle-cry once again. But in Englier of Gascony they mourned a great warrior, for he was soon after slain by the Saracen Climborin, no man of honor, but a good fighter. Yet Oliver, in his wrath, sent his soul to the devils who awaited it, and seven Arabs he unhorsed thereafter.

"My comrade is angered," said Roland. "Even beside me, he acquits himself well."

Horribly the second battle raged. On both sides, noble warriors fell to death. In the first four engagements, the French did well, but in the fifth, all the French knights were slain but sixty, who, before death, should sell themselves dearly.

Count Roland beheld the great losses among his men. He called his friend Oliver, the wise.

"What shall we do?" he asked. "Behold how many retainers strew the field! Well may we weep for France the Fair. What barons she has lost! O, my King, my friend, where are you? Oliver, brother, what can help us? How can we send him word?"

Oliver answered, with some heat, that it was now too late to blow the horn for assistance, and that never more should his sister, Aude, be betrothed to Roland, if he should see her again. "Valor with sense is no madness," he said, "for moderation is of more worth than foolhardiness."

But the valiant Turpin dissolved the quarrel, and bade Roland blow his horn. Mighty was Roland's effort, and the bugle's voice was heard over thirty long leagues. Charles heard it, but Ganelon persuaded him that it was a jest, a wager before Roland's comrades. The bugle call came again, and the French host turned back—but too late. Not one but said to the other, "If we should see Roland before his death, what great blows we should deal by his side!" But they had waited too long.

Evening fell, but the Emperor rode in great wrath and fear. The King had Ganelon taken into custody, to be guarded by the cooks of the company. To the chief cook, Besgon, he gave him in charge, and Besgon set upon him a hundred scullions, who beat him and put him in chains. He was put, fettered, upon a pack horse, to his humiliation, and there they kept him, until Charlemagne should demand him again.

Roland looked over the hills and the heath. Alas, how many noble Franks he saw lying in death. Bitterly he bewailed his error. "Too late I see you dying for me," he cried, "and I cannot fight for you or succor you. I shall die of grief, if I am slain by nothing else!" Returning to the fight, he cut through the field with noble Durendal. Never again will any man burn so for revenge! As the stag before the hounds, so fled the Pagans before Roland. The French fought as never before. Marsile, after killing several noble Franks, met Roland, who struck off his right hand and slew his son. A hundred thousand Pagans fled the field in terror, but more than fifty thousand remained, under the Caliph of Carthage. They charged fiercely, and Roland knew that the French were doomed.

The Caliph rode a sorrel steed; he dug in his golden spurs, and he struck Oliver from behind, through the breast. Feeling himself wounded to death, Oliver grasped Hauteclaire, that sword of burnished steel, and smote the Caliph on the helmet, splitting his head down to the front teeth; shaking the sword, he struck him dead. Never could that cursed Pagan boast of him to any! Then he cried on Roland for aid. Seeing his dearest friend covered with blood and ghastly pale, Roland swooned away on his horse. Oliver, bleeding sorely, and troubled in his vision, struck Roland on the helmet as he approached, for he could not recognize him; as far as the gilded nose-piece his blade penetrated, but he did not harm the flesh beneath. Realizing his error at Roland's gentle reprimand, he begged forgiveness, and the two companions parted forever. Feeling the approach of death, Oliver dismounted; lying on the ground, he confessed his sins loudly to Heaven, praying God to bless France, Charles, and Roland; and so his heart failed. Roland, the brave, wept for him. "Never have you done me harm," he said, "and it is my grief, since you are dead, that I must live." Roland fainted again, and only his strong stirrups held him to his saddle. Before he recovered, he had lost all his companions except for Turpin and Walter de l'Hum.

The three stood alone against the Pagans, who rode upon them with lances and spears; they dared not approach for hand-to-hand combat, although there were a thousand foot-soldiers and forty thousand horse among them. Their first cast of spears slew Walter, and four spears passed through the body of Turpin, whose horse fell under him. Pierced by four spears, the Archbishop yet sprang lightly to his feet; running to Roland, he cried, "I am yet unconquered; a good vassal is never taken alive!" Drawing this sword Almacé, he threw himself into the thick of the press. It was clear to those who found him after the battle that he had spared no one, for Charlemagne discovered him surrounded by four hundred Saracens, dead and wounded. This is attested by the Annals, and by him for whom God does miracles, the Baron St. Giles, who was on the field of battle, and who made the charter in the monastery of Laon. He who does not know this cannot know very much about the matter.

Count Roland fought like a true knight, but he was very weary, and his head throbbed painfully from the bursting of his temples when he had blown the horn. But he wanted to know whether Charles was on the way. He blew his horn once again, feebly, and Charles knew, when he heard, that Roland must be near death. He ordered his clarions blown, and the Saracens, hearing the mighty voice of sixty thousand trumpets in the distance, trembled with fear and said to one another, "Soon must Charles be here with us!" Four hundred armed men rushed to attack Roland, who determined never to yield to them as long as life remained in him. Into the thick of the charge he rode, Turpin beside him. He, who never loved a coward, called to the Archbishop, "Sire, you are on foot and I on horseback. For love of you I shall make my stand at this place. Together shall we meet both good and evil, nor can any mortal man cause me to part from you. Let us give the Pagans back their attack again. The best of all blows are those of Durendal!"

"A traitor is he who withholds his blows," answered the Archbishop. "Charles is coming back, and be sure that he will avenge us!"

The Pagans cried, "Alas for the day of our birth! Dread for us the dawning of this day! We have lost our lords and barons. Charles, the noble, comes with his mighty host. We hear the clear-voiced trumpets of the French, and loud is their cry of 'Montjoie!' Count Roland is so fierce and proud that no mortal can ever subdue him. Let us take aim at him, and then leave it at that." They cast at him all manner of weapons, but, although Veillantif was slain, Roland passed unscathed in his shattered armor. Then the Pagans fled. Count Roland, his steed dead, had no means of pursuing them, but against his will remained behind.

He went to help Turpin, whom he found in mortal agony. Unlacing his gilded helmet, and removing his white hauberk, he cut up his tunic to make bandages for his deep wounds. Embracing him, he begged that their dead companions be gathered together and identified. "Go, and return quickly," answered the Archbishop. "The field is ours, by God's grace!" Lamenting, Roland sought out the dead and brought them to Turpin for blessing. But when he saw Oliver lying in death, among his loved Peers, he could not help but weep. He paled, and fell to the ground in a swoon.

Turpin, greatly moved by the sight of Roland lying senseless, seized Roland's horn. Staggering, he turned towards the stream, meaning to fetch water for his comrade. But too great was his weakness. Sooner than a man might take a hundred paces, his heart gave out, and he fell in the agony of death. Roland came to himself, and, rising in great pain, he beheld the noble Archbishop lying upon the green grass in the attitude of prayer. Death had taken him while he confessed his sins to God. In great battles and in glorious sermons, he was ever his lord's champion against the unbelievers. May God grant him His sacred blessing!

Count Roland crossed his friend's hands and closed his eyes. Now he felt that his own death was very near. His brains issued forth from his ears. He prayed God to call his Peers, and for himself, he prayed to the Angel Gabriel. Taking his horn and his sword, he climbed upon a knoll, where, under two fair trees, there were four great blocks of marble. There he fainted, for his death approached. All this time a Saracen, who had feigned death, watched him. In his pride, the Pagan arose and seized him, crying, "Vanquished is Charles' nephew! I will bear home his sword!" As he pulled at Durendal, Roland came a little to himself. Grasping his horn, he smote the Pagan dead. "Pagan churl," he cried, "hadst thou the presumption to lay hands on me? Never shall man hear of this, but he will think thee a fool." Roland tried to break Durendal, the beautiful, for fear that it should be wielded by a lesser man, but the noble steel refused to shatter against the rocks.

"Ah, Durendal," he moaned, "how beautiful art thou, and how holy! In thy golden hilt there are many relics: a tooth of St. Peter and some of the blood of St. Basil, my lord St. Denis's hair, and a fragment of St. Mary's garment. Pagans should not own thee; thou shouldst be served by Christians. May never coward wield thee! Wide are the lands that I shall have conquered with thee, for the venerable Charles to hold in his power—lands of might and riches!"

Feeling death in his heart, Roland lay down upon the grass. Beneath him he placed his sword and his cracked horn. He turned his face toward the Pagans, that men might say that he died victorious.

"God, by Thy power, forgive my sins, great and little, which I have committed from the hour of my birth until this, the day when I am slain!" So saying, he held out his right gauntlet to God, and the angels of Heaven descended for him. St. Gabriel took the pledge from his hand, and God sent also his Cherubim and St. Michael of the Peril of the Sea to him; together they bore the soul of Count Roland to Paradise.

Charlemagne had reached Roncesvalles. He had but little time for grief, for he saw the dust of the retreating Pagans in the distance. Leaving guards for the slain warriors, he led the pursuit. Charles saw the sun setting, and he dismounted; prostrating himself on the turf, he prayed to God to stop the sun in its descent. There came to him an angel, bidding him ride on, promising that night would not cheat him of his just revenge. The Emperor remounted. For him God worked a great wonder, for the sun stood still in its course. In Val-Tenebrus, by the River Ebro, he overtook the retreating Saracens. Some he slew; the rest, for fear of him, threw themselves into the flood and were drowned.

The French made camp for the night, and Charles lay down, fully armed, upon the ground. He was weary, but sleep was long in coming to him. At last, at the end of his endurance, he slept. The Franks were asleep all around him. There was not even a steed that was able to stand; if one of them wanted grass, he reached for it lying down. Much has he learned who has suffered hardship! As Charles slept, he saw in a vision the Angel Gabriel, who remained all night at his head, bringing him dreams of conflict and trouble. He saw his armies overtaken by a great storm and attacked by wild beasts, monsters, and devils, crying on him for aid. But a great lion stopped his path, and assaulted his body; Charles did not know which of them was to win that struggle. Yet he did not awake, but dreamed again. This time he was in his place at Aix, holding two chained bear-cubs. From the wood came thirty bears, with human power of speech, begging for the return of their kinsmen. A hound ran from the palace gates to attack the mightiest of the bears; the King was not permitted to see which of the beasts was victorious.

Marsile, meanwhile, bleeding to death from his severed hand, fled until he reached Saragossa. Before the altar of Apollo, he fell in a swoon. His men upbraided the false god bitterly, threw him down from his altar and trampled him under foot. From the idol of Termagant they took his jewels; and Mahound they threw into a ditch, to be eaten by swine and hounds. Bramimunde, Marsile's queen, wept and tore her hair. "Emir Baligant is a confessed craven," she cried, "if he fail to fight that proud people who have such arrogance that they take no heed for their lives!" It was long before Marsile recovered. Never would he dare to face Charles again, but sent letters to Baligant in Egypt, swearing that, unless the Emir came to his aid, he would become a Christian and make peace with the Emperor, who had stayed seven years in Spain, winning greater victories every day. But the Emir was far away, and was long delayed.

Baligant summoned warriors from forty kingdoms, and equipped a great fleet in the port near Alexandria. Great was the force that sailed up the Ebro to relieve Saragossa. The Emir embarked with seventeen attendant kings to wait upon him, and other powerful vassal lords without number. Under a laurel, upon a throne of ivory, Baligant held court. He announced to his assembled nobles his intention to attack Charles in France, and he chose two of his knights, Clarifan and Clarien, to visit Marsile, bearing promise of aid, with a golden gauntlet as pledge and a wand of beaten gold. The ambassadors found the King in Saragossa, silent in his deep sorrow. To Queen Bramimunde they addressed their greetings, but this violation of etiquette stirred Marsile to speech. He gave them word that he owned Baligant as rightful lord of Spain, since his only heir had fallen in the field, and he himself felt death to be near. He told them of the camp of Charlemagne, near the Ebro, and gave to them in trust the keys of Saragossa. Baligant, upon receiving the news, was almost insane with grief, but listened to the advice of Clarien, and thought his victory over Charles almost a certainty, since Roland, Oliver, and the Peers were dead, and since the encampment of the Franks was so near. He visited the palace at Saragossa, received the fealty of the ailing Marsile, and spurred at the head of his men to battle; from time to time, he cried, "Forward, warriors; see, the Franks already are in flight!"

Charles, at daybreak, returned to view the carnage at Roncesvalles. He saw the meadow crimson with the blood of his barons, and he could not restrain his tears. Upon the hilltop he saw his nephew beneath the pine tree, and he swooned in anguish.

"Roland, my friend," he cried, "may God have mercy on thee! Never has there been so great a knight, for starting battles, and for winning them. My greatness is passing. With what a bad lord thou camest into Spain! It seems to me that I have no remaining comrade under the sky. If I yet have kinsmen, not one of them is so valiant. Henceforth shall I reign in sadness. Ah, sweet France, how desolate art thou now!" He tore at his white beard in his grief, and a hundred thousand Franks fainted upon the ground.

By the command of the Emperor, the dead were gathered together for burial. Many were the holy men who absolved them. Myrrh and incense were burned, and carefully all the slain were embalmed. The hearts of Roland, Oliver, and Turpin were removed from their bodies and placed in a coffer of white marble. Their corpses were wrapped in rich silk and deer-hides, and driven in three triumphal coaches with the army.

Before Charles had well departed from that field of sorrow, two messengers arrived from Baligant, declaring war in the name of the Emir. The Emperor was the first to arm; mounting his steed Tencendur, he dug in his gilded spurs and dashed forward in the sight of his men, calling on God and St. Peter. The French followed his example; armed and astride their horses, they held a tournament to exhibit their peerless skill in arms. "The man who would despair when surrounded by such vassals as these is indeed a fool," said Charles, when he beheld them. Under Heaven might one behold no race more valiant or mightier in the field. Ten divisions there were, all warriors of exceeding prowess; nor would they ever cry mercy for fear of death. The Emperor was noble in the saddle. Over his coat of mail he had spread his hoary beard, and, for love of him, the hundred thousand Franks of his division did the same.

They passed the hills, the deep valleys, the dangerous ravines. They emerged from the pass and the wastelands, and they crossed the Spanish border. On level ground, they took their position for combat. On both sides, the clarions sounded. Baligant heard from his scouts that the battle was near, nor did he wish to delay. Noble in his armor, he mounted his charger. Handsome was his figure, bright and proud his countenance; he was of valor often tested. Ah God, had he been a Christian, what a baron he might have been! He spurred his horse until blood flecked his sides, and jumped a ravine fully fifty feet across. His son Malpramis was no less chivalrous than he, for both were learned in the Pagan faith and in ways of courtesy, and both were very fierce and keen in battle. To Malpramis, the Emir granted the honor of the first blow. Marvelously strong in numbers were the Saracen divisions; in the smallest of them, there were at least fifty thousand knights. From many strange lands they came, and they were marvelous to look upon. The men of Micenes were there, who have huge heads and spines ridged with bristles like those of hogs; from Occiant the Wild came a host of heathens with hides so hard that they have no need for armor. Never was there so great a force of savage and godless men. Seeing the terrifying army behind the dragon banner, the Franks called upon God to protect Charles and award the victory to the righteous. The Pagans prayed devoutly to their gods. Then the Franks charged, shouting their war-cries of "Précieuse" and "Montjoie." The warriors on both sides were great in prowess and courage, but God had judged against the Pagans. The battle was hard, fiercely fought. Malpramis and Canabeu, Baligant's brother, were among the first to fall; the Emir was sorely grieved, and wished to die at once. But he threw more divisions into the battle, and the French were soon hard pressed; Ogier, the Dane, who was never a coward, rallied the dismayed Franks to a new attack, however, and the standard of Mahound fell before them. Day had passed and evening had fallen before the two kings met in combat. Both were mighty men, and neither feared to die. That combat could never cease until one or the other should admit himself to be wrong. Charlemagne was in dire peril; once he reeled in the saddle and almost fell, but St. Gabriel appeared to him, crying, "Great King, what are you doing?" At the voice of the angel, strength and self-possession returned to Charles, and he struck the Emir upon the helmet with the Sword of France, cleaving his head even to his white beard. The Pagans fled, for God had not willed that they should stay upon that field. The Emperor pursued them. Few were the Saracens who escaped.

The pursuit lasted as far as Saragossa, where Queen Bramimunde, seeing the army of the Emir in full flight, cried on Mahound for help. Marsile, hearing her screams, died instantly of grief, struck down by his misfortune. Saragossa was taken, for its defenses were weak, and that night the Franks slept within the walls, which was their right as conquerors. Bramimunde surrendered the towers to Charles. He who is aided by God always attains his purpose! With iron hammers, the French destroyed the idols; and if any Pagan refused baptism, Charles imprisoned or killed him. But Charles took Bramimunde with him to fair France, for he wished to accomplish her conversion by love, not by force, for he wished her only good. The army returned in triumph to France, where, at Saint-Romain, the barons were buried in sepulchres of white stone.

Reaching Aix, Charles summoned men from all his territories to sit in judgment; then began the trial of Ganelon. Before the trial began, there came before Charles the fair Aude, sister to Oliver, asking for Count Roland. Hearing that he was dead, she fell dead at Charlemagne's feet. The King thought at first that she had swooned, and tried to lift her by her hands. When the French saw that she was dead, there was great wonder and grief among them. Her body was carried to a convent of holy nuns, where Charles endowed for her a monument of unsurpassed richness.

Ganelon was dragged before the throne. His hands were bound, and he was tied to a stake by serfs, who were whipping him with ropes and staves. No other reward did he merit. In great anguish of body and spirit, he awaited judgment. The trial took place on a great feast-day, the Day of St. Sylvester. Ganelon bore himself well, and, had he been loyal, would have looked like a true baron. Thirty of his kinsmen were with him. He argued that vengeance, when declared publicly, was no treason, that he had laid no plans against Charles, his rightful lord, but taken private satisfaction for Roland's malice and hatred. The decision wavered; at last, Pinabel of Sorence stepped forward. He was a good speaker, correct in the phrasing of his thought. He defended Ganelon, and offered himself as his champion. There was no one there so great a fool as to offer combat with the famed Pinabel, save only the youthful knight Thierry, Geoffrey's brother, an Angevin duke. Pinabel offered his gauntlet in acceptance of Thierry's challenge, and both parties were set at liberty with hostages. Great was Pinabel's might, but God awarded the victory to Thierry, in token of a justice greater than the letter of the law. Ganelon's thirty kinsmen, who had bound themselves as his hostages, were condemned to death by the Franks, and all of them were hanged. He who betrays a man condemns not only himself, but others, to death. All agreed that Ganelon should die in torment. They bound his hands and feet to four spirited horses, which were then urged toward a stream in the middle of the field. Ganelon died the death of a traitor and a coward. If a man betrays another, it is not right that he should boast of it!

The Emperor had avenged his kinsmen, and now he summoned his bishops. The Queen of Marsile had been converted to the True Faith by the wisdom of Charles, and at the baths of Aix she was baptized, and renamed Juliana. Her godmothers were high-born ladies of France. Knowledge of the truth made her a Christian.

The day was over, and the King returned to his chamber. St. Gabriel came to him once again with a message from God.

"Charles," he said, "call up the armies of thine empire! Thou shalt enter by force the country of Bire, bringing aid to King Vivien in Imphe, a city which is besieged by the Saracens. The Christians call out to thee."

The Emperor had no wish to go.

"Ah, God," he murmured, "how filled with trouble is my life!"

He wept, and with his fingers he plucked at his white beard. Thus ends the history which Turoldus set down.

SUGGESTIONS FOR FURTHER READING

Editions:

Stengel, Edmund. Critical edition, Leipzig, 1900

Sherwood, Merriam. English translation, London, Longmans Green, 1938

Critical Works:

Boissonade, P. *Du Nouveau sur la Chanson de Roland,* Paris, 1923

Fawtier, Robert. *La Chanson de Roland: Etude historique,* Paris, 1934

THE POEM OF
THE CID

THE POEM OF THE CID: INTRODUCTION

The *Poem of the Cid,* the national epic of Spain, was written at about the same time as the French *Song of Roland.* In approach and technique, the two works reflect basic differences in the two parallel cultures. In the Spanish poem, for example, we find as an accepted ideal a more modern definition of loyalty, one which Charlemagne could hardly have understood. The Cid's first loyalty is to his king not as a person but as a symbol of his nation; national, rather than feudal fealty, is the basic motivation of his repeated attempts to be reconciled with his lord. This submission is often described in feudal terms, because the new words had not yet evolved. Other differences, perhaps more startling, are that the *Cid* makes more use of humor, is more given to realism in detail, and shows a considerable feeling for a rough-and-ready democracy.

The Cid (Arabic *El Seid,* the Lord) was a practical man, accustomed to coping with details of administration. He was also a brilliant tactician and leader of men. Like many first-rate leaders, he knew when to be harsh, when to be gentle; when to appeal to his followers' self-interest, when to disregard it entirely. Like a good Spaniard, he never undervalued money, though he considered it, as any ambitious man must, a means rather than an end. All these qualities he needed in order to survive in the stormy world of medieval Spain.

Rodrigo Díaz de Bivar, sometimes called Ruy Díaz, and later known as the Cid, was born (1040) in the city of Burgos, within that rugged northern part of Spain which had resisted Saracen conquest. For several centuries Spain had been the scene of struggle between Saracen and Christian. Southern

Spain had succumbed rapidly to the Islamic conquest, and many of the local rulers had turned Moslem and assumed high positions in the courts. The common people had not found it difficult to exchange one set of masters for another; in fact, the new rulers were more tolerant and more lenient than the old. In the mountain areas, however, resistance had been strong, and the conquerors had not thought the rough, unpromising area worth the struggle to subdue it. Tough little kingdoms grew up almost unperceived, and began to drive the Saracens back from their borders.

After the downfall of the Gothic monarchy, Moslem and Christian—Berbers and Saracens, lumped under the generic name of Moors, and Spaniards and Frenchmen—had fought inconclusive wars in the Peninsula. (One of them was the war in which Roland was killed.) In 1013, the Berbers captured Cordova, and the Saracen Empire fell apart, leaving the various governors as independent rulers. Garci Sánchez, one of them, called himself "King of the Spains." His sons-in-law, Sancho of Navarre and Bermudo of Leon, fought a war over succession to the title. Eventually, Sancho won, and united Leon, Navarre, Castile, and Astorga. His sons warred among themselves, as their ancestors had done; finally, Fernando, his second son, achieved an uneasy supremacy. It was during the disturbed second decade of Fernando's reign that the early legends of the Cid's youth began to be preserved in ballads and stories, associating him with the growth of Fernando's empire.

These legends have some basis in fact. Don Quixote remarked, "That there was a Cid there is no doubt; but that he did the deeds men say he did, there is doubt aplenty." The Cid was never, indeed, quite the champion of Christianity that the legends make him out to be, or as he appears in the poem. Rather, he was a soldier of fortune, who made the best bargain possible. This fact probably accounts for his practical approach to life. Although a Christian, he took service with the Mohammedans from time to time. Naturally, the legend slides over this phase of his existence. It is true, however, that he served faithfully whatever lord he happened to be serving; he never was a double-dealer; and it was his fidelity that made him most valuable as the greatest of the *guerrilleros*.

When Fernando died, he divided his kingdom among his three sons. Sancho, the eldest, received Castile; Alphonso, Leon and the Campos Góticos; and García, Galicia and Portugal. Sancho believed that a kingdom united by so much bloodshed should be united, if necessary by force; and within two years he had begun to carry his belief into effect.

It is at this point in history that the chronicles first mention Ruy Díaz, Sancho's ensign and right arm, as playing a leading part in the wars to which the partition gave rise. The loyalty of Ruy Díaz to his lord and his cause was so great that he would sacrifice even his reputation, if necessary, to gain power for the group led by Sancho. The battle of Golpejar, which Ruy Díaz won for Sancho through a violation of the code of chivalric combat, was one of the turning points in the conquest of Leon. It had been agreed that the battle would be settled in one engagement, and this the forces of Sancho had lost. At night, when the warriors of Golpejar were relaxed and unsuspecting, the Cid marched on the fortress and took it easily.

This maneuver, although condemned by some historians, was actually a manifestation of the modernity of the Cid's thinking. His ability to take a realistic view of any situation and combine practicality with daring is evident throughout the *Poem of the Cid*. The muddled condition of the Spanish nation during its centuries of civil and foreign war had created a situation in which the old laws of class distinction had relaxed to meet the difficult circumstances of living, especially in the rugged northern kingdoms. Men who could fight and think independently used the new opportunities to raise themselves out of the rigid constraint of medieval social stratification which had been imposed by the Gothic monarchy. The old legal code, moreover, had been revised to meet the new needs. And even within the limits of old traditions, an almost modern feeling of democracy was apparent. Adverse conditions have always been levelers of rank.

On the assassination of Sancho, the Cid took service with Alfonso, the heir. His independence of spirit was again asserted, according to tradition, by his daring in volunteering to administer to Alfonso the famous oath of innocence, in which Alfonso was required to swear himself innocent of Sancho's murder, before the nobles would acknowledge him as King. After the ceremony was completed, Don Ruy tried to kiss the King's hand in token of acknowledgment, but was refused. The *Poem of the Cid* begins with his consequent banishment from Castile. The ancient enmity of Leon and Castile thus plays a dominant part in the establishment of a background and a motivating thread for the epic.

Perhaps the chief reason for the Cid's attainment of epic stature is that he combines real achievement with the embodiment of Spanish ideals. The naturalness of his personality is reinforced by considerable detailed description of his individualizing qualities, of the group of eccentricities which distinguish him from other men and from the abstract heroes of fantasy. The human imperfections which result from his practical solutions to real problems enhance, rather than weaken his epic nature. His sense of humor, his employment of trickery, his realistic relations with his family ally him with the epic heroes of Homer.

The *Poem of the Cid*, like the *Song of Roland*, is built upon the ballads and lays of the *jongleurs;* it, too, is meant to be sung or chanted. It employs an eight-beat line, with middle and terminal rest-beats well marked. The language is used with great flexibility; often there are one or more unstressed syllables between beats, and rests and rest-beats are often substituted for speech-beats. These characteristics, with the strong stresses and marked rest-beats, tend to confirm the theory that the *Cid* is written for oral presentation, as well as to account for the metrical irregularities of the lines when they are read silently. For example:

"Tó dās lās sùs mēs ná dēs /' ēn gránt dē lèyt ēs tá vān /"

In addition, the lines reflect the Spanish tendencies to accent strongly the terminal pauses and interchange primary and secondary accents within words.

The language is rich and vivid, but maintains a virile, disciplined tone. It lacks some of the lyrical refinement of the *Song of Roland;* but it is by no means to be considered "primitive." The poet is a mature artist and a complete master of his formal and linguistic materials. The tone is objective throughout, but not so rigidly so as that of the *Roland.* The narrator achieves, through conversational intervention, an atmosphere of immediacy and informality which is highly appropriate to the material, as well as to its intended method of presentation. The general impression is more dramatic and less lyrical than that of the *Song of Roland;* but both poems contain an epic combination of these elements.

THE POEM OF THE CID: THE STORY

Returning from battle to his native city of Burgos, the Cid Ruy
Díaz de Bivar found the postern gates ajar and beheld desolation on every side. He rode with his company of sixty lances
through the streets of Burgos, and the weeping citizens
crowded to the balconies and windows to watch him pass. Arriving at his own dwelling, the Cid found the portals barred.
He learned that King Alfonso had unjustly placed him under
sentence of banishment, allowing him only nine days of grace
before exile; and had threatened with death and confiscation
of property any citizen foolish enough to give him or his followers aid or shelter. "What worthy vassal, had he worthy
lord," the citizens exclaimed.

The Cid left the city and rode for Arlanzon. His immediate
problem was to provide food for his men. The citizens were,
of course, forbidden to sell him any provisions. Martin Antolínez, blood relation to the Cid, decided to cast his lot with
him, realizing the King must sooner or later seek his friendship
if the Cid were successful in his plans for conquest against the
Moors. Antolínez provided food for the entire company, and
rode out of Burgos with Ruy Díaz.

The Cid's next requirement was money. Although he despised trickery, it was apparent that he could not achieve his
purpose through open methods. He ordered that two chests,
handsomely bound in leather and securely fastened, be filled
with sand. Martin Antolínez bore these chests to Rachel and
Vidas, two Jews of Burgos. He told them that the coffers were
filled with rich plunder, which the Cid, because of his present
predicament, could not carry with him; and he asked the Jews

to keep them as security for a loan of six hundred marks. Rachel and Vidas, believing the story, agreed to the bargain, and they conveyed the chests from the Cid's camp at night, "that no Christian might spy."

Before leaving Castile, Ruy Díaz and Martin Antolínez separated, in order to take leave of their families. Antolínez rode to Burgos, and the Cid went to St. Peter of Cardeña, the convent in which his wife, Ximena, resided with their daughters, Sol and Elvira. He left an ample allowance for their protection, and intrusted their spiritual and material welfare to their confessor, the Abbot of St. Peter's. The family heard Mass together at dawn the following morning, and parted from one another "as parts the nail from the flesh."

During the remainder of the period of grace, many soldiers left their homes to join the Cid in his exile. At sunset of the ninth day, when the Cid surveyed his army, he counted at least three hundred lances.

Moving at night, the Cid placed as much distance as he could between his company and possible pursuers, and arrived at the River Henares, where he made camp, near the town of Castejón, and lay in ambush all the night. He took Castejón by surprise and occupied the city with only a hundred of his men. Minaya Albarfañez, the Cid's best knight and closest friend, led the remaining forces on a raid to Alcalá, and returned with rich plunder. The spoil was divided, and the Cid took the usual leader's share of one fifth, which he sold to Guadalajara with some profit. He left Castejón at dawn, setting free its inhabitants. His act of generosity, in refraining from sacking the town and killing or enslaving its inhabitants, was highly praised by the Moors, who blessed him as he rode away.

The company pitched its tents for the second time outside the famous fortress city of Alcocer. The people of Alcocer, Ateca, Teruel, and Calatayud had for some time paid the Cid large tributes, so great was their fear of his power, but now they closed their gates. The siege of Alcocer lasted fifteen weeks. Finally, the Cid invented a stratagem by which he shortened the siege. He marched away in full force, leaving a single tent behind him, as though he found it impossible to take along all his supplies. The troops of Alcocer believed that he was short of rations and weakened by a hopeless siege, and they left the city in hope of waylaying him and capturing rich spoil. Ruy Díaz seemed to flee, but when they were far from the open city gates, he maneuvered his forces between them and the city and forced an entrance.

The neighboring towns were by this time thoroughly aroused, and Calatayud sent a message to King Tamin of Valencia warning him of the Cid's growing power. Tamin sent two kings, Galba and Faris, with three thousand Moorish soldiers, planning to recruit more men from the native populations of the threatened territories. A vast force finally besieged Alcocer and cut off its water supply, forcing battle. The Cid gave commands that no man should break ranks without his order; but Vermúdez, his standard-bearer, found that command too hard to endure. He spurred into the midst of the foe, and the Cid sent his troops to the rescue. They joined in fierce battle, and the Cid won the victory. Galba was slain by Martin Antolínez, and Faris fled to Calatayud, where he took refuge. The Cid's spoil from the battle was enormous; every man serving under him was now independently wealthy. The Cid sent to King Alfonso a gift of thirty fine horses. Alcocer was sold to Faris for three thousand marks' ransom.

Minaya Albarfañez went to King Alfonso as ambassador. He gained freedom to come and go as he pleased, and his property and life, originally forfeit because of his allegiance to the Cid, were restored to him. Also, Albarfañez was granted permission to take along with him any men who wished to join the Cid's forces; Alfonso promised to release their persons and property, as well as those of the men who had comprised the original company of exiles. Although Alfonso received the gift of horses, he did not agree to meet the Cid for reconciliation, saying that such haste to make peace with a vassal so recently banished would not be becoming in a king. However, his attitude seemed more peaceful, and he allowed Minaya to take money and letters to the Cid's family. Two hundred swordsmen and countless infantrymen took advantage of Alfonso's new lenity, and they accompanied Minaya on his return to the camp in Tebar wood.

The Cid conquered Huesca, Monyón, and Zaragosa, and his tributes grew to immense proportions. Messages of alarm from the oppressed cities sped on every hand to the Saracen leaders. The proud Count Raymond of Barcelona raised an army with the purpose of meeting the Cid in battle and recovering the honor which he felt that he had lost. The Cid, discovering Raymond's intentions, offered peace, saying that he did not mean to steal anything belonging to Raymond. Raymond refused the offer, and attacked. The armies of Ruy Díaz spurred from the thick pine forest of Tebar and won a decisive victory. Raymond, taken prisoner, refused food, saying that he preferred death to dishonor. The Cid promised that, if Raymond would break his fast, he should be set free, with all honor; Raymond, who had expected death or shameful usage, after three days finally took advantage of the Cid's kindness. He swore not to molest the Cid again at least within the year—and was set free.

Having manned the pass, the Cid led his forces toward the sea, gaining much territory to the east, including the cities of Zeluca, Almenara, Burrana, and Murviedro; he now held the critical area which blocked the entrances and exits to Valencia. Valencia sent an army against him, but he defeated it through a clever encircling maneuver devised by Albarfañez. Two Moorish kings were slain on the field. The army of Ruy Díaz moved through Guera and Zativa, ravaging the coastal area and hemming in Valencia even more securely. The King of Morocco, being himself at war on his borders, could send no immediate aid. On the other hand, reinforcements for the army of the Cid arrived almost daily from Aragon, Navarre, and Castile. In the tenth month of the siege, Valencia surrendered. The banner of the Cid flew over the Alcazar. So impressed was Ruy Díaz with the beauty and wealth of the land that he vowed to make his home here. The spoil was beyond counting; "the men-at-arms are changed to mounted knights."

Despite his joy in the conquest, the Cid was still heavy at heart because of his estrangement from King Alfonso. He swore never again to cut his beard, in token of his fealty and his grief. Minaya Albarfañez was sent once again to the King, bearing a gift of a hundred steeds, with magnificent trappings and arms, to request permission for his family to join him in Valencia. On this mission, Albarfañez was accompanied by Don Jerome, a famous priest and man of war, whom the Cid had created Bishop of Valencia. Alfonso was impressed by the gifts and by the stories of the Cid's achievement. He freely granted the petition, and praised the Cid in the warmest terms. Ximena, Sol, and Elvira came with great ceremony to Valencia, escorted by Avengalvón, the Cid's Moorish ally, with a guard of honor of two hundred lances. No sooner were they reunited with Don Ruy than King Yusef of Morocco besieged the city with a vast Saracen army. The Cid was glad that the attack took place while his womenfolk were in the city, for he was confident of victory and felt that watching the battle would give them a valuable lesson in "how bread is won." After a long, bloody engagement, the Cid greeted his wife and daughters on horseback, covered with blood and bearing a naked, gory sword, and said to them, "Regard ye the bloody sword, the sweating steed—in this manner are the Moors overcome on the field of battle!" His family, justifiably overcome, fell on their knees before him in gratitude and relief.

The Cid sent to King Alfonso a gift of two hundred beautifully caparisoned horses, pleading again for a reconciliation and hinting that his daughters, richly dowered, might consider offers of marriage. The King was well pleased with the gifts, and remarked that no other vassal had served him so well. The Lords of Carrión, Fernando and Diego, envying the Cid's success, secretly begged from Alfonso permission to marry Sol and Elvira. When permission was granted, Fernando and Diego began to live in a somewhat better style, for they felt that their fortunes were made. Alfonso ordered Minaya Albarfañez to tell the Cid of the marriage which he had arranged, and to assure the Cid of his love. He further offered to meet the Cid in formal reconciliation, allowing him to name the place of meeting.

When the news was conveyed to the Cid, he was of two minds. The marriage was not very pleasing to him, although the house of Carrión was a fine aristocratic family; but he submitted with grace, saying that his daughters belonged to his lord, to dispose of as he would. The place of meeting Don Ruy was set on the bank of the great river Tagus, and Alfonso, being informed of the arrangement, sent word that the interview would take place in three weeks. The Cid made elaborate preparations to entertain his lord, and the gathering occurred as planned, both leaders bringing large escorts of festively garbed knights. Rich gifts were exchanged, and mutual love was declared. In token of submission, the Cid threw himself face downward on the ground before Alfonso, biting the grass; nor would he rise until the King had once more formally accepted him as vassal. When Alfonso renewed his command that Sol and Elvira be betrothed to Diego and Fernando, the Cid delivered his daughters into the King's protection, requesting him to give them in marriage himself. The King appointed Minaya Albarfañez as his deputy in this office, since he himself could not be present at the wedding. The Lords of Carrión accompanied Don Ruy to Valencia, and many noble lords and ladies of the court accepted the general invitation to the ceremony.

Fernando and Diego were given a sumptuous welcome in Valencia. A palace was prepared as their dwelling, and the Cid sent his best gentlemen to attend them. Among the attendants were Pero Vermúdez and Muño Gustioz, two of the Cid's best knights, who were instructed to watch the Lords of Carrión closely and report all that went on in the palace. The Cid and his nobles went in festive dress to welcome the Lords of Carrión with a magnificent banquet. The wedding took place, with Minaya Albarfañez acting for the King in giving Sol and Elvira in marriage. After fifteen days of celebration, the wedding guests departed, laden with rich gifts. The Cid's new sons-in-law remained in Valencia, where they were for two years treated with all love and honor, even as though they had been his own sons.

One afternoon, as the Cid lay sleeping among his vassals in the great hall, a lion broke loose from its cage and rushed among the company. The faithful knights drew their swords and surrounded their lord's couch, protecting him with their bodies. But Fernando and Diego hid themselves in terror. The Cid was aroused by the commotion, perceived the lion, pushed his way through the ring of terrified men, seized the beast by the neck, and returned him to his cage. He then looked for his sons-in-law, but failed to find them among the knights who defended him; when Diego and Fernando were discovered in their hiding places, they were made the object of general derision. The Cid severely ordered his knights to cease tormenting them, but Diego and Fernando decided that their humiliation required that they revenge themselves on the Cid. However, they did not, as the feudal code of honor requires, challenge him openly, but showed fair countenances and began to plot treachery in secret.

Shortly after this incident, Valencia was again besieged by the Moroccans, under King Bucar. Following their usual cowardly pattern of conduct, Diego and Fernando planned an extended visit to their lands in Carrión. But they were overheard by Gustioz, who reported the matter to the Cid. The Cid promptly invited Diego and Fernando to remain in the city and protect their wives, while those who knew how to fight the Moors went out and won the battle. He shamed them into altering their decision, and they too went out to the battle.

The forces of the Cid left the city arrayed for battle. Bishop Jerome, as usual, begged the honor of striking the first blow, and acquitted himself nobly. The Moors were utterly routed, and King Bucar fled the field. The Cid pursued and, overtaking him, cut him in two as far as the waist, striking through armor, flesh, and bone with a single stroke of his sword. The Cid captured in the battle two swords of great worth, the blades Tizon and Colada, which he prized especially because he won them in fair fight with two valiant Saracen knights.

The army returned rich with plunder, and the Cid's possession of Valencia was now quite secure. He was especially pleased with the conduct of Diego and Fernando, who had not, apparently, been laggards in the fight, for both boasted of killing Moors, and were not contradicted in this claim by Pero Vermúdez, who was with them in the struggle, having been ordered by the Cid to look after them. But when tales of battle went round that evening, no soldiers could recall seeing either of them in the fighting. However, the Cid sent good reports of both men back to Castile.

The brothers decided to return to Carrión, and, despite the kindness which the Cid had shown them, they plotted to humiliate him through his daughters. Telling the Cid that they intended to take Sol and Elvira to visit their dower cities in Carrión, they set forth. The Cid gave them a bridal present of three thousand marks, as well as the two "blades of honor" which he had won at the last siege of Valencia. Also, Diego and Fernando bore away their share of the plunder, which was very great, and several fine steeds and rich garments which the Cid gave them at the hour of parting. They stopped at Molina for a night, in compliance with Ruy Díaz's request that they bear his greetings to the Moor, Avengalvón. Avengalvón entertained them royally, and provided them with an escort of two hundred knights, which he himself led as far as the Ansarera. But the brothers plotted to kill him for his gold, as soon as they could create an opportunity to be alone with him. Avengalvón, however, was informed of their treacherous intention, and departed in great wrath, swearing that, were it not for the love he bore the Cid, he should certainly kill them and return Sol and Elvira to their father.

In the oak forest of Corpes, a rugged, desolate spot, the brothers fixed their camp. All night long they made show of love to Sol and Elvira. In the morning, having seen the treasure safely loaded on the beasts of burden, they sent all their retainers ahead of them to Carrión, remaining behind with their wives. They then began to insult and revile the two women, strip them nearly naked, and beat them with their saddle girths. After beating them and kicking them with sharp spurs until they tired, they left the women for dead, exposed to the cold and the wild animals, and rode away. They felt justified in their brutality, maintaining that this insult to the family of the Cid had wiped out the insult to their own family which occurred in the episode of the lion. They said to one another that Sol and Elvira had never been fit mates for Lords of Carrión, not even as concubines; forgotten was the fact they had originally begged Alfonso to grant them these ladies in marriage.

Feliz Muñoz, however, had followed the brothers at a safe distance, as he had been ordered to do by the Cid. Finding the two women near death, he brought water to revive them. After they had recovered somewhat, he placed them before him on his horse, wrapped in his mantle, and conveyed them to St. Stephen's. Here Diego Tellez de Albarfañez gave them his hospitality while they recovered, and the citizens helped to restore their spirits by offering them all possible honor and encouragement.

Word of the crime had reached Valencia. The Cid sent Minaya Albarfañez, Pero Vermúdez, and Martin Antolínez, with an escort of two hundred knights, to bring his daughters back to Valencia. After welcoming Sol and Elvira, he dispatched Minaya to King Alfonso with his complaint against the Lords of Carrión. Since the King had taken the women under his protection and had bestowed them in marriage, the insult now lay on the Crown of Spain, and must be avenged.

King Alfonso assembled his court at Toledo, sending messengers throughout the land to summon all his nobles. Both the Lords of Carrión and Don Ruy were asked to appear. The court assembled with great magnificence. Don Ruy arrived on the fifth day, at the head of a large company of well-equipped knights. He was a very impressive figure, and public opinion was with him from the outset of the case. As he rose to declare his grievances, all eyes were upon him. He first asked that Diego and Fernando return to him the swords Colada and Tizon, noble blades given in honor, which the owners had for the first time dishonored. The brothers were commanded to return the blades. The Cid next demanded the return of the three thousand marks which were his bridal gift, as well as the horses, apparel, and other presents with which Fernando and Diego left Valencia. The court decided that this demand, too, must be met, and on the spot. The Lords of the Carrión had spent some of the money, and must borrow heavily on their lands in order to pay; the penalty was, in fact, quite ruinous to their fortunes.

The Cid then questioned the brothers as to their motives in humiliating his family. He defied them to name one wrong that he had ever done them, and insisted upon redress. Diego and Fernando boldly asserted that the superiority of their ancient family made no answer or redress necessary; Lords of Carrión, they said were fit mates for daughters of emperors. Their only unworthy act, therefore, was their unbecoming condescension in agreeing to the marriage; this act they had redeemed, reasserting their family honor by casting off these women of inferior rank and serving them as they deserved. Count García took their part, adding an insult to the Cid's cherished beard, which seemed to strike more resentment from Don Ruy than any hostility which had gone before.

Pero Vermúdez answered the Lords of Carrión. He related how, in the battle at Valencia, Fernando had turned in panic from the first Saracen he saw, that he was pursued and would have been slain, but for the intervention of Pero, who himself slew the Moor. Later he had not contradicted Fernando's boast that he had done the deed, feeling that a better reputation would give the young man needed self-confidence. Pero then repeated the story of the lion. Last, he asserted that Sol and Elvira were in every respect superior to their former husbands, offering to prove the truth of all that he had said, by personal combat in the field. Fernando accepted the trial by combat. Diego answered the challenge, and was challenged by Antolínez. Asur González now strode into the court; he was flushed from breakfast, and he hurled insults at the Cid and his supporters. Muño Gustioz replied that Asur, who "breakfasts before he prays," disgusted all the noble company, and the two exchanged challenges. Minaya Albarfañez and Gómez Pelaget also quarreled with one another.

At this point, the attention of the assembly was focused anew on two knights who knelt before Alfonso, asking as a boon the hands of Sol and Elvira in marriage. The knights were Ocaria and Ximenez, Infantes of Navarre and of Aragon, and their request was granted. Now Diego and Fernando, who scorned the daughters of the Cid, must bow before them and reverence them as queens. The court was adjourned, the date for the trials-by-combat having been set at three weeks hence, in Carrión. The Cid departed for Valencia, leaving his knights under the protection of Alfonso, who swore that no treachery would be allowed. Diego and Fernando asked that the two swords of the Cid be barred from the combat, for they feared to fight against these honorable blades which they had insulted through treachery. But Alfonso decided that the combatants might choose any swords which suited them best; so the Cid left Tizon and Colada with his knights, exhorting them to use this honorable steel in defense of the right.

The day of the combat arrived. Although the Lords of Carrión brought with them many soldiers, obviously planning treachery, their fear of Alfonso was so great that they attempted nothing. It was apparent to the King that the brothers were reluctant to have the trial take place, for, as he declared, if they had been willing, they would have accepted the challenge at Toledo, when it was given, instead of petitioning for delay. At any rate, there was now no road of escape for them. Pero Vermúdez unhorsed Fernán González and wounded him so severely that he conceded the combat, even before swords were used; he had nearly swooned with fear at the sight of the sword Tizon when Vermúdez unsheathed it. Antolínez, with the sword Colada, drove Diego from the field. Gustioz overcame Asur González with his lance, wounding him badly. The judges unanimously awarded the victory to the champions of the Cid.

The Lords of Carrión were disgraced for life; no longer

could they claim the title of men of honor. The fact that they did not die in combat was for them a worse punishment than death, for they must forever face the derision which they fear.

> "Who ill treats and deserts a sweet lady,
> May a like or even more dire fate befall."

The three champions returned to Valencia, where they were received with honor and rejoicing. The marriages of Sol and Elvira were celebrated with even more splendor than were the first nuptials. The Cid had reached the pinnacle of earthly honor and realized all his ambitions. His descendants were kings of Spain. He died, record the closing lines of the poem, on Pentecost.

SUGGESTIONS FOR FURTHER READING

Editions:

Ramon Menéndez Pidal. Madrid, 1908-1911
> For good readers in Spanish, still considered the best and most comprehensive.
> > v. 1—Critique of the text; grammar
> > v. 2—Vocabulary
> > v. 3—Text of the poem

P. Selden Rose and Leonard Bacon. Berkeley, University of California Press, 1919. Good English translation.

Other Books:

R. Menéndez Pidal. *The Cid and His Spain* (Sunderland tr.). London, John Murray, 1934

D. Butler Clarke. *The Cid Campeador and the Waning of the Crescent in the West.* New York, G. P. Putnam's Sons, 1902

NIBELUNGENLIED

NIBELUNGENLIED: INTRODUCTION

The *Nibelungenlied*, like the *Beowulf*, is a poem embodying materials drawn from Germanic history, mythology, and legend, a story of "old, unhappy, far-off things, and battles long ago." The version presented here was written down toward the end of the twelfth century, in the dialect called Middle High German. It contains the story of Siegfried, dragon-slayer and winner of the treasure of the Nibelungs; his courtship of Kriemhild, sister of Gunther, King of the Burgundians, and their marriage; his winning of Brunhild, by a trick, for Gunther; the feud between Brunhild and Kriemhild; the murder of Siegfried by Gunther's vassal, Hagen; the marriage of Kriemhild to Etzel, King of the Huns, and Etzel's invitation to the Burgundians; the death of Gunther and Hagen in Etzel's hall; and finally, the death of Kriemhild.

We recognize parts of this story from our knowledge of its most recent version, that found in Wagner's operas called the *Ring of the Nibelungs.* We notice, also, that Wagner's version is in many respects quite different from that of the *Nibelungenlied.* Wagner saw the story as one in which the most important personages were Siegfried and Brunhild, and, like many Germans of his time, he thought of them as figures drawn from the Germanic pantheon: a culture-hero, almost a demigod, and a Valkyr, a battle-maiden, the chooser of the slain destined for Valhalla. In order to attain his artistic objective, he wrote two operas, *Das Rheingold* and *Die Walküre,* which tell of the events preceding the story of Siegfried and the rival queens found in the *Nibelungenlied.* In the central opera, *Siegfried,* he tells the story of the dragon-slaying and the winning of the hoard, and includes an event scarcely glanced at in the *Nibelungenlied*, the betrothal of Siegfried and Brunhild. And in the final opera of the cycle *Die Götterdämmerung* (*The Twilight of the Gods*), he tells of the murder of Siegfried and the self-immolation of Brunhild on his funeral pyre, this last incident also not found in the *Nibelungenlied*.

Wagner's version, also, makes much more use of Germanic mythology than does the *Nibelungenlied*. The Middle High German poem, written in a thoroughly Christian atmosphere, could not well bring in Wotan, the principal deity of the Germanic pantheon; but Wagner's presentation of the story demanded the presence of these gods. For such materials he went to the versions of the story current in medieval Scandinavia, preserved in the Eddas, and, most completely, in the thirteenth-century Icelandic *Volsungasaga*.

The *Volsungasaga* tells a story very like that found in the *Nibelungenlied*, but it contains also other elements not found in the Germanic poem, especially the story of the birth of Siegfried (called Sigurd in the Norse), and the events which took place after the death of Gunther (Gunnar) and Hagen (Hogni). Although it was written down some two hundred years after the *Nibelungenlied*, it was not in the least influenced by that poem; rather, it is another version of the same story, drawn from the same source.

And here we must repeat what we said earlier, that the *Nibelungenlied* is a poem embodying elements drawn from Germanic mythology, legend, and history. In the *Nibelungenlied*, it is true, the mythological elements are of the slightest, if indeed, strictly speaking, they exist at all. Folklore material is there in plenty: the slaying of the dragon, for instance, and the *Tarnkappe*, the hood of invisibility, are matters met with in many fairy tales. Basically, however, the story is legend founded on history.

The historical fact underlying the legends, found widely throughout the Germanic-speaking areas, is the destruction of the Burgundian capital at Worms, in 437, by the Huns, whose king was Attila. We recognize that this must be the same name as Etzel, found in the *Nibelungenlied,* and Atli, in the *Volsungasaga.* The Burgundian princes, as we know from an early document called the "Law of the Burgundians," were named Gibica, Gundahari, and Gislahari: and these must be the same names as Gibich, father of Gunther, Gernot and Giselher.[1] The treacherous invitation of Etzel at his wife's prompting, and his killing of Gunther and Hagen, must be a legendary reflection of the defeat of the Burgundians, for people do not celebrate their defeats in their stories; rather, they adapt history to legend in order to explain their defeats. Modern examples of this phenomenon are not lacking.

The adaptation of history to legend is the prerogative of the epic poet, who need have no concern with fact as such. Theodoric of Verona, or Dietrich von Bern, another famous German legendary and historical figure, died in 526; yet the *Nibelungenlied*-poet has him present at the death of Kriemhild, which must have been nearly a century earlier. Probably the poet was not in the least aware that he was mixing up his centuries, for he was a poet, not a historian, and, just as Wagner was to do many centuries later, he used whatever material he had as his artistic necessities demanded.

The Germanic values of the *Nibelungenlied* still prevail, beneath the courtly façade. Gunther is a medieval prince, adept in political intrigue; but it is not difficult to see in him, as in King Siegfried, the earlier "bestower-of-rings" and "shield-of-knights." This courtliness, however, owes something to the expanding influences of French models. None of the earlier Germanic stories takes any great interest in romantic love; and love between man and woman is one of the primary forces of the *Nibelungenlied.* In this the epic is the product of its time, the late Middle Ages; for romantic love was not earlier a source of the question of loyalties.

The *Nibelungenlied*-poet could have found easy scope for lyricism in the magical background of the poem. The ring and

---

[1] There was another prince, Godomari; but the name Gernot, found in the *Nibelungenlied,* is not the same name. Gutthorm, found in the *Volsungasaga,* has a very similar name.

girdle of Brunhild, the winning of the Hoard, the awakening of Brunhild within the circle of fire—these episodes, and many more, could have carried him from his artistic purpose. Fortunately, these temptations were not victorious; perhaps, if they had prevailed, the *Nibelungenlied* would be only another interesting lay of medieval Germany. As in other poetry of epic stature, however, the mythological tradition behind the creation of the work is either told in episodic, narrative fashion, or implied. In the *Nibelungenlied*, most of this material is implied. It is very difficult to trace the mechanical techniques by which the effect is accomplished. Why does Brunhild tower over Kriemhild, in spite of their mutual ownership of the magical objects of power, and the greater number of lines which are given to Kriemhild and her revenge? Why, without a single explicit line of proof, does Hagen tower above Gunther, worthy to be the nemesis of Siegfried and the last of the men of Nibelung to die in battle? Even without any knowledge of the Eddas or the *Volsungasaga*, any perceptive reader can feel their stature.

Keeping the mystic elements in the background, the poet of the *Nibelungenlied* saves his lyric power for more human and personal topics, as does Dante in the episode of Paolo and Francesca in the *Divine Comedy*. The German poet's description of Siegfried's first meeting with Kriemhild is scarcely to be rivaled:

"Even as the full moon stands before the stars, so pure in her radiance that all clouds must run away before her, so did she stand in beauty among her ladies."

For Dante's Francesca, "the greatest pain of all is remembrance of past happiness in present woe"; for Kriemhild, "all pleasure, no matter how sweet, must at last turn to pain." But, whether the emphasis be upon fate or upon the Christian eternity, the sweetest passages in both epics are those of human love.

Scholarly search for the author of the *Nibelungenlied* has, to date, been inconclusive. A bishop of the late tenth century

—Pilgrim of Passau—had created most of the main incidents of the story, as his own version of popular legend; he is accepted as a main source for the poem. A Minnesinger known as *"Der Kurenberger"* is known to have written at least fifteen detached stanzas in the same metre. Yet, although the "folk-epic" theory of the nineteenth century has long been in disrepute, no valid scholarship has established the identity of the poet. The uniformity of style, as well as the method of incorporating myth, points to a single author. Karl Lachmann, the Germanic scholar, has found at least twenty lays of ancient origin which seem to form a part of the poem; his research, although of the "folk-epic" school, has indicated to many modern critics the probability of individual authorship; it is unlikely, they argue, that these vastly rich background sources could have been co-ordinated in such a manner by a "folk-author." Furthermore, his nineteen "twelfth-century additions" would appear to indicate a uniformity too great for a "folk epic." It is, in fact, unlikely that any poem of epic stature could have been other than individual in authorship. An epic cannot have "the quality of growth, rather than of authorship," although centuries of growth may lie behind it.

Some critics believe that the *Nibelungenlied* was, in its earliest form, meant to be sung rather than read. Its verse-form, a four-line strophe, instead of the couplet-form of the later romantic epics, seems to corroborate this theory. There can be little doubt that the early lays of which it is formed were sung in courtly circles. But the music of the German epic is not the music of the Minnesinger; there is now little question that it was meant to be read. There were, as we have seen, many versions of the story available, but this does not mean that it grew by itself from the songs of minstrels. The story of the fall of the Burgundian kingdom must have inspired many poets, even as the absorption of the Geats led to the creation of the semi-mythological Beowulf. But, as the *Beowulf* is now accepted as the creation of an individual, so must the *Nibelung-enlied* have been a unification of many poetic tales by one author. Its simplicity and uniformity of diction, its classical richness, so well disciplined, seem ample testimony, combined with the usual linguistic and literary tests, of its single authorship. But it is very pleasant to think of the poem as recited to the sound of harps. Its meter, with the marked caesura, the measured half-line of three feet, with the last half-line of each strophe extended to four feet, seems admirably suited to such presentation. However, the careful artistic variation of accent indicates that it was meant to be read.

The fact that it was meant to be read, and its great popularity, are attested by the number of manuscripts and fragments—twenty-nine—still extant. Three complete early copies of the poem still exist. The longest of these (Manuscript C) was discovered in 1775, and shortly after was printed. Its widespread appeal to Germans led to further investigation of the subject, and two other complete manuscripts came to light: Manuscript B, probably the earliest, and A, a rather careless copy of B. The B-text is the basis for most modern editions. The story itself lived on in popular memory after the decay of the chivalric epic as a literary form; as late as the sixteenth century a ballad, *Das Lied vom hürnen Siegfried*, was printed, and in the eighteenth century a prose chapbook appeared, not long before the literary revival of interest in medieval story. And it was that revival of interest which led Wagner to the composition of the *Ring*.

NIBELUNGENLIED: THE STORY

In the land of Burgundy there once lived a maiden of noble birth, peerless in beauty and gentility. Her name was Kriemhild, and through her it was fated that many a noble warrior should die. Her three brothers, Gunther, Gernot, and Giselher, were heroes of rare valor; Gunther, the eldest of the three, was king over the wide lands of Burgundy, served by countless powerful vassals, among whom were the Margraves Dankwart, Gere, and Eckewart, Hagen of Tronje, Ortwein of Metz, and the renowned minstrel-knight Volker the Fiddler. Gunther's court at Worms upon the Rhine was known afar for wealth, honor, and chivalry.

One day, as she lay attended by her ladies, the fair Kriemhild dreamed that she had reared a falcon, strong and free in beauty, and that it was slain before her eyes by two great eagles. Her mother, Queen Ute, told her that the falcon represented a noble husband, who would be in great peril of his life. Kriemhild swore that day that she would die a maid, since wedded happiness must end in weeping.

Meanwhile, in the kingdom of Netherland, there grew to young manhood a prince named Siegfried, son of the mighty King Siegmund and his fair queen, Siegelind. Siegfried had for his tutors men rich in wisdom; his surpassing beauty of form and his princely chivalry won the love of many fair ladies of the court; and his bravery, strength, and skill in warlike sports were already far-famed.

When the young prince reached the age of knighthood, King Siegmund held high festival, and four hundred esquires assumed the garb of knighthood with him. After the ceremony,

the new-made knights held tournament, and Siegfried surpassed all others. At the banquet following the sport, Siegfried,
by his father's order, bestowed lands and castles upon all his
sword-companions. The nobles all swore fealty to the prince,
and offered him the crown of Netherland; he refused, with true
courtesy, to take the throne from his father, resolving, instead,
to win knightly honor by subduing Siegmund's hostile border-
lands.

Hearing of the beauty of Burgundian Kriemhild, Siegfried
at once desired her for his bride. His kinsmen tried to turn
him from his purpose, fearing for his life at the hands of the
powerful Gunther; he remained inflexible. Siegmund persuaded him to ride in peaceful fashion as a guest to Gunther's
court; force will never, he explained, win the heart of a maiden.
Siegfried chose twelve knights to bear him company, and
Siegelind prepared rich armor and fine garments for the journey. The company departed in an atmosphere of gloom, for
their friends feared never to see them more.

Upon the seventh morning, the company arrived at Worms,
where Gunther's folk marveled greatly at their rich apparel
and noble bearing. No one knew the travelers; Ortwein of
Metz suggested that Gunther consult Tronje Hagen, who knew
men from many far kingdoms. Viewing the newcomers in
secret through a castle window, Hagen instinctively recognized
Siegfried as the famed conqueror of the Nibelungen. He told
Gunther how Siegfried was once called upon to divide the famous Nibelung Hoard between the princes Schilbung and Nibelung, and was promised the marvelous sword of King Nibelung.
The two brothers quarreled with Siegfried's judgment, and he
refused to finish the task, whereupon the two brothers attacked him. He slew them both with the sword, Balmung,
conquered their warriors, killing twelve giants and seven hundred ordinary men, and forced the surviving nobles to pledge
him eternal fealty. The sorcerer dwarf Alberich, seeking vengeance for his slain masters, challenged Siegfried to mortal combat. He was vanquished, despite his magic, forced to swear
loyalty to his conqueror, and to relinquish to him the fabulous

hood of darkness, the *Tarnkappe*, which made the wearer invisible and gave him the strength of twelve men. Siegfried then slew the dragon which guarded the Hoard; bathing in its blood, he was rendered invulnerable to weapons. Having bound Alberich in slavery, he left him as guardian and chamberlain of the Hoard. All these marvels Hagen told Gunther, advising him to treat the stranger prince with highest courtesy, since his hate was a thing of terror.

The King, therefore, welcomed Siegfried courteously; to his amazement, the knight answered his greeting by challenging him to fight for his throne. The King replied with some heat; but Gernot and Giselher averted the quarrel. Gunther once again greeted Siegfried, telling him that all his possessions should be his, as the right of a noble guest, if he would but accept peace. Having established his courage, Siegfried accepted the offer, and the company was royally entertained at court, where Siegfried won great popularity. In every tournament, the prince was supreme, and Kriemhild, watching the sport through the palace windows, was stirred more than she would confess.

Siegfried remained as Gunther's guest for more than a year. Although many lovely ladies languished for him, he remained faithful to Kriemhild, whom he had yet seen only in dreams. Kriemhild, too, spoke to her women many fair words of the lover whom she had never met.

One day messengers arrived at Gunther's court, reporting that Luedeger of Saxony and Luedegast of Denmark had united to challenge the Burgundian throne, and were massing their armies for attack. Gunther called upon his nobles for aid, and Siegfried promised that, given a thousand men, he would repel the invaders. The King granted his request, and he set forth with a picked company, among whom were his original escort of twelve, as well as Hagen, Volker, Ortwein, Sindold, and Dankwart, the finest warriors in Burgundy. Siegfried's army passed through the Rhine territory, through Hesse to the land of the Saxons, leaving the enemy country in ruins behind them. Ortwein and Dankwart led the rear guard; and

Siegfried left Hagen and Gernot in command of the main force, riding alone into Saxony. He located the main force of forty thousand men, and saw a warrior fully armed in gold guarding the van; the two knights engaged in single combat, and Siegfried overcame his opponent, who proved to be King Luedegast. The King pledged his lands to Siegfried in return for his life. Forty of the enemy knights tried to rescue their leader, but Siegfried retained his captive, killing all but one of the Danes, who carried the disastrous news to Leudeger.

Giving his royal captive into Hagen's charge, Siegfried led the attack on the army; Volker the Fiddler was standard-bearer, riding before the host. Although outnumbered by more than forty to one, the Burgundians defeated the Danes and Saxons; Siegfried wounded Luedeger in single combat and took him prisoner. The victorious army returned to Worms with more than five hundred captives. Gernot, as advance messenger, visited first the King, then the lady Kriemhild, who, overjoyed to hear of Siegfried's distinction on the field of battle, loaded her brother with costly gifts and hastened to join in the preparations for the warriors' homecoming.

The army returned. The wounded were well cared for, and all the knights were richly rewarded. The festival continued for six weeks, with constant tournament and feasting. At one of the banquets, Siegfried, as a mark of royal favor, was at last introduced to Kriemhild. For twelve days thereafter they were together constantly, and their love, which had fed only upon dreams, became real and beautiful.

At the final banquet of the festival, Luedeger and Luedegast, recovered from their wounds, were, by Siegfried's request, set free, in exchange for an oath of friendship with Burgundy. There was a great ceremonial leave-taking; the knights bade farewell to Gunther, Kriemhild, and Ute, and departed with many costly gifts. Siegfried also intended to return to his homeland; but Gunther persuaded him to remain. Truly, it was not difficult to turn Siegfried from his purpose of leave-taking, for the fair Kriemhild had his heart in thrall. Day after day passed in pleasant pastimes with her, and Siegfried thought very little of his kinsmen and home.

From across the Rhine there came to Gunther news of Brunhild, maiden queen of far Iceland, a woman matchless in strength and beauty. Her love might be won, said the messengers, only by the warrior who could vanquish her in three contests—throwing the stone, broad-leaping, and hurling the shaft. If the suitor failed in but one of these trials, he was put to death; but if he should win, the Queen pledged her word to be his bride. Many knights had died in Iceland for their audacity; for the Queen had magical prowess in feats of arms.

Fired by the challenge of winning such a princess, Gunther resolved to marry Brunhild or die. Siegfried counseled him against the enterprise; but Gunther remained fixed in his purpose. Hagen advised that Gunther take Siegfried with him to Iceland. "He can do well," insinuated Hagen, "the things that you must do with Brunhild." Gunther swore that, should Siegfried choose to accompany him, and if he were successful, he should pledge life and land to grant his every wish. Siegfried's answer was simple and direct. "Give me your sister," he said, "give me Kriemhild and I shall go with you." Gunther agreed, and the two knights set sail, taking with them only Dankwart and Hagen, as Siegfried advised. Kriemhild commended to Siegfried the safety of her brother; and he swore that he would protect him with his life.

The warriors embarked, and a stirring breeze filled the sails. Siegfried took the helm, for to him was known every highroad of the sea. Favored by the winds, they soon beheld the castle towers of Brunhild's court. Siegfried counseled all the knights to bear themselves with humility before the young Queen; also, he told them that the purposes of the journey would be better served if he should play the role of vassal to Gunther. "Not to meet any wish of yours do I swear such service," he told Gunther, "but for the sake of your sister, the fair Kriemhild, who is to me as my very soul."

As they were speaking, the ship glided so near the castle that they could see the women who watched the ship from the case-ments. "Choose," said Siegfried to the King, "which of these maidens, were you free in choosing, you would fain have as queen." Gunther promptly singled out a beauty in white. "Well have your eyes guided you," answered Siegfried, "for it is indeed the stately Brunhild who now compels your heart and soul unto herself."

The ship now landed, and Siegfried, in his self-assumed role of servant, held the stirrup for Gunther before mounting him-self. The ladies of the castle watched the knights as they rode toward the castle, marveling at their rich dress and stately bearing. Gunther and Siegfried rode before, dressed in white and mounted upon white chargers; Hagen and Dankwart brought up the rear, riding black steeds and identically dressed in black. The massive gates of Brunhild's castle were opened, revealing the fourscore-and-six towers within. The Queen's retainers received the guests, telling them that no one might wear arms within the castle.

Brunhild, hearing from one of the ladies that Siegfried was among the knights, called for her finest robes of state and went in person to greet him. "Is the mighty Siegfried at last come hither for love of me," she cried, "then he shall pay for it with his life!" Attended by a hundred beautiful damsels and five hundred knights, she addressed her welcome first to Siegfried, assuming that he must lead the party, "I thank thee, my lady, high and noble Brunhild," said Siegfried sardonically, "that you are pleased to greet me before this noble knight, who stands here before me; for he is my master, whom methinks it were more fitting to honor first." When he told Brunhild of Gunther's suit, adding that the love of so great a king must be high honor to her, she seemed amazed and angry, replying in her pride that Gunther must first defeat her, then claim her as his bride. And should he lose, she ordained, not only he, but his followers must die. "Do nothing in haste," she said in scorn, "for well may you forfeit both life and honor." Siegfried urged Gunther to accept the challenge without fear, since he should be protected from Brunhild by an art of which Siegfried was master. Brunhild ordered that the trial should begin immediately, and she departed to array herself for battle.

Siegfried slipped away quietly to the ship, where he wrapped himself in the hood of darkness, returning to the arena. Seven hundred warriors, all armed, were present to witness the contest and declare the victor. Brunhild waited, armed in gold; her shield was three spans in thickness, of steel-reinforced gold, studded with huge emeralds: three servants could barely carry it into the ring. Gunther, Hagen, and Dankwart, seeing her lift the massive thing without apparent effort, became nervous and wished for their armor. Brunhild overheard the conversation and scornfully bade their armor and weapons be brought to them. Now twelve men bore into the arena a great, rough, unwieldy stone. Brunhild flung back her silken sleeves and raised her arms as a signal for the opening of the contest. Gunther, standing fearful and perplexed, suddenly felt a light touch on his arm, and heard his invisible companion bid him be silent. "It is Siegfried," continued the voice, "a friend who holds you dear. Let your heart be free from fear before the royal maiden. Give me your shield in hand and leave it for me to wield, and pay attention to what you are hearing. Make the motions yourself—leave the rest to me." Gunther's heart was filled with hope, and he obeyed.

As quick as lightning, Brunhild hurled her spear at the shield which Gunther seemed to hold. Sparks flew hissing from the metal, as the sharp point penetrated, ringing upon the mail rings of Gunther's armor. Gunther and his invisible companion staggered beneath the force of the blow; and, but for the hood of darkness, both would surely have been slain. Siegfried quickly recovered, and sent the spear back with equal force; not wishing to kill Brunhild, he reversed the shaft, so that the point might not pierce her body. Nonetheless, she fell beneath the blow. Regaining her feet, she cried, "A shot, O Gunther, befitting a hero!"

Wrathful, she raised the great stone and flung it far from her, springing lightly after it. But Siegfried, even while carrying Gunther's weight, threw it yet farther, and his leap, too, exceeded the mark. Flushed with anger, Brunhild admitted her defeat and commanded her men to pay service to Gunther as their rightful lord. Greeting the Queen with loving courtesy, Gunther received her vow, took her proffered hand, and led her into the palace, where they were betrothed. Siegfried hid the *Tarnkappe* and pretended to be just returning from the ship. When Hagen told him of Gunther's victory, he said to Brunhild, "These tidings bring me joy, for so is your haughty spirit tamed; there lives yet one man who is your master, it seems."

Brunhild asked that, before leaving for Burgundy, she be given time to call her kinsmen together and settle her affairs. This having been granted, she sent messengers throughout the kingdom to summon all her warriors. Gunther feared treachery; but Siegfried promised to bring immediate re-enforcements, of which the King knew not. Wearing the hood of darkness, Siegfried boarded a small boat and set sail for an island, known to him alone, where dwelt the Nibelungen men who guarded the Hoard. In the disguise of an unknown warrior, he presented himself at the castle of Alberich, where he overcame the giant porter who challenged him. Alberich, hearing the noise of battle, armed himself, and attacked Siegfried with his golden scourge. Siegfried's shield was broken at the first blow of the mighty weapon; but he sheathed his sword, not wishing to slay his chamberlain, and overcame him with his bare hands, pulling his long white beard until he howled with pain and rage. "Were I not pledged to serve the mightiest warrior on earth," Alberich cried, "I and all my vassals would be yours to command." Pleased to find his treasure so well guarded, Siegfried revealed his identity and summoned all the Nibelungen men to gather in the great hall. Choosing a thousand of the best knights, he set sail once more for Brunhild's kingdom. All the warriors were armed with surpassing richness, and the silken-winged vessels were laden with good war-steeds.

When Brunhild saw the splendid ships approaching, she sought Gunther and asked whose they were. "They are my own good men, in truth," he answered, "that I left upon my

journey, lying near by. I have sent Siegfried to call them to
me, and now, O Queen, they are here. Go forth yourself to
greet them, that they may know we see them gladly." Brunhild
obeyed, yet in her greeting she ignored Siegfried.

The guests were given lodging, and the great company assembled in Brunhild's hall. The Queen appointed Dankwart
as her chamberlain, to apportion her treasure among the wedding guests; so lavish was his hand, however, that she began
to fear the loss of all her wealth, and asked that some of it be
reserved for her personal use at Worms. Much to the amusement of Siegfried and Hagen, she refused to trust any man of
Gunther's to fulfill her request, but insisted that her old chamberlain fill her coffers for her. Appointing her uncle as warden
of her lands, she bade him swear allegiance to Gunther. She
chose as escort eighty-six maidens, one hundred ladies, two
thousand knights, and the retinue of the Nibelungen men to
complete the wedding company. After fair leave-taking, they
embarked for Burgundy. Brunhild insisted upon reserving the
wedding ceremony for the arrival at Worms.

When they had journeyed nine days toward Burgundy,
Gunther asked Siegfried to put ashore and ride as messenger
to Worms; for Kriemhild's sake, he assented. Arriving at court,
he sought Kriemhild, who rewarded him with twenty-four
armlets of beaten gold. Although Siegfried was too nobly born
to accept a herald's fee, he received the gift for her sake, afterward distributing it among her women.

The court prepared to welcome the royal bride, and messengers sped throughout the land summoning Gunther's
kinsmen to the wedding feast. A band of knights and ladies,
led by the royal family, rode to the strand to greet the ship.
Jeweled bridles and lordly arms flashed in the sunlight; surely
so fair a company had never been seen before. Siegfried rode
beside Kriemhild, while Ortwein attended the Queen. The
knights, as was the custom, jousted as they rode.

The ship landed, and Gunther led forth his fair bride; Kriemhild and Ute saluted her in honor and friendship, as befitted
her rank. At last all the company were landed and mounted

upon their steeds. The tournament was resumed, until Gunther ordered Hagen to end it, before all the ladies should be buried in dust. The horses were allowed to rest until the air should be cooler, while the knights and ladies amused themselves with feasting and courtly pastime in the sumptuous tents prepared by Ute. At sunset, they escorted Gunther and Brunhild to the castle, where a great banquet had been prepared.

Before Gunther was served with water, Siegfried reminded him of his bargain. Summoning Kriemhild into the hall, Gunther told her of his pledge and prayed her to redeem it with her free assent. Truly, Kriemhild was in no way unwilling to accept Siegfried as her lord. A ring was brought, and the couple was united with high ceremony.

Seeing Siegfried seated beside Kriemhild in a place of honor, Brunhild could not restrain her angry tears. Gunther asked the cause of her sorrow, swearing that he and all his vassals were at her service, ready to avenge her every wrong. "My grief is for the sake of your sister," Brunhild answered, "whom I see here seated beside a mere steward of yours. If she must be thus dishonored, it shall forever be a cause of sorrow to me." She swore that, until she learned the reason for the match, she would never share Gunther's bed as his wife. The King replied that Siegfried's lands were as wide as his own, and that he was most worthy to wed any princess. Brunhild began to realize how she had been deceived, and her countenance was lowering and wrathful.

The attendants escorted the royal couples to their chambers. Left alone, Siegfried and Kriemhild rejoiced in their love; but with Gunther and Brunhild it fared differently. Brunhild approached her couch clad in purest white, and her beauty and stateliness fired Gunther's passion. Yet she refused his love, demanding once again an explanation of his obligation to Siegfried. Gunther tried to force her to his will, but he met with ill success; Brunhild bound him hand and foot and hung him from a nail on the wall. Forgetting his attempt to prove himself master, Gunther pleaded with his bride to let him down, swearing that he would never touch her without her consent.

She ignored him and went to bed, while he hung there all night, alternately imploring and cursing. When morning came, she threatened to call in his knights, that they might see what manner of man they had for King; finally, however, she relented and let him free. He returned to his couch, that the attendants might suspect nothing; but he took great care to lie as far as possible from Brunhild.

Siegfried and Gunther, with their brides, met that morning at Matins, where both were consecrated and crowned. Six hundred squires were knighted in honor of the double nuptials, and after Mass the knights held tournament before the palace casements. Gunther stood apart, brooding alone among the revelers. When Siegfried asked him how he had fared the night before, Gunther poured out the entire tale of his unbelievable humiliation. Siegfried wisely concealed his amusement, swearing that before another night had passed he would teach Brunhild her duty as a wife. He planned to come invisibly into Gunther's chamber, wrapped in his hood of darkness, extinguish the lights as a token of his presence, and subdue Brunhild. Since he swore to leave her virginal, Gunther agreed.

Late that night Siegfried came to the royal bedchamber. Brunhild saw no one but Gunther and marveled that he needed another lesson so soon. Finding greater force than she had expected, she began to resist in earnest, and Siegfried's life was in grave peril. He conquered her at last, and she begged him to spare her, promising never again to cross his will. "Now have I seen," she cried, "that Gunther can be lord over the mood of a woman." Siegfried rose from the couch as if to lay aside his clothing; unperceived, he took with him from the chamber Brunhild's ring and girdle. Gunther, left alone with his bride, found that she had become in strength as any other woman. In his own apartment, Siegfried avoided Kriemhild's questions, but planned to give her the ring and girdle later.

On the following morning Gunther was in festive mood, and for two weeks the revelry continued, unmarred by any sorrow. The monarch dispensed gifts lavishly among his guests, and all the treasure brought from the Nibelung isle was soon dealt away.

Siegfried, at the end of this time, took leave of Gunther. He refused the share in the kingdom of Burgundy which was to have been his marriage portion, asking instead that Hagen and Ortwein, with their vassals and kinsmen, might own him for lord and follow him to Netherland. Hagen refused with contempt. "Let other men, who serve you, bear you company," he cried, "for as we have always followed the Burgundian kings, so shall we remain henceforth by their side." Ortwein accepted the offer, and Eckewart went with Siegfried in Hagen's place.

In Netherland, Siegmund and Siegelind rode out with their nobles a full day's journey to welcome the prince and his bride. At Xanten castle a lordly festival was held in their honor, and before all his warriors Siegmund gave his crown and his power to Siegfried.

Siegfried became a wise and just monarch. Incredibly wealthy, feared in war, and lord over many mighty vassals, he reigned in joy for ten years. When Kriemhild bore him a son, the boy was christened Gunther, in honor of his uncle. In the same season, Siegelind died, and Kriemhild came to full power as queen; she was a good mistress to her vassals and much loved. Across the Rhine, Brunhild, too bore a son, who was named Siegfried. In both courts there was peace and happiness. But Brunhild seethed under her mask of serene obedience. She envied Kriemhild's glory and power, and she had received no token of service from Siegfried.

One day she confided to Gunther a desire to see Kriemhild. Gere was sent as messenger to Netherland to invite its monarchs to visit Worms. "However high and mighty he may be, however far away he may dwell," said Kriemhild, "what his master commands Siegfried cannot fail to do." Gere returned bearing Siegfried's acceptance of the invitation; the magnificent gifts which he brought from Netherland caused much amazement at court. "Well may Siegfried give of his treasure," mused the dark Hagen, "nor could he give it all away if he should live forever. The Nibelung Hoard lies beneath his hand. Would that it might once come into Burgundy land!"

Having received messages that Siegfried, Kriemhild, Siegmund, and their train were approaching Worms, Ute and Gunther prepared to do them honor by riding out to greet them. Brunhild, however, seemed indifferent. Gunther commanded her to remember her own reception in Burgundy, and to greet her guests with like courtesy. "Fain would I do that," said Brunhild ironically, "for, in truth, I have good reason to love the lady Kriemhild well."

The meeting was joyful; dust rose in clouds from the meeting of the great retinues of mounted knights and ladies. They rode without delay into the town, the knights jousting as they went. When the guests had been conducted into their chambers at the castle, Brunhild glanced often at Kriemhild, who was fairer than the gold she wore.

At table that evening, Siegfried and his twelve hundred richly clad knights were most impressive to see; Brunhild could not help but rejoice in so lordly a guest. The feast lasted until dawn, when the knights, in high spirits, jousted before the ladies. At Matins, Brunhild and Kriemhild sat together in friendly manner; after Mass they bore each other willing company at table. Nor was there any hint of difference between them for fully eleven days.

Before Vespers on the twelfth day, the two queens sat together watching the tournament before their casement. Suddenly, in pride, Kriemhild declared, "Such a husband have I, that well might both these kingdoms lie beneath his rule." Brunhild retorted, "If none other lived beside himself and you, so might he indeed rule these kingdoms; but while Gunther lives, such a thing may scarcely be!" They quickly grew hostile, and Brunhild introduced again the subject which had long been tormenting her: "When first Gunther had his will of me, then he himself told me that Siegfried was Gunther's liegeman." Kriemhild proudly retorted that her lord was no man's vassal, but a greater king than Gunther. "Since you believe my husband to be your vassal," cried Kriemhild, "then today all our followers shall see whether I dare go into the chapel before the wife of the King." "If you will not own service," answered Brunhild, "then you, with all your women, must hold apart from my train on the way to the minster." "Truly, I shall be most glad to do so," retorted Kriemhild. They parted in great anger.

At Mass, Brunhild and her ladies appeared gorgeously arrayed; but Kriemhild and her attendants appeared in magnificent robes and jewels which none had seen until that day, for Kriemhild had brought them from the Nibelung Hoard, though her courtesy and tact had kept them hidden before. The queens met before the minster, and Brunhild, furiously jealous, forbade Kriemhild to go before her.

"If you could but have been silent," said Kriemhild, "then it were certainly better for you. You have now brought nothing but dishonor to yourself and your lord. In truth, how might a harlot expect to be a queen?" She showed the company Brunhild's well-known ring and girdle, saying that they had been given her by Siegfried, who told her that Brunhild had been his mistress before Gunther took her. Brunhild dissolved into furious tears, and Kriemhild, seizing the opportunity, passed into minster first.

Truly, no one paid much attention to Mass that day. After the service, Brunhild, with a band of armed men, confronted Kriemhild, who was attended also by warriors, and called upon her to prove her statements. Kriemhild looked to Siegfried for support; to her amazement, he denied the whole thing. "So should we ever govern women when they chatter heedlessly," he said to Gunther, and the two kings sauntered away arm in arm. The companies dispersed. Both the queens were in tears.

Hagen of Tronje at once sought out Brunhild in her chamber. When she told him of her wrongs, he swore that Siegfried should pay for his insults with his life. Hagen then went to Gunther, in whose mind he skillfully implanted the idea that Siegfried's life counted for little, when, with his death, such wide lands and great treasures could belong to Burgundy. At Gunther's order, his knights attempted to kill Siegfried in tournament that day; but they were unsuccessful. Hagen and Gunther realized that open methods could never avail them against so great a warrior. Hagen swore to contrive means for Siegfried's death in secret, and the weak King infamously agreed to betray his friend.

Four days later, knights rode into Gunther's court, bearing tidings that Burgundy must prepare for war. They said that they were men of Luedeger, who had broken his treaty and challenged Gunther's throne. Gunther feigned despair; and Siegfried, suspecting nothing evil, declared himself, as always, ready to save the King from his enemies. The King gave Siegfried a picked army, including, of course, the dark Hagen, who planned the false alarm in the first place.

Before the knights departed for battle, Hagen sought Kriemhild, who commended Siegfried's personal safety to him. Hagen swore to protect him in battle, but declared that, in order to do so, he must know if there were any weaknesses against which he should guard him. Kriemhild told him that, when Siegfried bathed in the blood of the dragon Fafnir, a linden leaf clung to a spot between his shoulders, where he was now vulnerable to weapons. "Sew a little token on his tunic," said Hagen, "that I may know where to shield him in the heat of battle." Kriemhild obeyed, little knowing that she betrayed her lord to his death.

The knights rode away; when Hagen had well noted the cross upon Siegfried's tunic, he sent two of his men to bid Gunther order the army to return to court, carrying news that Luedeger had disbanded his men and withdrawn the challenge.

At Worms, Gunther announced his intention to hunt that day in the Vosges. Siegfried, still in high spirits from his earlier anticipation of battle, at once offered to attend him. In hunting dress, he took leave of Kriemhild, who suddenly feared for his life, remembering what she had told Hagen. She begged him to remain at home, telling him that she had dreamed of disaster through this hunt. "I know of no one here who bears us hatred," answered Siegfried, "for all of your kinsmen have been generous to me." Kriemhild tried to detain him with her embraces; but he laughed at her fears, and in a moment he was gone. Never would Kriemhild see him again alive.

The hunters rode forth in Gunther's train; Gernot and Gisel- her both remained at home. Before the great forest the knights made camp. Hagen proposed a contest, in which each should take his huntsmen and go a separate way, so that the King might judge which of them was the most skillful. Siegfried, with but one tracking hound, slew as many beasts as the dog was able to start. Two wild boars, a mighty lion, four ure- oxen, an elk, a great bison, and a stag fell before his hand, for in all ways, even in sport, was Siegfried a perfect knight. At the request of his huntsmen, who feared that he might wipe out all the wild-life in the forest, Siegfried ended the chase. On the way back to camp, a huge bear ran out of the thicket, started by Siegfried's horse. He gave chase, captured it alive, and tied it to his saddle horn, thinking to give sport to the men in camp. When he loosed it from its bonds, however, the men were terrified; Gunther ordered all the dogs freed, and some of the knights ran after it as it fled, pursued by the yelping pack. Only Siegfried could overtake it on foot; he slew it with one blow of his sword, and all the men accorded him the honor of the day.

The tired hunters began their feast, only to find that the wine had been omitted. "I thought that today we should hunt in the Spessart forest," said Hagen, "and there I sent the wine." "You are not very bright," cried Siegfried; "for seven good horses laden with wine and mead should be here at this mo- ment. Must the King's hunters fare thus?" "Be not so angry," said Hagen, "for I know of a cool spring that flows not far from here. Let us slake our thirst there." As if in playful mood, Hagen proposed a race to the fountain. Siegfried won easily, but waited, with his usual courtesy, until the King should arrive to drink. While Gunther drank, Hagen stole away Siegfried's weapons, which he had laid aside against a tree. As Siegfried bent to drink, Hagen pierced him between the shoulders, wounding him to the heart. Mortally wounded, the hero sought his weapons; finding only the shield, he rushed upon Hagen with it, beating him into insensibility and nearly killing him.

Bleeding dreadfully, Siegfried fell among the flowers, which were stained crimson with his life-blood. "O cowards most base," he cried, "to you was I ever faithful, and thus am I repaid. You have laid eternal shame upon your kindred; thenceforth with shame be parted from the company of all true knights." The huntsmen hurried to the spring, where they found Gunther weeping over the dying hero. "He who has done evil need not mourn," said Siegfried to the King in scorn, "for he merits only reviling thereby." Hagen showed no remorse, but stared at Siegfried with hate, exulting aloud that Burgundy was at last free from his mastery. "Had I suspected your treachery, be sure that I should have guarded myself well from you," said Siegfried faintly, "but most of all do I weep for Kriemhild. Woe is it to me that I ever bore a son, whom in time people will scorn because those to whom he must give the name of kinsmen are murderers. Gunther, if you be not entirely parted from true faith, do no further harm to Kriemhild, but let her come to rejoice that you are her brother." His words were silenced in the agony of death, and all but Hagen wept.

The knights were bound by Gunther to conceal the truth, agreeing that Kriemhild should be told of her husband's death at the hands of robbers. "I care not if Kriemhild knows all," said Hagen, "for she who has so sorely grieved my lady, fair Brunhild, may, for all I care, weep forever more. I myself shall bear him home." They made camp for the night, and then crossed the Rhine to Worms. Never have knights spent so evil a day in hunting; for the quarry that they slew many a noble maid was doomed to weep and many a valiant warrior should die.

Hagen, in fierce and wanton humor, ordered Siegfried's body to be laid at Kriemhild's door, where she must pass it on her way to Matins. Her chamberlain found him there. When she heard that before her gate a noble knight lay dead, she recalled her conversation with Hagen, and, knowing in her heart that the dead man was her husband, she fell in a deathlike swoon. Recovering her senses at last, she bade her attendants lead her to him; finding her fears true, she sent Siegfried's men to carry the news to his father. "Your shield bears no mark of a sword," she cried, "but you have been murdered. Oh, if I knew who had done it, he should die at once!"

When Kriemhild's messengers arrived at the chamber of Siegmund, he was awake, for his heart had warned him of disaster. He and his hundred men armed themselves and hurried to Kriemhild's side, accompanied by Siegfried's thousand warriors. She restrained them from a show of immediate violence. "Gunther has so many brave knights," she said, "that if you offer battle you must all be lost together. Lord Siegmund, let this thing stand until a more fitting time. Be sure that I shall ever seek to avenge my husband. He who has parted us, when once I am sure of his guilt, shall find in me his certain doom. Remain here with me now, and help me prepare my lord for burial."

Siegfried was buried in state; high and low alike mourned him. Gunther, Hagen, and his followers came to the funeral Mass; Kriemhild accused them of the deed, and when they approached the casket of gold where the dead knight lay, his wounds began to bleed anew. "Gunther and Hagen, you have done this thing," cried Kriemhild, "and may God give me vengeance!" Open conflict nearly broke out, but Kriemhild once again restrained Siegfried's men while Mass was sung. More than a hundred Masses were chanted that day, and Siegfried's treasure was dealt out by Kriemhild among all those who would promise to pray for his soul.

Kriemhild lay in her chamber after the burial of Siegfried, very near to death. Siegmund begged her to leave this hostile land and come to Netherland, where she should continue to reign as queen, for her husband's sake. Giselher, Gernot, and Ute prevailed upon her to remain. "How can I stay, and continue to look upon the face of him who has done this thing to me?" she said. "Whoever has in this way harmed you," answered young Giselher, "you may spurn his service. Take

whatever is mine, dear sister, and stay here with your mother."
Siegmund returned to Netherland without Kriemhild, swearing
to care for her son and raise him as a prince and a knight. He
refused any escort from Gunther, and departed without offering the hand of friendship to any there. But Gernot and
Giselher rode after him to the Rhine, and they swore that they
were guiltless in the murder of his son, nor had they heard of
any who were hostile to him. Siegmund permitted young
Giselher to escort him to his homeland. Returning to Burgundy, Giselher was faithful servant to Kriemhild; he and
Margrave Eckewart tried in vain to comfort her. But Brunhild
sat apart, nor did she ever show the least pity to Kriemhild.

At Worms, Eckewart built a home for Kriemhild, where she
lived without joy, weeping and praying. She spoke no word to
Gunther or Hagen for fully three years, nor would she allow
them in her presence. Hagen would not rest in his accomplished villainy, but ever tried to persuade the King that the
Nibelung Hoard should be brought to Burgundy. "Then,
truly!" he said, "may your sister be more friendly to us."
Through Ortwein, Gere, Gernot, and Giselher, Kriemhild became reconciled with Gunther, and admitted publicly that
Gunther was not guilty. "But it was Hagen's hand that slew
him," she said, "and I shall hate him in my heart forever."

There was peace again among the royal kindred. Kriemhild
emerged from her mourning, and spoke to all but Hagen, who
dared not venture within her sight. The Hoard was brought to
the Rhine, for Kriemhild had been persuaded to share her
bridal portion with her kinsmen. Gernot and Giselher, with
eight hundred warriors, received it from Alberich, who, if he
had dared, would have offered battle, but prophesied that the
curse upon the Hoard would destroy the house of Burgundy.
All Kriemhild's storehouses and towers could barely contain
her wealth, and through it she made many knights faithful to
her. Her growing power made Hagen apprehensive; and he
suggested to Gunther that the treasure be taken from her by
force. "I swore that I should never do her more evil," said
Gunther. "Let me, then, bear the guilt for you," responded

Hagen; and Gunther weakly agreed. The King rode away on a journey, commanding all his kinsmen and vassals to go with him, and Kriemhild was left without protection. Hagen, who had, through stealth, secured the keys to her treasure-houses, stole the Hoard and commanded that it be sunk in the Rhine. Kriemhild's wrath was great at this second injury; but she bore it quietly, praying for revenge.

After thirteen years, the monarch Etzel, having lost his wife Helke, sent the Margrave Ruediger of Bechlaren to urge his suit for the hand of Kriemhild. Ruediger was welcomed with honor by his old friends at Worms, and he persuaded the royal family to aid him in his proposal to Kriemhild. Hagen reminded Gunther that Kriemhild's new power might well give cause for fear to any that had wronged her; but Gunther and his brothers agreed that, after her many injuries in Burgundy, it would be treason to deny her honor. Kriemhild agreed to see Ruediger; but she was cold to his message until he secretly found an opportunity to tell her that the arms of Hunland were ready to help her against her enemies. Then she yielded, and prepared to leave the court with the Margrave. Her treasure she distributed among her women, reserving a thousand marks for Masses for the soul of Siegfried. Eckewart swore to follow her with his five hundred knights, and a hundred of her maidens also accompanied her. Gunther and Gernot rode with her to the city of Vergen on the Danube, and they swore before they left her that, if ever she should be in need, they would ride to Hunland to serve her.

The company passed through Bavaria, stopping at Passau, where they were entertained by the noble Bishop Pilgrim of that city. They rode on through Everdingen; crossing the Traune into Ruediger's lands, they were received by his lady, Gotelinde, who had ridden out to Ense to meet them. They rested there until morning, and Kriemhild was received with friendship and courtesy. Proceeding to Bechlaren, they were entertained royally with feasting and tournament. When Kriemhild departed, she and Gotelinde exchanged rich gifts and oaths of friendship. They continued on their journey, entertained on the way by several of Etzel's powerful vassals; at last they reached Traisenmauer, the King's stronghold, where Kriemhild awaited Etzel's arrival. Four days later he came, and noble thanes, both Christian and pagan, were in his mighty retinue. After the nobles had passed in review before Kriemhild, Etzel and Dietrich of Bern arrived, with many other knights of high fame. The King dismounted and greeted his bride; as she lifted her veil for his kiss, the company marveled at her beauty.

With tournament and feasting the marriage was celebrated. The festival lasted seventeen days, and the generosity of Kriemhild caused much wonder among the knights, who had believed her to be penniless. Etzel and his thanes tried to exceed each other in gift-giving, and many a man from giving stood bereft even of his own clothing.

On the eighteenth morning they set sail at Miesenburg for Etzelburg, where Kriemhild was welcomed with high courtesy by Princess Herrat, Etzel's niece and Dietrich's betrothed. So plentifully did Kriemhild deal out gifts there that soon nothing remained to her of the treasure that she had brought from over the Rhine; but she gained many loyal servants. Never before had she wielded so much power. Her every request was instantly granted by the enamored Etzel.

For seven years Etzel and Kriemhild lived in happiness and peace. She bore him a son, who was baptized Ortlieb; she had made many converts to Christianity, and her lord was among them. More and more knights pledged allegiance to her, and she was widely famed for her beauty and virtue.

After five more years had passed, she saw that her power was great enough to carry out her plans. Everyone in Hunland obeyed her will, and at each season twelve great kings were seen to bow before her throne. Once again she began to think to revenge herself on Hagen. One night, as she lay in Etzel's arms, she told him that she was lonely for her kinsmen. Glad to serve her, Etzel sent his famous minstrels, Werbel and Schwemmel, to carry his invitation to Worms.

Hagen warned Gunther that Kriemhild had some design in

bidding them attend her in Hunland. But Gernot replied, "Though Hagen may well fear for his life in Hunland, this is no reason for her kinsmen to forego her company."

"Since, friend Hagen, you well know your own guilt," added Giselher, "stay here at home and take care of yourself; let those who are not afraid come with us to see my sister." Hagen, angered, agreed to go with them, but strongly recommended that Gunther take with him as many of his best knights as he could. Three thousand men gathered near Worms in answer to the King's summons; of these, Hagen chose a thousand, among whom were Dankwart and Volker. They prepared to leave by the week's end, taking with them rich apparel and well-made battle gear.

Brunhild and Ute begged Gunther to remain at home, but even Hagen realized that his word had been passed and he must go. Rundold was appointed chamberlain of the kingdom and guardian of Brunhild's child. Kriemhild, in Hunland, received her messengers with joy. "It is Hagen who has my special favor," she said, "for he is a most noble knight. I am pleased that we shall see him here so soon."

Gunther and his knights arrived at the Rhine, to find the waters swollen in flood. Hagen was sent to find means to cross. As he strode, full-armed, along the bank, he came upon the Rhine maidens bathing in a pool near a waterfall. He stole away their garments and refused to give them back until his questions had been answered. In reply to his question about the voyage to Hunland, the first maiden told him that it would be safe and attended with all honor. Pleased, Hagen returned the clothing and started to walk away; but he was halted by the second maiden. "My sister lied but to regain her robe," she said; "for if you go into Hunland, you must surely be betrayed and die." A maiden said that all the knights of Burgundy were fated to perish in Hunland, and that only the King's chaplain would escape. "Little joy would it bring my royal masters if I should tell them that we must die in Hunland," said Hagen, realizing the derision that such a message would bring, "so show me, wise woman, how we may safely cross to the opposite strand." The Rhine maidens directed him upstream to the dwelling of a boatman, warning him that this man was a warrior of might, and true to Gelfrat, lord of this border. "If challenged, give your name as Amelrich," said one, "and the ferryman will answer. Let Gunther guard himself if he would cross this march, for Gelfrat and his brother Else are lords of warlike mind."

Hagen proceeded upstream, where he found the boatman's cabin. He shouted across the flood, giving his name as Amelrich and offering a golden armband as guerdon for his passage. The ferryman rowed across, but recognized that Hagen had deceived him and challenged him to fight. Hagen slew his opponent and flung him headless into the Rhine. Righting the boat, he steered it to Gunther's men. After many crossings, all the knights were brought across the river. On the last trip, Hagen saw the royal chaplain beside his baggage, and, remembering the phophecy, he threw the man into the river, hoping to cheat fate. But the chaplain swam to shore, and Hagen realized that the Rhine maiden had foreseen the truth.

When the boat was emptied, Hagen struck it in pieces with his heel. The others were dismayed, and asked how they should cross on their return. "This thing was done," Hagen said, "so that, if there should be a coward in our company, he shall die shamefully, even though he should flee from us." Volker agreed that the act was wise, and the company proceeded on its way. Volker guided them through Bavaria, for he knew the land well. As the army marched, Hagen revealed his encounter with the Rhine maidens and told the prophecy to the knights. Many were sore afraid, but they obeyed Hagen's counsel and paced their steeds slowly through the hostile territory, that no man might say they were afraid. Gelfrat, having heard of the death of his boatman, attacked the rear guard, which was commanded by Hagen and Dankwart. He was slain by Hagen and his brother Else was also defeated, so that the attacking forces withdrew in disorder. Four Burgundians were killed, but the Bavarians lost more than a hundred men. The company continued undisturbed through Bavaria. Reaching Passau, they were welcomed by Bishop Pilgrim.

After resting at Passau, they continued to the border of Etzel's land, where they found Eckewart guarding the march. Hagen, finding Eckewart asleep on duty, took his sword from him in jest, but returned it in token of respect. Eckewart warned him to be wary in Hunland, for he had heard that Kriemhild plotted his death. He conducted the visitors safely to Bechlaren, where they were received with honor by Ruediger. Gotelinde and her daughter greeted the guests, and Gunther's men pitched their tents near the castle. The royal party was entertained within, and Giselher, who loved Ruediger's daughter upon sight, took her as his bride. The strangers remained with Ruediger until the fourth morning, and then they departed, after exchanging gifts. The Margrave gave to Gunther a coat of mail of magnificent workmanship; to Gernot he gave his famous sword, little dreaming that by the same blade he should die. Hagen, having admired a rich shield that belonged to Gotelinde's dead son, was given it in token of friendship. Ruediger escorted his guests to Etzel's castle, where he parted from them regretfully.

Lady Kriemhild watched her visitors from a high casement. "Now does my heart rejoice," she mused, "for here are my kinsmen come with new-wrought shields and shining armor. He who would be rewarded by me must now remember all my wrongs. To my true followers shall I ever be gracious."

Gunther was received with honor. Many of the greatest knights in the history of chivalry rode out to greet him; Dietrich of Bern and Hildebrand led the escort. Dietrich was grieved to see the heroes of Burgundy, and warned them as best he could. "Do you, then, not understand that Kriemhild still mourns the Nibelung hero?" he said. "May she be forever weeping," answered Hagen in defiance, "for Siegfried has been dead for many a year. She should now be entirely devoted to her lord, the King of Hunland." "Let us not speak of the manner of Siegfried's death," said Dietrich, "but, while my lady Kriemhild lives, you may look for injury. Beware her vengeance, for it is long abiding!" In honor, the Burgundians could not now turn back; Dietrich knew this, and mourned.

Attended by her train, Kriemhild went forth to greet her guests. She kissed her brother Giselher, and Hagen, having seen, made fast his helmet band. "After such a greeting," he said, "let all warriors guard themselves; for widely does the welcome differ between master and man." Kriemhild answered scornfully that Hagen should never have friendly greeting from her. "What do you bring from Worms," she asked, "that I should ever make you welcome here?" "Had I known," said Hagen, "that you would expect a present from every thane, then I am wealthy enough, surely, to have brought you a gift —if, that is, I had thought to do so." Kriemhild demanded to know where Hagen had hidden her treasure; he answered that for many years no one had known of it, as his masters had commanded him to sink it in the Rhine.

Kriemhild asked Gunther's warriors to surrender their weapons for safe keeping; they refused. "Why will my own brothers not give me their shields?" wondered the Queen; "I fear someone has warned them, and if I knew him, he should not live long." Dietrich defied her, saying that he himself had warned her kinsmen; fearing his anger, Kriemhild was forced to hold her peace. Etzel, who had watched the quarrel from a distance, heard nothing, but marveled that Hagen, his friend in youth, should have so wrathful a mien. Hagen and Dietrich clasped hands in friendship, and Hagen besought Volker to tell him what had happened.

Hagen and Volker strode across the courtyard and seated themselves under Kriemhild's window, where they glared fiercely at the astonished Huns. Kriemhild wept and called her true warriors to her, "Avenge me upon Hagen," she told them, "for he must die." Four hundred knights followed her to the bench where the two warriors insolently remained seated before her. Hagen drew from its scabbard Siegfried's famous sword and laid it across his knees; Volker unsheathed his famous weapon—a long, heavy broadsword named "Fiddle-bow." When Kriemhild accused Hagen of the slaying of Sieg-

fried, he admitted his guilt and defied her. She ordered her
men to slay the strangers; but they looked fearfully at one another and no man dared begin the attack. They at last dispersed, leaving the Queen alone. Kriemhild sought her chamber, and Hagen and Volker hurried to tell Gunther of the
incident. Gunther was feasting in the great hall with Etzel,
who, knowing nothing of Kriemhild's plot, greeted the two
warriors in friendship. They remained with him until nightfall, when Etzel dismissed his guests to their lodging at Hagen's
suggestion. As they left the hall, Kriemhild's warriors pressed
upon them from every side; but Hagen and Volker warned
them away, and the party passed without disturbance. The
chambers were sumptuously appointed, and the knights were
weary; but they feared to sleep. Hagen and Volker armed
themselves and guarded the entrance; and Volker charmed the
others to rest with his music.

Near midnight, a party of Huns approached stealthily; but,
seeing the door well guarded, they fled. Volker wished to pursue the cowards and slay them; but Hagen warned him against
leaving the rest of the party unguarded. Kriemhild, who heard
of the second failure of her men, was angry, but planned other
means to attain her purpose.

The morning bell sounded for Matins, and Gunther and his
men began to dress themselves for chapel. Hagen told them to
wear full armor and be ready for possible violence. When
Etzel beheld his guests in armor, he was astonished, and asked
if anything were amiss. Kriemhild watched Hagen in anxiety,
knowing that if he betrayed her plot, all would be hopeless;
but Hagen answered merely that it was a custom of Burgundian knights to wear their armor for three days during high
festival. Too proud to tell what had happened, Hagen doomed
his companions to certain death. In the tournament following
the service, Kriemhild's men were in murderous mood. Dietrich
and Ruediger withdrew their knights from the field, having
sensed the temper of the situation. The Huns fought in earnest
with Gunther's men, but Etzel saw nothing but knightly sport,
as the mass mellay was at an impasse. Volker thirsted for

blood; singling out a gaily dressed fop of the court, he ran him through the body and slew him. Hagen, seeing this, cut his way through the press and took his place beside Volker. The two held off the kinsmen of the slain man, who sought vengeance, until Etzel ended the tournament, judging that the murder was accidental. The company left off combat and passed into the castle.

Kriemhild turned to Hildebrand and Dietrich in her distress, but she was refused with little gentleness by both. But there was a knight named Bloedel whom she could bribe with offers of high position; him she sought, and he swore to do her bidding.

The warriors gathered that night in the hall, and Kriemhild sat with them, bringing with her her young son Ortlieb. She asked her guests to take the boy and raise him to knighthood in Burgundy. Since this request conformed to common custom among princes, Etzel was grieved and shocked to hear Hagen reply that in his opinion, the prince was doomed to die in Hunland, at a very early age. Bloedel seized the moment of uneasiness and forced his way into the hall with a thousand men. Dankwart, who had previous warning of the attack from one of Bloedel's men, stopped him in the outer passage. He had only unarmed squires with him; but they fought valiantly, seizing footstools and tables to shield themselves. Finally Dankwart stood alone among his foes; nine thousand squires and twelve knights lay dead. Bleeding from many grievous wounds, he gained the door and burst into the hall. "Too long, my brother Hagen, you sit at table;" he cried, "to you and to God I cry, for knights and squires lie slain in their lodging." Dankwart then guarded the portal, so that the Huns could not enter.

"I wonder," mused the grim Hagen, "what the Huns outside are whispering to one another. I imagine that they would avoid the service of the chamberlain who keeps the door and who brings to his friends such high tidings of court." He continued, "Long since have I heard the tale of Lady Kriemhild's woe; without vengeance, it seems she can no longer bear it.

Now shall we quaff a memory-cup and pay for her loyal cheer; the young prince of Hunland shall be the first installment." With these words he smote off Ortlieb's head, which rolled into the Queen's lap. In a frenzy of battle, he also slew the tutor, struck off the right hand of the minstrel Werbel, and killed everyone within reach. Gunther, Gernot, Giselher, and the others joined the fray. Dankwart held off the Huns outside the door, while Volker guarded it within.

Kriemhild, terrified, called to Dietrich to help her from the hall before Hagen reached her. He shouted above the din of battle, and, hearing him, Gunther commanded his men to cease fighting. Dietrich asked that he and his men might leave the hall unharmed, since this battle was none of their choosing, and Gunther granted the request. With Kriemhild on one arm and Etzel on the other, Dietrich led out his six hundred men. Volker stood beside the door all the while; if any of his enemies tried to escape with Dietrich's knights, he lopped off their heads. After Dietrich's exit, the combat continued until no Huns were left alive in the hall. Gunther's exhausted warriors laid aside their swords, and Volker and Hagen passed out before the hall, where, leaning on their shields, they taunted their foes.

The Burgundians, at Gunther's order, cast out the dead, so that they fell headlong down the staircase; many who yet retained some spark of life were slain by the fall. The kindred of those cast out began to weep, whereat Volker said, "Indeed, the Huns are cravens, who weep like women. Rather should they try to keep their wounded alive." A margrave among the Huns, believing that Volker's words were prompted by kindness, bent above one of his dying kinsmen, striving to carry him away. Volker pierced him with his spear as he stooped, and the others fled in terror.

Soon many thousand knights stood before the palace, but they did not dare attack, for fear of the two warriors at the door. "It were more seemly," remarked Hagen, "that the people's King stood foremost in battle, as do my royal masters." Hearing the taunt, Etzel snatched his shield and would force his way through to Hagen, but his warriors restrained him by force. At Kriemhild's call, Iring, Margrave of Denmark, challenged Hagen, refusing aid. Unable to hurt Hagen, he turned upon Volker, Giselher, Gernot, and Gunther, mad with battle fury. Giselher wounded him, but, regaining his feet, he attacked Hagen, whom he managed to wound before fleeing to Etzel. Hagen's taunts drew him again into battle, and Hagen this time slew him with his mighty spear. Irnfried tried to avenge his brother, but was also slain.

Now more than a thousand knights forced their way into the hall. All were finally slain, and a momentary quiet prevailed. Volker stood before the door, inviting any who sought death to enter and try their luck. After two more attempts, the Huns were discouraged from further attack, and the Burgundian force was decimated. The three princes of Burgundy emerged to parley with Etzel, having realized that they must eventually be overcome. "Let us at least, since we must die, fight with you in the open air," cried Gernot. Kriemhild responded by swearing that, if Hagen should be given up for hostage, the others should go free. Gernot replied that, rather than give up a warrior to his death, they should all prefer to die. In answer, Kriemhild bade her men set fire to the hall. The knights within were perishing with thirst and heat; Hagen bade them drink the blood of the fallen and tread the burning brands into the lake of blood beneath their feet. When day came, Etzel believed all the Burgundians to be dead, but six hundred lived to repel his twelve hundred knights.

Ruediger, in agony, watched the slaughter. Should he bring his men to the aid of his friends, or should he follow his rightful lord? The higher loyalty won, and he led five hundred men against the hall. The Burgundians at first believed that he came to aid them; but soon they learned that he meant to slay them. Hagen, whose shield had been broken in conflict, asked Ruediger for his own, which he received. Even grim Hagen was moved to tears by the gesture; and this gift proved to be Ruediger's last to any man, for he was slain by Gernot, whom he also killed. None of the men of Bechlaren came forth alive.

Kriemhild, having heard no sound for some time, angrily accused Ruediger of making truce with Hunland's enemies. Volker answered from within the hall, "That is untrue, my lady. You have fiendishly belied Ruediger, for he and all his men lie still in death. Look about you, Kriemhild, for men to obey your commands. Ruediger, the hero, was faithful unto death." In proof of his words, Volker ordered the Margrave borne upon his shield to the door of the hall; Etzel and Kriemhild lamented their loss.

Having heard of Ruediger's death, Dietrich of Bern thought to avenge him. Hildebrand went to parley with the Burgundians, in an attempt to recover the body of Ruediger, he was sorely wounded by Hagen. Many died in the fray, including Volker, Dankwart, and Giselher of Burgundy, and Siegstab, Wolfwein, Helfrich, Wolfbrand and Wichart among the men of Dietrich. Dietrich armed himself and sought Hagen, who stood alone with his King amid the ruins of the hall. Refusing to yield themselves as hostages, the two surviving Burgundians fought, but were taken captive. Dietrich led them before Kriemhild, praying her to be merciful to them. Both were led away to Kriemhild's dungeons, after she had sworn that she would do them no further harm. They were imprisoned separately, and Kriemhild sought Hagen in his cell, offering him freedom if he would restore her treasure. He defied her, and was shown, for answer, Gunther's head. "Now, at last," he cried in horror, "have you accomplished your heart's desire. The noble King of Burgundy is dead, also young Giselher and Sir Gernot. No one knows of the treasure but God and me; nor shall I ever, O she-devil, reveal its hiding-place to you!" Taking the sword of Siegfried from its sheath, Kriemhild struck off Hagen's head.

"She shall reap no gain from the deed," cried the wounded Hildebrand, "for by me shall the valiant knight of Tronje be avenged." He slew her with his sword, nor did she receive aid from Etzel, so great was his disgust.

So lay all the dead warriors. Only Dietrich and Etzel remained to weep for their kinsmen. Who once stood high in honor now lies low in death.

Nor can it be told further   what later did befall,
But that good lords and ladies   saw you mourning all,
And many noble squires   for friends in death laid low.
Now has the story ending   this is the Nibelungen woe.

SUGGESTIONS FOR FURTHER READING

Translations:

By Daniel B. Shumway. New York, 1937
By Arthur S. Way. Cambridge, 1911

Other Books:

Robertson, J. G. *History of German Literature*, New York, 1902
Weston, Jessie L. *Legends of the Wagner Dramas*, London, 1896

THE

LUSIADS

THE LUSIADS: INTRODUCTION

Os Lusíadas, the *Lusiads,* is the product of the greatest age of Portugal. This small country, with a population of perhaps a million, was the pioneer in the expansion of empire in the early years of the Renaissance. Situated on the western coast of the Iberian Peninsula, hemmed in on the east by a mountain range, the Portuguese, like the Scandinavian sea-rovers of a few centuries earlier, had no room for expansion except over the sea. Every circumstance was favorable to such an expansion. First, there was the great spice-trade, for many years in the hands of the Venetians, who transported the products of the Orient from the Near East to Europe. A nation which could find an alternate route to India, a route not controlled by the Eastern, Mohammedan peoples, could swiftly become one of the richest and most powerful nations in the world. Second, there was the Iberian drive toward the conquest of the Moslems, a drive intensified by the wars between Mohammedan and Christian in the Peninsula, wars which were not to terminate until the end of the fifteenth century. The same impulses which thrust Columbus westward from Cádiz in 1492 pushed Vasco da Gama eastward in 1497.

For its time, Vasco da Gama's voyage was the more important. The New World was precisely that—a land still, for the most part, in the Stone Age, and susceptible of only the most rudimentary development without the expenditure of more capital than anyone at the moment could spare. The East, on the other hand, was a fully developed area, susceptible of exploitation with only the minimum expenditure of capital and men. It was to this fact that the Portuguese Empire owed its rapid early development. Possessed of better ships and seamen than the Orientals, having the initiative in the attack, and knowing precisely what they intended to do, the Portuguese could, by establishing trading-posts which tapped the interior of the country—as at Goa in India and Macao in China (both still Portuguese, by the way)—control the East-West routes of trade in the goods most desired by both sides. Such trading-posts could, as they still do, provide bases as well for the propagation of the Faith. It is hard to say which of the two desires—for worldly wealth or for the spiritual welfare of the heathen—was the stronger. Both are almost inextricably intertwined in the records of the time, as in Columbus' journal and the *Lusiads*.

The history of the movement toward the East begins more than a hundred years before Camoens wrote his poem. Early in the fifteenth century, Henry the Navigator, Prince of Portugal, began the study of exploration in what we should call today a scientific manner. He established a school of geography and an observatory for the study of navigation, and began a systematic series of examinations of the possibilities of Africa as market and as source of supply. One group of explorers worked down the west coast of Africa, and returned with slaves and gold from what is now the Gold Coast and the northern coast of the Gulf of Guinea. One of their castles still stands at Cape Coast, not far from Accra. Another group rediscovered the Madeira Islands. A third, working overland from North Africa, crossed the Sudan, and reached the belt of green forest which circles the Western Desert. Still another tried to penetrate into Ethiopia, searching for the shadowy figure of Prester John, well-known to medieval legend as the ruler of a Christian people somewhere far off—in Africa, probably, or perhaps even in Central Asia.

These exploits were immensely profitable to the Portuguese, not only in gold dust and slaves, which were very marketable commodities around the Mediterranean, but principally in the impetus which they gave to further exploration. Between 1488 and 1493 Pero de Covilham made his way, by the old spice-route, to India, and on his return voyage visited Ethiopia. His reports to the King clearly indicated that a voyage around Africa might be feasible. Bartolomeu Dias actually sailed around the continent in 1488, but his men forced him to turn back just short of the town of Sofala, which Pero was to reach two years later. The explorations of de Covilham and Dias were the foundations on which Vasco da Gama, hero of the *Lusiads*, was to build.

In 1497, Vasco da Gama set sail from Portugal, in ships in which nowadays no sensible man would embark for an afternoon's cruise: two square-riggers, a fore-and-aft rigged caravel, and a supply vessel, included in the fleet to permit very long voyages. After a hard voyage, they rounded the Cape of Good Hope, made several landings on the east coast of Africa, and on May 20, 1498, they landed in India. With this voyage the Portuguese Empire began.

For the next few years the Portuguese, having assumed the dominant position in the spice-trade previously held by the Venetians, were occupied in establishing themselves and consolidating their conquests. Following their earlier pattern of controlling trading-centers, the Portuguese in 1511 settled in Malacca, the strategic control-point for commerce with the Far East. From here they moved northward to Formosa (a Portuguese word meaning "beautiful") and established themselves on the coast of China, at Macao, not far from the rich port of Canton. Some of their vessels sailed as far north as Japan, though the Portuguese never established any depot so firmly there as at Goa and Macao. It was their control of the spice-trade of the Far East which impelled the Spaniards to send Magellan (himself a Portuguese) around the world in 1519-1522. Though Magellan did not live to finish the voyage, he was no unworthy countryman of the more successful Vasco da Gama.

The *Lusiads* and its author were products not only of their peculiar time and place but also of the greater force which we call the Renaissance, the Revival of Learning. One of the most notable characteristics of the Renaissance period is a new feeling of nationalism, replacing the older feeling, usually connected with the Middle Ages, that national boundaries are less important than those of religious conviction. A second is the new spirit of quest, of curiosity about *this* world, which finds its most obvious manifestations in the explorations of men like Columbus, Vasco da Gama, the English seamen of the Elizabethan period, and later in the development of the scientific spirit. A third is the great reverence for classical learning, transmitted through the Middle Ages, but reinforced in Camoens' time with the new knowledge of Greek literature. In such a climate of thought, how could Camoens have produced anything other than the *Lusiads?*

He was born about 1524, in Lisbon, and educated at the University of Coimbra. As a member of the lower nobility, he had access to the court, and there he had an unhappy love-affair with one of the Queen's ladies. At the age of twenty-four, he was banished from the court, and enlisted in the army for the campaign against Ceuta, in North Africa, where he lost an eye. Some time after his return, he had a duel with an official, whom he wounded, and as a result was banished again, this time to India. His father, a ship's captain, had made the voyage earlier and died in a shipwreck off the Indian coast; his grandfather had married a relation of Vasco da Gama. His own literary training and his reading, coupled with these earlier and almost innate influences, must have strongly influenced him to the composition of which Vasco da Gama and his exploits were the subject. After several campaigns in India (reflected in the *Lusiads*) he was sent to Macao, where he had a minor official position, but even here he got into trouble, and was shipped back to India, accused of malfeasance in office. On the voyage, he was shipwrecked; we know from his own account that he saved only the manuscript of his greatest poem. After reaching Goa in 1561, he spent some years at various official tasks, in and out of difficulties, and then (1567) started the return voyage. He got as far as Mozambique, where again for two years he awaited a vessel; and finally, in 1569, he returned to Portugal.

But the Portugal to which he returned was not the country he had left. The country had reached its highest pitch of prosperity almost a quarter of a century earlier, when Luis de Camoens was shipping East to seek his fortune in a land of what seemed limitless wealth. Much of that wealth had, it is true, been brought to Portugal, and the country was prosperous. But in 1569-70, Lisbon was visited by the plague, and recovered slowly. The King was Sebastian, only sixteen years old, but already two years on the throne. He was a religious idealist; one could without much injustice call him a fanatic; who saw himself as a Crusader destined to win the final battle over Islam. Physically weak and sickly, he seems to have been little better mentally. Paying no heed to the advice of his generals and sea-captains, he determined to conquer Morocco, and, still trusting his own intuition, he was defeated and killed at Alcazarquivir. Soon after his death, Portugal became a part of Spain. Fortunately for himself, Camoens died shortly before the catastrophe.

The *Lusiads* was published in 1572, with a Prologue and an Epilogue dedicated to the unfortunate Sebastian. In them, Camoens makes plain his feeling of insecurity concerning the future of Portugal. He perceived, perhaps better than many of his contemporaries, that the foundation of Portugal's greatness was in its control of trading-routes and in commerce, not in a desire, left over from the Middle Ages, to propagate the Faith by force of arms.

But, being a Portuguese, Camoens could not exclude from his mind the necessity for the conversion of the paynim—or their extinction. The *Lusiads* is shot through with references to enmity with Islam, an enmity derived from centuries of conflict with Moslem invaders of the Peninsula. It appears most obviously in the passages in Canto I and II, which deal with Vasco da Gama's reception at Mombasa, and in Cantos VIII and IX, dealing with the wars in Calicut and the conversion of the "good" Moor, Monsaide.

As a product of the Renaissance, the *Lusiads* is informed on every page with national spirit. The Portuguese are shown as everything that heroes should be, and sometimes, especially in the Prologue, as more than heroic. Ulysses and Aeneas are thrown into the shade by the exploits of Vasco da Gama; Roland is merely a soldier like another. The great men of the past are mere prologues to the swelling act of the imperial theme.

Aeneas and Ulysses, however, furnished the models for Camoens' treatment of his hero. Though he probably knew little or no Greek, he was full of the learning of his time and place, which means that he knew Latin literature, especially the *Aeneid*, thoroughly. Like Aeneas and Ulysses, da Gama made a long and successful voyage; like them, he enjoyed the favor of the gods. It is interesting that Venus, Aeneas' mother, not the cool and reasonable Athene, was the patroness of da Gama. In this, of course, Camoens is probably continuing the cult of courtly love, a late medieval literary convention, but still viable in his day. This treatment of a late medieval theme, its binding-up with the themes of the Renaissance—nationalism and the seeking mind—are the inevitable product of the local and temporal matrix of the *Lusiads*.

Another curious combination is that of Christianity and paganism, symbolized by the constant presence of the Christian God and His Faith in the poem, together with the operations of divine will through the agency of pagan deities. Milton, certainly Camoens' superior as a classical scholar, and as deeply soaked in his own religious feeling, could never have done as Camoens did; he felt it necessary to point out that pagan divinities were the offspring of the fallen angels. But Camoens seems to find it not inappropriate to derive the descent of the Portuguese from Lusus, the son of Bacchus; or to take them to an island magically set in the ocean by Venus, where Vasco da Gama marries Tethys; or—most notably—to have a prayer addressed by da Gama to God answered by Venus.

This mingling of theology and mythology was never more successful than in the *Lusiads*. Why, it would be hard to say. Perhaps because the work is composed in the ottava rima, an eight-line stanza borrowed from Tasso, the Italian poet, who wrote the minor epic called *Jerusalem Delivered*. Following the story through these stanzas is difficult, because the thought tends to halt at the end of each, and one has to make the slightest effort to begin the next. Since the prayer is made in one stanza, and Venus is described as answering it in the next, there is not the same carry-over between the two that one would find in Milton's blank verse.

The ottava rima has other values, principally that it allows of lyrical passages which are harder to attain in more connected meters. The passages which spring to mind are the appearance of Venus before Jupiter (Canto II) and the really magnificent speech of the Giant Adamastor in Canto V. Either, of course, could have been composed by a poet of genius in hexameters or blank verse; but the rhyme and the stanza-pattern give an effect which is rivaled only by some of the stanzas in Chaucer's *Troilus and Criseyde*.

THE LUSIADS: THE STORY

CANTO I: Sing, you goddesses of the Tagus, the bravery and
resourcefulness of Vasco da Gama, who led his heroes across
unsailed seas, spreading the knowledge of the Faith and the
glory of Portugal! No more of the heroes of old time, of
Ulysses and Aeneas; their glories are now eclipsed by another,
the representative of a greater line; no more of Roland now,
but sing of the illustrious scions of Portugal, Juan and Sebastian, whose domains are the whole earth!

On Mount Olympus, the gods sat in conference, considering
the destiny of the East. Imperial Jupiter, in the center of the
gathering, spoke to the assembled deities: "Long have you
known of the bravery of the Portuguese, how with small numbers, though valiant, they repelled the invading Moslem and
the powerful Spaniard; how they warred victoriously even
against imperial Rome. Now it is destined that they shall excel the great empires of old, the Greeks, the Persians, the Romans, and by their own strong arms win dominion over the
Eastern seas. Even now they are passing a hard winter, buf-
feted by the seas and the winds, and have come into an ocean
where they will one day discover the place of the sun's rising.
I am determined that, after their hard voyage, they shall come
to a friendly port in Africa, where they may refresh themselves
after this long voyage, and store their ships for a longer journey."

Bacchus, who had long ruled the East, knew of the prophecy
which foretold the arrival of the Portuguese in India, and he
knew, also, that their conquests would be remembered as the
greatest the world had seen. Should the prophecy come true,

his fame as ruler of the East would be gone forever. Opposed to him was Venus, who recognized in the conquering Iberians the old Roman virtues which she had cherished in Aeneas; and she knew, also, that wherever this conquering people ruled, she would be greatly honored. Between the two there was contention, and neither would yield to the other.

But Mars, who perhaps remembered his old love for Venus, intervened in the quarrel. "O Father of all the Gods! Remember that long ago your word was given to support this valiant people in their conquest of India. Further quarrel is beneath our dignity. I pray you, dispatch your messenger, Mercury, to the fleet, that he may guide them to a place where they may refresh themselves and learn the way to the East." To this speech of Mars Jupiter bent his head in acquiescence, and sent the gods to their own homes.

It was early spring where the Portuguese were sailing, around the great Cape, in the channel between the African coast and Madagascar. About them lay many small islands, which seemed deserted; but from one of these some small lateen-rigged boats appeared, heading toward the ships. They were manned by dark-skinned sailors, armed with short swords and daggers. The Portuguese were astonished at the sight, and asked one another what or who these people might be.

As the Portuguese fleet came up, the boatmen signaled them to stop: the ships were turned toward shore, the sails furled, and the anchors dropped. Up the sides came the visitors, chattering and smiling, with friendly gestures. The Captain, da Gama, received them with good cheer, offering them food and wine, which they drank with pleasure; the natives asked in Arabic who their visitors might be. The sailors replied that they were Portuguese who had sailed all seas, and were now searching for the road to India. And, they asked, who were their guests?

One of the boatmen answered that they too were Moslems, not natives of the island, but from Mozambique; they offered a pilot to guide the Portuguese on their way to India, and invited them to visit the Governor, who would give them further assistance. Then they departed.

During the night the sailors rejoiced that they had come upon so pleasant a spot, and in the morning, when the sun rose, they prepared the ships for a visit by the Governor. He came aboard, bearing gifts, for he believed that his visitors were Turks. Vasco da Gama, however, told him that he and his men were Christians, and had no dealings with the infidel Turk. Then, because the Governor had asked to see the weapons, Vasco da Gama ordered his men to show their arms, though he did not fire off any cannon. The Governor, now knowing with whom he was dealing, began to form in his mind a treacherous plot to attack the Portuguese unaware; when the Captain asked him for pilots, he gladly assented, and then, because it was night, took his leave.

Bacchus, observing all these things, determined to help the Moslems in their designs, for he had no desire that his worship should give way to that of the True God in India. Assuming the form of an old Moslem, a friend of the Governor's, he came to the Governor's palace, where he reported that the newcomers were piratical Christians, who had laid waste many towns along the coast. Then he advised the Governor to lay an ambush for the Captain when he and his men came ashore for water; and, if this did not succeed, to provide them with a pilot who would lead them to death. To all of this treachery the Moslems gladly agreed.

Mistrusting the tone of the Governor's reply to his request for a pilot, Vasco da Gama had his men in the boats arm themselves well. When they approached the shore, the Moslems received them with warlike shouts and a volley of arrows. But leaping ashore the Portuguese returned the fire so valiantly that the Moslems broke and scattered, running every way, unable to rally, while from the ships came a bombardment which reduced the town to rubble. Some of the Moslems tried to escape by sea, but the Portuguese round-shot sank their canoes, and they drowned. Then the Portuguese, unhampered by Moslem treachery, took on all the water they needed.

The pilot, however, was still meditating evil. With smooth words he described the land they were seeking, and the course thither, deceiving the Christians, who trusted him. He went on to say that not far off there was an island inhabited by Christians; and the Captain asked him to steer the vessel to that port. But the pilot lied; the island was all Moslem. He turned the ships toward it, but Venus, aware of his perfidy, sent foul winds. Unable to make head against them, the pilot suggested that they try for another port, where the inhabitants were partly Christian and partly Moslem. The Captain, believing his false report, headed for this new island, called Mombasa; but Venus, always careful, prevented his ships from crossing the bar into the harbor, and they anchored outside.

Boats put off from the city, with peaceful messages; but Bacchus had also come to the Governor of Mombasa, and he too planned nothing but treachery. What can a man do, when at sea the winds assail him, and on land he suffers from the deceit of mankind?

CANTO II: It was evening when the messengers from the city arrived, bearing an invitation from the King to cross the bar and anchor in the port, and an offer of the rich prizes of the East, jewels and spices. The Captain, however, was unwilling to attempt an entrance to the harbor in the dusk, and answered that next morning he would gladly come ashore and pay his respects to the ruler. When he asked whether there were any Christians in Mombasa, the emissaries falsely replied that there were many.

Some of Vasco da Gama's crew were condemned criminals, assigned to him for dangerous exploits. Two of these he detailed to go ashore, bearing gifts to the King, and to reconnoiter the city. They were well received, for the Mohammedans did not wish them to know of any treachery. In one house, Bacchus had gone so far as to set up an altar like a Christian shrine, where, in the appearance of a Christian, he made a show of adoring the True God. The scouts were completely deceived by this show of piety, and reported, when they returned to the ships in the morning, that there were Christians in the town.

Having heard their tale, and given the envoys from the King a hearty welcome, the Captain ordered the anchors hoisted, and, under topsails, the ships made their way toward the harbor mouth. Venus, however, had not been deceived; summoning the nymphs of the sea, she placed them before the ships, keeping them from entering the harbor. Though the sailors tugged at the sheets and swore, the ships could not cross the bar. The noise of the sailors at work, and the shouting of the sailing-master that he spied a rock ahead, so astonished the Moslems that they believed their plot had been discovered; and, like frogs leaping from a rock into a pool, they threw themselves from the ships and made off. The Captain ordered the ships to anchor in order to avoid the rocks. Now it became clear to him that the inability of the ships to enter the harbor was directly due to supernatural influence, protecting him from the wiles of the infidel; and he uttered a heartfelt prayer of thanks to Divine Providence, imploring that God would lead him to a safe haven.

Venus heard his prayer, and sped off to the seat of great Jupiter. Looking more beautiful than ever, she approached the Father of the Gods and, mingling her cajolery with tears, implored him to avert his wrath from her and her beloved Portuguese. Tenderly embracing her, Jupiter replied, "My child, have no fear, for I swear that your dear Portuguese will eclipse the glory of the Greeks and the Romans; their voyages will be more famous than those of Ulysses and Aeneas. Even Neptune shall tremble before the mighty Vasco da Gama, and the warlike Turk will bend in homage. These ports which now deny them water will one day pay them tribute. The Portuguese will capture and hold forever Goa, the Queen of the East; they will defeat the forces of Calicut and Cochin; all the oceans of the East, even as far as China, shall be their oceans, the infidel inhabitants their subjects. Even should all the heroes of the past be brought again to life, these could not match the valor of the Portuguese."

With this, he sent his messenger, Mercury, to lead Vasco da

Gama to a safe port. First he went to Malindi, where he inspired the people with a friendly curiosity about the Portuguese; thence he flew to Mombasa, where in a dream he appeared to the Captain, and directed him to flee from the treachery of the Moslems, who were again preparing an ambush, and to sail northward to Malindi, where he would have a kindly reception. Awakening from his dream, and knowing that he had received a divine command, the Captain ordered the anchors weighed and the sails hoisted. As the seamen hauled up the anchors, a number of small boats scattered from around the ships; they were filled with infidels, who had been trying to cut the cables so that the ships might drift into their clutches.

The next day they fell in with two small ships, one of which escaped; from the crew of the other they learned that the King of Malindi would help them on their way. They sailed on to the north, and before long they had reached the port.

The King of Malindi, knowing of the Portuguese valor, received them with presents of food, which da Gama repaid with beautiful cloth and coral. He sent ashore a messenger, who knew the language, to pay his formal compliments.

The messenger, inspired by Minerva, said to the King, "Your Majesty, your fame as a just and warlike monarch is known throughout the world. We have come here not as pirates, but in search of India, the emissaries of our own great and terrible ruler. We have been received elsewhere with treacherous attacks, but know that here there is no danger of such treatment. Surely we have been guided here by Heaven! My master sends me to pay his respects. It is not from any suspicion of you that he has not come to pay them in person, but because of our King's commands that he is never to leave his vessel in a harbor; and, as a king, you know the value of obedience to the royal order. He assures you that we will remember forever your magnanimity, and will, to the best of our power, repay it."

The King, struck with the power of a ruler who could command obedience so far from his palace, replied graciously,

"Your Captain's obedience is very praiseworthy; indeed, I take it as a sign not of bad manners, but of high loyalty and devotion to duty. I myself will visit your Captain tomorrow, for I am eager to see him and your ships. And if you require help, you shall have all you need."

At dawn of the next day, the King of Malindi and his court were rowed out to the ships in a magnificent barge. Vasco da Gama, showing his visitor every courtesy, met him in a small boat, to the sound of trumpets. Many canoes darted to and fro across the bay; from them came the sound of native flutes, while the Portuguese fleet saluted the monarch with cannon. Entering da Gama's boat, the King was rowed through the fleet, the salute thundering about him. Then he asked the Captain to tell him of the glorious exploits of the Portuguese.

Canto III: Vasco da Gama began, "O King, it hardly befits a man to tell of the glories of his own nation, lest he seem to boast. But I am ready to obey your command, and will try to be brief in my account. My own nation lies in Europe, the region between the Arctic and the Tropic of Cancer. Far in the north are the Scandinavians, inhabiting a land of ice and snow; eastward of them are the uncouth Muscovites, and south are the German tribes. Still to the south lies the Italian peninsula, the home of a brave race; beyond Italy is Gaul. In the southwest is the glory of Europe, the Iberian Peninsula, extending from the Pyrenees to the Gates of Hercules, and containing two great nations, the Spaniards and my own Portuguese.

"Afonso of Spain, the sixth King of that name, was a great warrior for our Faith. Henrique, the second son of a king of Hungary, came to him from a desire to win glory in that glorious war. As a reward, the King of Spain made him Lord of Portugal, and gave him his daughter, Teresa, as a bride. After service in the First Crusade under Godfrey of Bouillon, Henrique returned home, where he died, leaving one son, still a child.

"This boy, named Afonso for his grandfather, was disinherited when his mother remarried and took the land for herself, saying that it had been given as her dowry. The quarrel was decided at the battle of Guimaranes, won by Afonso, but the peace which followed was a short one; for the Castilians attacked him, and after being worsted in the first encounter, besieged him again at Guimaranes. He would have been defeated had not his countryman, Egas Moniz, advised him to secure his freedom by submission; Moniz, indeed, went to the Spanish King with such an offer, which was accepted, and the siege lifted.

"Afonso, however, refused to carry out his part of the agreement; and Moniz, unable to compel him to do so, went, with his wife and children, barefoot before the King, offering his life and theirs in payment for the broken promise. The King of Spain, touched by this magnanimity, forgave Moniz.

"Now Prince Afonso directed his attention to the Moors, who were in possession of the country to the south of the Tagus. He gave them battle at Ourique, though he was outnumbered by a hundred to one. As the dawn rose, Afonso saw a vision of Christ crucified, and the miracle so inspired the troops that they hailed him as their King. Then they fell upon the Moslems, who did not flee, but encountered them bravely. Many a great deed was done that day; but at the end, the Moors turned and ran, and our men gathered in much booty. As a token of the victory, Afonso took for his coat of arms five blue shields, one for each of the Moorish kings defeated, surrounding a cross, a token of the miracle which had presaged his victory.

"Thereafter he carried the war to the rest of Portugal, and eventually beyond its borders. But his impiety on making war against his mother was finally punished by his being captured at Badajoz; because age was now upon him, he handed over his kingdom to Sancho, his son, a valiant lad, who carried on the war.

"The Moslem, stung by the Portuguese victories, reacted by attacking Sancho at Santarém. Afonso, who was at Coimbra, heard of the siege, and joined forces with his son to win a glorious victory. He was not to enjoy his fame long, however, for within a short time he died.

"Sancho continued his attacks upon the infidel, intending to drive him out of the country. He was aided in this endeavor by a German fleet, which was returning from the Holy Land. After the capture of Silves, Sancho turned his forces to the east, where he subdued a part of Leon. It was his son, Afonso II, who won the battle of Alcácer do Sal, and proved himself a valiant warrior; but his grandson, Sancho II, was a mild and indolent man, who could not enforce his will as a king should, and who lost the kingdom to his brother, Afonso the Brave. It was he who finally won the whole country from the Moslems.

"His son, Diniz, showed himself a wise ruler, for he instituted laws and built cities, as a king should do when he has pacified his country. This was the age of peace and tranquility; and when Diniz died, he left his kingdom to his son, Afonso IV, whose daughter married the King of Castile.

"In Afonso's reign, the Saracens again attempted to overrun Spain. The King of Castile sent his wife to implore her father's help against them, and immediately he set forth. The two kings encountered the infidel at Tarifa, where, though greatly outnumbered, they routed their enemies with great slaughter.

"He returned to Portugal, hoping to enjoy a tranquil old age; but his own impetuous and cruel nature betrayed him. His son, Pedro, was of marriageable age, and many matches were proposed, but he would have none of them, for his heart was set on Inés de Castro, who returned his affection, and who had married him in secret, though she was not of royal birth. Thinking that if she were out of the way, he could marry his son as he chose, Afonso summoned her and her children before him, where, in spite of the mother's plea for herself and her children, he cruelly ordered them put to the sword. But he did not long outlive this evil act; and when his son succeeded to the throne, he had the murderers returned from Spain, whither they had fled for refuge, and put them all to death.

His unhappy life had made him a hard man, and the execution of justice, in other things than in this, was swift and sure.

"His son, Fernando, however, was as mild as his father was severe, and under his lax rule the Castilians invaded the land. You see what can happen to a country whose king is weak and easily led by impulse! He became enamored of Leonor, wife of Meneses, and the two eloped; and their adulterous passion was the cause of great suffering in Portugal!

CANTO IV: "As when in the dark night the wind roars and the tempest rages, men are frightened, but with the dawn they see before them the safety of harbor and the bright sunlight vanquishes their fears, so was it in Portugal when Fernando died, and João I, the heir of Pedro, became king. First the people rose against the friends of the late monarch and his mistress, and put them to death, not even the Bishop of Lisbon was spared. Then the forces of Castile, led by Juan I of that country, invaded the land, for he had married Beatriz, daughter of Fernando and Leonor, and through that alliance claimed Portugal for his own. From all the cities of Castile he drew his forces, intent on pressing his title to the throne. But João was quick to face him. At the conference of nobles which he assembled, some were faint-hearted, but not the noble Nuno Álvares Pereira! With his hand on his sword he exhorted them to remember the valor of their forefathers, how these had thrown back the infidel and the invading Spaniard, and had won the country for themselves. Inspired by his words, the nobles and the commons together gathered their arms, now covered with the rust of a long peace, and sallied forth to battle. The two forces met; the trumpets sounded the charge, and battle was joined. Nuno was like a lion in the battle, and João no less valiant. Fired with the ardor of those who defend their country against a foreigner, the Portuguese pressed the Spanish back, until João remained on the field of battle, victorious. Nuno, desirous of greater glory, pursued the Spanish into Andalusia, where, at Seville, they acknowledged the freedom of Portugal.

"But what warrior can rest, having no enemy to attack? The next exploit of João was to set out across the ocean, and to drive the Moslem from Ceuta, which lies across the Pillars of Hercules; his capture of the town protected the Peninsula from attacks across the Strait.

"Not long after this, he died, and was succeeded by his son Duarte, whose brother Fernando surrendered himself in order that his army might escape the Saracen. He could have won his own freedom by yielding Ceuta, but he chose a hero's captivity rather than a coward's freedom.

"His successor Afonso, and João, Afonso's son, conquered much of the African coast, and again subdued the proud Castilians. After Afonso's death, João sent a great expedition to seek the road to India. Past Naples and Sicily they traveled, past the mouth of the Nile, past Ethiopia, to the Persian Gulf. There, alas! they died, without having accomplished their mission, and far from their homes. Manoel, the successor to João, thought always of carrying out their great project. One night, in a dream, he felt himself carried high into the air, where he could see the whole world. In the East he saw two fountains, from which came two old men. One of them spoke: 'Manoel, now the time has come for you to send to our countries and secure tribute of us. I am Ganges, and my companion the Indus: we are the rivers of India.'

"When Manoel awoke, he summoned his council, of whom I was one, and, explaining his vision, he entrusted to me the task of realizing it. I gladly accepted the commission, and set about recruiting men and ships. Finally, all were gathered in the harbor of Lisbon, and, after we had visited the church of Belém to implore God's blessing on our venture, we embarked. All around us men and women were in tears, for they knew not whether they should ever see us again; our resolution was fixed. On the shore stood an old man, who lifted up his voice against our going: 'What folly, what lust for power is this, that leads so many to their destruction? The search for glory is called noble, but it leads only to the grave. Are there no nearer enemies, none of the cursed believers in Mahommed? Why will you seek enemies at the end of the earth, when they lie all about you? Why squander your substance in these journeys? Cursed be the man who first launched a ship!'

CANTO V: "But paying him no heed, we spread our sails with a cheer, and soon the heights of Cintra were far astern. This was the eighth day of July, 1497. Southward we sailed, past the dry hills of Morocco, past wooded Madeira, past Senegal, to the Canary Islands, which lie below the Tropic of Cancer. After taking on food and water, we continued our way southward, keeping the coast of Africa steadily to port: we passed Sierra Leone, the mouths of the mighty Niger and the Congo, and crossed the Equator. Here we saw for the first time the Southern Cross, and the Great Bear dropped into the sea astern. We passed through storms, which it would tire me to tell of, and you to hear. We saw the St. Elmo's fire, which gathers on the tips of the spars; and once we beheld the sea sucked up into a great waterspout. For five months we sailed so, until one morning a sailor called from the masthead, 'Land ho!' Ahead, to the east, lay a hilly country; I landed, and, taking a sight, found that we were south of the Tropic of Capricorn. The men who were with me found a black-skinned stranger, and brought him to me; he could not understand our speech, nor did he seem to recognize the samples of gold and spices which we showed him, but was glad of the presents which we gave. Next day he brought back several of his people, to whom we also made presents. One of my soldiers, Veloso, went to their village, but they attacked him, and he barely escaped with his life.

"For five more days we sailed along, the wind fair. One night a cloud appeared ahead, black as night, and took the form of a great giant, who spoke to us in a voice that might have come from the bottom of the sea. 'O daring people, now you have come to my place, to the seas which I have until now protected against all comers! To no mortal have its secrets yet been opened, and for him who learns them will be hardship, the storm and the tempest, wrecks, raids by the Kaffir—all these shall be my revenge! The next fleet that comes this way shall feel my power! And every year your ships shall know catastrophe, until you shall prefer death to the storms with which I shall visit you.'

"I asked the monster who he was, and he replied, 'I am Adamastor, the spirit of this cape which marks the southern tip of Africa. With my brothers, the Titans, I warred against great Jupiter, for I hoped to secure Thetis, Peleus' wife, for myself. But my brothers were defeated, and I was tricked by Doris, Thetis' mother, into believing that this rough and inhospitable cape was her daughter. In my despair, I prayed to be changed into these rocky headlands, and so now you behold me.'

"With these words, the figure disappeared, and I prayed that we might be spared the dangers it had foretold. In the morning, we beheld the cape and, shifting our course to the east, rounded it. We landed, and bartered with the kindly natives for fresh meat; but they know nothing of any country save their own.

"Leaving them, we sailed northward again for many days, the weather often foul, and made land again on the Feast of the Epiphany. From the natives we got meat and water, but no help in our quest, so that some of the men were in despair that we should ever reach India. But they were Portuguese, and remained faithful to me.

"From this river we set forth again, and headed well out to sea, for that is a dangerous coast; but, when we had passed it, we turned the ships' heads again toward land, hoping to meet with assistance. The next people we saw were also Negroes, but their language had a few words of Arabic. They were sailors, too, for we could see their ships. We were able to learn from these natives that ships like ours sailed across that sea, and returned to a land where men's skins, like ours, were white. Taking advantage of the good harbor, we careened our ships and cleaned their bottoms, grown foul from the long voyage, and were about to set forward again when we were attacked by a dreadful sickness, which rotted men's bodies. Some of our companions were buried there, and with the remainder put again to sea. We came first to Mozambique and then to Mombasa, homes of Moslems, whose perfidy you know. And now God has brought us to your fair land, and you have heard all my story."

The King praised da Gama's valor and prudence, and the assembled courtiers repeated to one another with amazement the portions of the story which most impressed them.

CANTO VI: For several days the King of Malindi entertained the Portuguese, until they were ready to depart. Then, with kindly words, he sent them on their way to India.

Bacchus, desperately trying to prevent them from attaining their goal, came to the sub-marine court of Neptune for assistance. The Sea-god called into council all the deities of his kingdom: Triton, with his rough, shaggy hide covered with shellfish; lovely Amphitrite and Leucothea. Bacchus, by permission of Neptune, addressed the throng: "You have seen," he began, "the audacity of these mortals, who venture where none have ventured before. They make themselves masters of the sea, and of the sea-gods! But it is not only for this reason that I have come. They wrong me, too, when they decide that they will assume the sovereignty over the lands which I won in the East. Jupiter and the Fates are resolved to give my lands to these puny mortals, and, therefore, I have come from Olympus, seeking help from you." Immediately Neptune sent a message to Aeolus, god of the Winds, ordering him to unbind the tempest, and to wreck the daring fleet.

It was calm on the surface of the ocean, though a storm was brewing far below.

The sailing-master, feeling the wind change, called all hands on deck to shorten sail. The wind struck with a roar, setting the ship on her beam-ends and ripping the sails out of the boltropes. With difficulty, they brought her to, and righted her; then the soldiers were set to the pumps, for she had taken much water. As they worked to save the ship, they could see that Paulo da Gama, the Captain's brother, was in worse plight than they, for his mainmast had gone by the board, and he could not control the vessel. Coelho, in the third ship, had got in all sail before the storm struck; but even so, under bare poles, he was making heavy weather of it.

Vasco da Gama, looking at the mountainous seas, prayed for deliverance to Heaven, but still the winds roared. Venus, from Olympus, looked down and saw her favorite almost overwhelmed by the ocean. Calling together her nymphs, she descended to the abode of the sea-gods, where by their amorous blandishments they induced these deities to leave off their wrath.

As dawn broke, the seas went down; and from the mainmast the lookout called that land was in sight. The pilot from Malindi, knowing that he had guided the vessel safely to port, told Vasco da Gama that the voyage was a success: the land before him was the port of Calicut, in India. Fortune favors the brave!

CANTO VII: O Lusitanians, though you are few in numbers, you are valiant for your Church! See how the Germans and the English, far in the north, make up their own kind of Christianity, and disrupt the peaceful world! And the French—have they carried out the promises of Charlemagne and St. Louis, to drive the infidel from the Holy Sepulchre? Have they leveled their cannon—new and terrible invention—against the Turk? Only the Portuguese remember their ancient fidelity.

But let us return to Vasco da Gama, now that he has come safely through the storm. As they came toward the coast, small fishing boats gave them direction to the harbor, which they entered. This land of Malabar, whose port is Calicut, is the richest of the provinces of India: richer even than the Punjab, Orissa, or Bengal, where the people worship the Ganges, for this is the kingdom which once belonged to Porus, the richest of all kings.

The Captain sent a messenger ashore to inform the ruler of his arrival; as he passed through the town, a great crowd of people surrounded him. One of these, a Moor named Mon-

saide, hailed him in Spanish. The messenger told him whence
and why they had come, and asked to be taken to the King's
palace. Because this lay a short distance from the town,
Monsaide asked the messenger to come to his house for some
refreshment. After a time, they returned to the ships, where
Vasco da Gama received them with courtesy. The Moor told
the Captain something of the country; how it had been divided
into several small states after its king, Perimal, had been converted to Islam, and had gone to Medina to live a life of devotion. The people, however, remained Hindus, and practised
the religion of their forefathers.

As he finished his account, a messenger came from the royal
court, bearing permission to land. Quickly Vasco da Gama was
rowed ashore, where he was received with honor by the Catual,
a high officer; together they set out for the King's court. On
the way, Monsaide acted as interpreter, pointing out to the
Captain the statues of the local gods, and the carvings depicting earlier history.

On their arrival at the palace, they were presented to the
venerable monarch of the place, the Samorin. Vasco da Gama,
seated beside him, made the offer of alliance sent by the King
of Portugal: to conclude a treaty permitting the Portuguese to
trade with Calicut, and to grant military aid to the Indians
against their enemies. The King answered that he was honored to receive ambassadors from so great and so distant a
nation as Portugal, but that he would have to consider their
offer and consult about it with the chief men of his kingdom.
In the meantime, he continued, Vasco da Gama and his men
were welcome to the land. They accepted his invitation, and
that night, Vasco da Gama and his men slept in the palace.

Next day, the Catual summoned Monsaide and asked him
to tell what he knew of the Portuguese. The Moor answered
that he knew little, except that they came from beyond Spain,
and had proved themselves valiant and resourceful in war. He
advised the Catual to visit the ships and to see for himself what
the Portuguese were like.

The Catual took his advice, and was received by Paulo da

Gama, who was surrounded by rich banners, bearing pictures of great historical scenes. The Indian took greater interest in these than in the discharge of the cannon with which he was saluted, and asked that they be explained to him.

CANTO VIII: Monsaide, as the Catual had requested, told him the meaning of the pictures on the banners. They were, he said, the heroes of Portuguese history, beginning with Lusus, from whom Lusitania takes its name, the son of Bacchus, who many ages before had come to what is now Portugal, because it was the fairest land under the sun. Other pictures showed Ulysses, building the first city in Portugal; Viriato, the shepherd, who defied the Roman legions; the glorious kings of Portugal. After many questions about these matters, the Catual, greatly struck by the nobility of his guests, quitted the ships and returned to the city.

Within the town, the soothsayers, consulting the oracles, found that the men who had come from afar were destined to become their rulers. Bacchus, too, brought his powers to bear, for he appeared to the chief priest three times in a vision, warning him to be on guard against the visitors. This evil old man called his leaders to a council, where they decided to spread the tale that the newcomers were pirates, not to be trusted. By means of bribery, they got the chiefs of the country on their side, and these influenced the King to believe the priests' lying stories.

The King summoned Vasco da Gama to an audience, where he advised the Captain to tell the truth, and all would be well. But he replied with spirit, denying that he was anything but a loyal subject of his King, sent to discover new countries, and that he asked only a token to carry home to his lord. The King believed him, thinking that his chiefs had misunderstood the Portuguese; in this, however, he was deceived —they were corrupt. He dismissed da Gama to return to his ships, so that the Portuguese might begin to trade.

The chiefs, however, put him off with fair words, even in the small matter of a boat to take him back to the fleet. They hoped that, before long, the pilgrim fleet would be returning from Mecca, and with these ships they would be able to defeat the Portuguese. Seeing that the chiefs were bent on doing him some mischief, the Captain, being a prudent man, began to prepare his defenses. They would not let him call upon the King again, but demanded that he order merchandise sent ashore. Da Gama was willing, if they could provide boats, for he did not choose to risk his own small-boats in this venture. Seeing through their evil plans, he dispatched a letter to his brother, asking that the merchandise be set ashore for trading and that some articles be included which he could use for ransom, if it were needed. When the goods were brought, he was released, for the chiefs considered that having put the goods ashore the Captain would probably decide to stay. He did so decide; but, once on shipboard, he knew better than to risk his neck by putting himself again into the power of those treacherous Moslems.

CANTO IX: Da Gama's men in charge of the trading had very bad luck, however, for the chiefs kept the traders of the city from doing any business with them. They still hoped for the arrival of the fleet from Jidda, the port for Mecca, and endeavored to keep the Portuguese in harbor until it should come. But God did not desert His people: He put it in the heart of the trusty Monsaide to tell da Gama of their wiles. He sent a message to his two agents to return aboard secretly, for the weather was fair for sailing.

When the two attempted to leave the city, however, they were seen and captured. Da Gama gave as good as he got, for he detained on the ships several wealthy natives, who had come for the purpose of selling gems. When the wives of these traders saw the fleet weighing anchor and setting sail, they hastened to the King, who immediately ordered the Portuguese agents freed, and sent back to their ships with an apology. On their arrival, the Captain set his hostages free, and sailed from the harbor, his ships loaded with the spices of the East. Much of his success was due to the fidelity of Monsaide, the Moor, who, by divine inspiration, asked to become a Christian, and was received into the Church.

Venus, anxious to help her favorite, decided to break the monotony of the long voyage home by preparing a magic island for the venturers. She called Cupid to her aid—for without him she could do little—and he set about preparing a great store of his arrows. These he shot at the Nereids of the sea, so that they were inflamed with desire. Venus led them to the island, where she told them how she had acted on the occasions when she had fallen in love; and they, under the spell of the gentle passion, listened eagerly.

Far at sea, the sailors saw the island, lovelier than any they had known before. Dropping anchor in the smooth bay, they went ashore to see what they might find—fruit, perhaps, or good water. Little did they know what was before them!

Some of the nymphs showed a little maidenly reserve, but most of them fled, hoping to be caught—and caught they were. Tethys herself, who had long been a foe to the Portuguese, yielded to da Gama, a conquered queen. She led him to the top of a fair mountain, from which, she said, she had been bidden to point out to him the lands the Portuguese should in the future travel, the seas they should sail.

Canto X: On this mountain stood a magnificent palace, erected by the magic of Venus. Here they took their ease, while a nymph sang the song of the future. Vasco da Gama, she revealed, was to be the first of many valorous travelers, who would open the East to commerce with Portugal. This was not to be accomplished without difficulty, for some would keep their word to the Portuguese, others would break it. After Vasco da Gama, the next voyager was to be Pacheco Pereira, who, after many battles with the Samorin, should impose his will upon the Indians, though his own death was not to be in battle, but by sickness, forgotten by the King whom he had helped to make great. After Pacheco, Francisco de Almeida and his son Lourenzo would defeat the Samorin in a naval battle, in which Lourenzo would show his valor by fighting on after a cannon ball had carried away his leg. What could the heroes of antiquity learn from such a one! But his death would be avenged by his father with his conquest of the city of Dabul and his defeat of the Egyptian sea-power in the bay of Diu. His memory will live forever, though he himself was fated to die at sea off the Cape of Good Hope.

And there are to be many more of these valiant conquerors: Lopes de Sequeira, who is to open the trade-route into Abyssinia; Henry, worthy descendant of the Navigator, the last conqueror of Malabar, whose conquest Vasco da Gama had begun; Mascarenhas and Vaz de Sampaio and his lieutenant, Heitor da Silva. All these, and many more like them, will win fame and glory for Portugal throughout the world.

Then the nymph showed Vasco da Gama a great plan of the starry heavens, with their spheres centered about the Earth, and a model of the Earth, with all its countries rightly displayed. Well did the Portuguese know of that, for they had traveled over much of it! She told them, also, of the life of the Apostle Thomas, who many centuries before had traveled to India, and there miraculously raised a young man from the dead. Struck with awe at the great saint's power, the King and many others were converted. But the Brahmins, hating the True Faith, contrived that Thomas should suffer martyrdom at the hands of the unbelievers.

And now, Muse, I take my leave. Let all men remember the bravery of the Portuguese who were the first to sail those far oceans. And so you, O King, remember them; consider how cheerfully they spend their lives for you and the glory of your country. May your Majesty so act that the foreigner may wonder at the Portuguese soldier, as one more used to commanding than to being commanded!

SUGGESTIONS FOR FURTHER READING

Translations:

By Leonard Bacon. New York, 1950

By William Atkinson. Penguin Books, 1952

Other Works:

See the notes to Bacon's translation and those to the edition (in Portuguese) by J. D. M. Ford, Cambridge, Mass., 1946

THE DIVINE
COMEDY

THE DIVINE COMEDY: INTRODUCTION

The English historian Carlyle wrote that the chief aim of man is not to die well, but to live nobly. For the poet of the eleventh-century *Song of Roland,* the implied contradiction would have had little meaning. But to Dante Alighieri, writing of life in the Italy of the late thirteenth century, the increasing conflict between homage to Caesar and obedience to God was all too apparent. Florence, the city of his birth, was at that time the heart of Western civilization; it was also one of the few remaining cities which were relatively free from the expanding clutch of despotism. Yet, in the ferment of national development, all of those things which had once meant order and security seemed to be dissolving into chaos.

When Dante was born, in 1265, Europe had already seen its first great revival of learning: the twelfth-century renaissance; it had known teachers such as Anselm, Lanfranc, and Abelard; important universities had arisen at Paris, Bologna, Oxford, and many other places; Aquinas was writing his *Summa,* and Roger Bacon was laying the foundation for modern philosophy. The security established by the Peace of Constance had led to new civic liberties undreamed of a century past, and the city-states, left to govern themselves, developed intense political sentiment, combining themselves in ever-shifting patterns of alliance, splitting within their own walls into aggressive factions, and engaging almost continually in war.

The Church, too, which had been for centuries a sort of international government, was torn by the doctrinal schisms of the schoolmen, the increasing complexity of canon law, the multiplicity and frequent corruption of its monastic orders, and the disputes, which became ever more serious, over the papal succession. In its power and wealth, it had widened its old position in the social hierarchy, taking for itself more and more secular and political power. This movement placed Rome in a new light; no longer was it merely a universal spiritual authority and arbitrator. It had itself become a sort of separate kingdom, making alliances, engaging in wars, and—which to Dante seemed worst of all—using its spiritual influence to aid its friends and threaten its enemies. No longer could Church and State work together in a relationship like that of Charlemagne and Turpin; warlike prelates there were, indeed, but they might more likely be found fighting against their king than killing Saracens. In the last decade of the thirteenth century, the Pope and the Holy Roman Emperor were at war; and Florence, more than most of the city-states, was torn asunder by the battles between papal Guelph and secular Ghibelline. Dante, who was not so constituted as to be a passive observer, was in the thick of the fight, as soldier, ambassador, counselor, and political pamphleteer. The Guelphs at first claimed his allegiance; but later division of this party into White and Black factions caused him to change sides shortly before 1300, when the Whites went over to the Emperor. Soon after, he, with other leaders of his persuasion, was exiled from Florence. Heartsick for his beloved city, disillusioned by his fellow-exiles, he wrote the *Divine Comedy* during those years of 1302-1321, when he had learned "how bitter is the taste of another's bread, how weary the path up and down another's stairs."

The *Divine Comedy* unites the highest religious and moral ideals with the stern lessons of personal experience and observation. Florence is Dante's "beloved nurse"; but so often has she been raped by the greedy that she is on the point of death. Never can her citizens settle down to enjoy, in peace, the blessings showered upon them by nature and by art, but they must pay with blood for new things—because they are new, not because they are better. Italy had indeed become a "dwelling of pain," where men changed loyalties "like the aged hag, who finds no rest upon her bed of down, but turns and turns again in hope to find ease." How, then, can the individual find security, in this world of violence and instability? There is, for Dante, but one answer: man must turn again to God. It is the nature of Fortune to change; let men leave to Fortune the goods which are hers, let him look beyond, secure in the Old Faith, to that which never can betray him. In God he can find again the order and love which have departed from earth.

The poem is a sustained allegory which moves from disorder to order, from eternal torment to eternal blessedness, from fear to perfect security. Dante's voyage is the longest in epic literature, and—especially for modern readers—one of the most meaningful. Its end is perhaps the greatest of all human objectives —the rediscovery of order, through Faith and Reason.

Dante's guide through Hell and Purgatory is the ancient poet Vergil. What more appropriate figure could have been selected for the allegorical representation? Although, as we learn from his discourse with the poet Statius, Vergil had led others to salvation, he, perfect in intellect and in secular virtue, yet lacking the Faith, had not received benefit from his own arguments. Not only does Dante borrow extensively from the *Aeneid* in his description of Hell, but his style shows marked influence of the Latin poet. His preference for simile over metaphor, his adaptation of the *bel stilo*, and his incorporation of classical, as well as scriptural, examples bear witness to his debt.

Vergil—or Reason—can guide Dante through the two lower realms; but after he has reached the Earthly Paradise at the summit of the Mount of Purgatory, Beatrice appears to him, a symbol of spirituality, and Vergil disappears. Beatrice Portinari was a real woman. Dante had met her when he was nine years old, and had seen her again nine years later. The number nine was to him a perfect mystical quantity—the number of the Trinity squared—and, after her death, immersed in the study of St. Augustine and other great theologians, he saw her as an embodiment of the Church itself. In the *Divine Comedy*, she represents Faith, or, as in the mystic pageant of Church history, Theology. But she lacks neither human charm nor individuality. Sometimes she smiles at Dante with the dazzling radiance of divine mystery; again, her smile is as he remembered it when she lived on earth. The "young girl" whom she reprimands him for following signifies a schismatic philosophy which once tempted him; yet the figure is a delightfully feminine one.

Dante places the date of his vision at 1300, "midway upon the pathway of our life" for him. This choice of time permits him to use the epic device of prophecy; it was also the date of the first papal Jubilee, and it marked the beginning of bloodshed between the Blacks and the Whites which led to Dante's own exile. Dante had seen much of treason and of false friendship, and he places "those who betrayed where a special trust had been given" in the lowest circle of Hell, with Satan the arch-traitor. Although the *Divine Comedy* takes place entirely outside the earth of men, the level of human experience is preserved, especially in the *Inferno*, through the use of examples drawn from Dante's own acquaintance. His figures of speech, too, are drawn from things that he has seen. Although, like most moralists of his period, he distrusts nature as corrupt, he was by no means immune to its beauty. True, man in the "state of nature" is infected with mortal sin; wild, rugged landscape, lacking the order of art, is to be found only in Hell. Yet those who were "sullen in God's sweet air, made lovely by the sun" are punished in a particularly degrading fashion.

The satire of the *Inferno* was a political bombshell. It spares no rank or calling. Three Popes of Dante's own period are in the circle where fraud is punished; Emperor Frederick II lies among the heretics; the hells of usury and barratry are filled with the names of Italy's great families. His own friend and teacher, Brunetto Latini, because of the irregularity of his sexual practices, suffers in the rain of fire. While both factions are represented, the opposition is in the majority; yet one receives the impression of scrupulous honesty. The way of a Christian in a corrupt and dying world is not easy; the vast majority of mankind must be lost. Dante's sympathy with men like Farinata, who have fallen through intellectual presumption, reminds one of Milton's heroic treatment of Satan. Thirst to know is the greatest of all temptations for him; the greatest reward in Paradise is the satisfaction of all doubt. The *Inferno* is the most powerful of the three books; for it is here that Dante's knowledge of human passion emerges with greatest force, in the brief, vivid life-stories told by the damned. The figures of Paolo and Francesca, Latini, Farinata, and Ugolino are unforgettable in their power.

To the subtle minds of the thirteenth century over-simplification was not permissible. Let the poet of the *Roland* say, "The Christians are right; the Pagans are wrong." But may there not be greater mercy in Heaven for a good pagan than for a bad Christian? And can mere observance of religious forms constitute Christian living? The answers to such questions require subtlety and qualification, particularly at a time when every man's loyalty must be, to some extent, divided between opposing demands of Church and State. The unified philosophy of the *Divine Comedy* is reached partly by the examination of carefully selected individual cases. Can a priest break his vows, if he is assured first by his spiritual superior that his lapse will be forgiven and penance waived by the Church? What of an emperor who abandons the responsibilities of his birth, fearing that he may be forced into committing evil? On such problems, Dante gives moral judgment.

Still other questions are resolved in the "dialogues" which the narrator holds with Vergil, Beatrice, and the spirits of the departed. Some of these passages are rather long and difficult to understand, for Dante never leaves a problem unsolved or half-explained. In examining the Christian virtues, definitions gradually emerge, based upon a synthesis of many philosophies. In the effort to reconcile religion and science, a coherent theory of the structure of the universe is built which satisfies the requirements of both, as Dante knew them. Since most of this discourse takes place in the last two books, a certain amount of speed and excitement must be sacrificed; the problems of construction and description are also more difficult. Hence, the *Inferno* is the most popular book, and readers who have not gone beyond it have accused Dante of morbidity, and have wondered how anyone could call the poem a "comedy." Dante referred to the work as a comedy, because it ended, not in death, but in triumph; a greater victory than the attainment of the Beatific Vision in the *Paradiso* is difficult to imagine.

The universe of the *Divine Comedy* is, above all things, a universe of order. Even Hell is contained in and regulated by the greater order of God's eternal Now, in which all events are foreseen, but in which there is room for freedom of the will. Hell approaches most nearly to conditions of chaos, with its violent winds, earthquakes, and blasts of sudden fire; yet each region has its strict boundaries, so that each shade must be certain of receiving the punishment most proper to its sin. The landscape of Purgatory, too, is rugged; but here is an ordered, controlled ruggedness—a place for pain, but not for eternal pain. We find here, too, some influence of the beauty of conscious art; the terrace of pride is enriched by carvings surpassing any human sculpture, and suffering is relieved by song. On the mountain there is also the order of day and night, and the rest which comes with night. The sun and the stars are more brilliant here. In Paradise, all is pure order and beauty. Although all are equally happy, according to the capacity of each, yet there is a hierarchy of blessedness. Even this difference in degree brings joy, however, for "in His will we find our peace." Another medieval poem, *Pearl*, interprets the scriptural prophecy that "the last shall be first," by presenting a dead infant as a queen in Heaven, exalted over the greatest saints. In Dante's Heaven, the words are differently construed; here, as in the child's ideal game, everyone is "first," including the "last." The Heavenly Rose is in one dimension, like the Round Table of King Arthur, indicating brotherly equality under God; some assume places of greater eminence, so that Dante's human mind may grasp the analogy to "degree" on earth. Actually, none of the blessed have any "place," all share in one Paradise, according as their love makes them capable of receiving that of God. The idea has never been explored with such subtlety and imagination, and never, even in *Paradise Lost,* has the ineffable come so near expression.

Although Dante loved freedom, his was no ideal of "democracy." Although all men were brothers through their common descent and redemption, this equality was in spiritual, not temporal things. Unlike the English preacher John Ball and his followers, Dante did not use the argument of our universal parenthood to advocate that all goods should be held in common, or that no man should be another's master. Cacciaguida, speaking of the golden age of Florence, praises the days when each man did with joy the work appointed to him, and when over-reaching ambition and pride did not stain the city with the blood of her children. In the old order there was peace; drastic changes had brought war. Let the Church return to its former position, supreme in things of the spirit, but subordinate to the prince in temporal matters. Charles Martel, who was placed by one medieval writer in the flames of Hell, because he taxed the Church to pay the army, is seen by Dante in the Sphere of Venus—a spirit whose great love for his fellows might have prevented much strife, had he lived longer. The spirits with whom Dante speaks are well-known men; he learns in Paradise that it had been so ordered in advance, since no man would listen to his story if he named men of little renown.

In the entire work not one obscure serf or poor housewife is mentioned by name, even though the story of such a one might have been rich in human interest. Nor, in his chastisement of worldly prelates, does he mention their treatment of their tenants, although these prelates were infamous among the common people as the most rapacious of landlords. Usury, which, with the rise of capitalism, had been an ever-increasing problem to orthodox moralists, is severely punished in Hell; the charging of excessive rents is not mentioned. Dante, himself a man of good birth and considerable influence, spoke to men of his own class, to whom, as he had learned from his own experience, fell the greatest temptation. Furthermore, although the standard of literacy in Florence was higher than that of other medieval cities, the serf, if he could read at all, would have been incapable of understanding Dante's purpose. The peasant class was an inert group; revolts were rare and sporadic. Dante wanted to talk to the men who would, and should, change things.

In expressing these difficult ideas, Dante, like many other writers of his period, relies greatly on the use of emblem and symbol. In the traditional colors of liturgical ornament, the real and mythological animals of the bestiary and the family crest, the mystic numbers of theology, the vivid, well-known figures of the scriptures and classical mythology, and the signs and symbols of astrology, he finds abundant material for his purposes—material, furthermore, with which every educated person of his day was thoroughly familiar. Some of these figures are more difficult for the modern reader; the seven stars of the Southern Hemisphere and the seven nymphs who dance beside the chariot of Holy Church in the Mystic Procession may not be recognized as representing the cardinal and theological virtues, nor is it at once apparent that the two-fold animal nature of the Gryphon portrays the two-fold nature of Christ, as God and Man. The identities of the elders, too, seem confusing to the reader who is not thoroughly familiar with Revelation. As in any complex allegorical work, considerable knowledge must be brought to the reading before the power of the symbolism is apparent. Identification of the indirectly described historical figures, which was relatively simple to Dante's original audience, is a more difficult matter, over which scholars of Romance philology still wrinkle their brows.

Because numbers—especially the mystic quantities of three, seven, and nine—were so significant to Dante, the *Divine Comedy* itself is organized around them. There are three books, each consisting of thirty-three cantos, with one introductory canto to the first—a total of one hundred cantos. The imaginary date fixed for the narrative—1300—is meaningful in this sense, as well as in the ways mentioned above. The three steps of Purgatory, the triple ring of the Beatific Vision, the seven circles of Hell and the seven terraces of Purgatory, the single and double horns of the beasts of the chariot in the masque of theology—all these have a special significance which should not be ignored by any student of the poem.

The metrical structure of the *Divine Comedy* is elaborately planned to prevent any miscopying or partial suppression. Like the "rime royal" of Chaucer's *Troilus and Criseyde*, Dante's terza rima is an unbreakable meter; that is, it is very nearly impossible to alter a line without an obvious break in the structure. Terza rima rhymes *aba bcb cdc* . . . each group of three lines being linked to the preceding and following groups by the rhyme of the middle line in the first with the first and third lines of the next. Dante also provided against the excision of any group of lines within a canto by using exactly 136 lines to each: forty-five groups of three lines plus an end-line. The *Inferno* has thirty-four cantos, the other two, thirty-three each; and, finally, each of the three parts ends with the word *stelle*, stars. In a period when books were subject to the frequent errors of the scribe, or to capricious censorship by anyone copying them, the value of such a device is apparent.

Dante's love of simile has been mentioned, as part of his heritage from the classics. One of his most powerful techniques, giving roots to the mystic nature of his symbolism, is the sensitive use of simile borrowed from everyday life. Ugolino gnaws the head of his enemy with "teeth as strong as those of any dog chewing a bone." Matilda, dragging Dante through Lethe, speeds over the water "like a shuttle." The holes in which those who have practised simony are punished are compared to the baptismal font at St. John's in Florence. Metaphor is often used in a similar manner, reinforcing the simile; one of the spirits, in surprise at seeing Dante's shadow, "sharpens" his eyebrows at him. By such devices, as by the constant reference to contemporary history and personalities, Dante keeps our own world within call, giving his poem more immediacy than Milton's, and providing that concreteness on two levels of narrative, the lack of which removes Spenser's *Faerie Queene* from the realm of epic poetry. The use of the first person singular in narration, unique in epic poetry, makes the vast realms of the voyage in the *Divine Comedy* seem even less remote from the reader. Milton's adventure was in the past;

Dante's journey of discovery seems to have happened immediately before we read about it, and he makes us feel, as Milton does not, that the events described are going on now, as we read. We, too, may share in his vision and his victory.

THE DIVINE COMEDY: THE STORY

I. Inferno

CANTO I: *Vergil Finds and Rescues Dante*

> Midway upon the journey of our life
> I found myself within a forest dark
> For the straightforward pathway had been lost. . . .
> I cannot well repeat how there I entered
> So full was I of slumber at the moment
> In which I had abandoned the true way.[1]

Looking upward, I beheld a mountain, whose shoulders were still bathed in the light of the sun. I climbed it with great pain and difficulty; not only did the steepness of the hill impede my steps, but also the three beasts: a panther, the type of worldly pleasure and of my native city, Florence; a lion, emblem of ambition and of France; and a she-wolf, the symbol of avarice and the Papal Court. Alone, and threatened by these, I turned to flee.

Yet there came to me a voice, speaking in the language of reason, the voice of him who sang the song of Anchises' son, who came from Troy after its destruction. My master, Vergil, told me that I must follow another course if I meant to escape the wolf, for she was destined to beset my present way until the Hound should strike her dead. It would be best for me to follow him through the realms where the lamentations of the lost rise up unceasingly; thence to that hill where those in the fire are happy, because they hope to come finally to the place

[1] The verse-passages quoted in this summary of the *Divine Comedy* are taken from the translation by Henry Wadsworth Longfellow (1867).

of eternal love. Beyond that, however, a worthier soul must
lead me, for my guide might not pass the gate of the Eternal
City. Willingly I followed his steps.

Canto II: *Beatrice Appeals to Vergil*

As the day retired, I armed myself for the lonely journey.
O ye Muses, consider whether my courage shall be great
enough for this high endeavor! I am not Paul, nor am I Aeneas;
yet fettered though I am, let me begin, upon that dusky slope
whose way is death.

My guide reproached me for cowardice when I uttered my
fears; then he told me how it chanced that he had come to help
me. A saintly lady had called to him, asking him to help one
dear to her, though not dear to Fortune, who had gone astray
upon the hillside.

> "Beatrice am I, who do bid thee go;
> I come from there, where I would fain return;
> Love moved me, which compelleth me to speak."

Our Lady of Pity, seeing how I was astray, had sent Lucia to
ask Beatrice to help me, who had loved her always. The news
so heartened me that I turned to my guide,

> "Now go, for one sole will is in us both,
> Thou Leader, and thou Lord, and Master Thou."
> Thus said I to him; and when he had moved,
> I entered on the steep and savage way."

Canto III: *The Entrance Through the Gate of Lost Hope*

> "Through me the way is to the city dolent;
> Through me the way is to eternal dole;
> Through me the way among the people lost.
> Justice incited my sublime Creator;
> Created me divine Omnipotence,
> The highest wisdom and the primal Love.
> Before me there were no created things,
> Only eterne, and I eternal last.
> All hope abandon, ye who enter in!"

These words I beheld written upon a gate; and I said, "Master, the meaning of this is terrible to me."

"These souls," he answered, "cry to one another the lack of intellect's true insight. Here we must proceed without fear."

Placing his hand in mine, he led me to unknown things. Here, sighs, wails, and shrieks of every kind rent the damned air. A dreadful din, in every tongue, bound me in terror. My master reassured me, telling me that these shrieking ones were they who "lived their lives without either praise or blame," keeping unwilling company with those angels who had dared neither to stand for their God nor to rebel against Him, but were for themselves alone. Here I saw Pope Celestine V, he who made the great refusal of his temporal responsibility. Never have these cowards and vacillators dared to live; so, forever, they covet eternal death. But for death they never may hope, because they are of that accursed unliving-undying breed whom the world has forgotten, and will forget; both mercy and justice scorn them eternally. "We never shall trouble to discuss these creatures!" said my guide; "Look, and pass them by." As I gazed, I saw a vast multitude following a ragged banner, which moved swiftly and without purpose, as if it disdained repose. Naked they were, and plagued incessantly by stinging flies, so that their faces streamed blood and tears.

Turning to look beyond, I saw a great river, whose banks were thronged with souls; as Vergil later explained to me, it was the pressure of divine justice that caused them to thrust forward with such seeming eagerness. Upon the brink of the flood, we met an ancient man with flowing white hair, who cried out to the guilty souls to beware, and ordered me, a living man, to fly at once from those already dead. But Vergil quieted his rage; since he could do nothing to harm us, knowing us to be protected by a greater power, he bent his flaming eyes upon his passengers. Some wept, some cursed; but the demon ferryman herded them all together, beating the laggards with his oar, and they withdrew from that accursed shore which awaits every man who fears not God.

"Here all souls must come who die under the wrath of God," said my mentor, "and when Charon complained of you, saying that you should return by another road, to be ferried by a lighter bark, well should you understand his meaning!"

At this, the dread earth heaved itself in a gigantic spasm, giving forth a blast of air that lit the sky with a vermilion glow. My senses left me, and I fell to the ground.

CANTO IV: The First Circle: *Limbo, Home of the Virtuous Unbelievers*

A clap of thunder awoke me; I found myself on the other bank of dismal Acheron. Vergil bade me follow him into the dreadful gulf of Hell; his face was pale with compassion, which I at first believed to be fear. Reassuring me, he led me into the topmost circle. Here I heard no shrieks of lamentation, but only sighs, as of men who are sad, but suffer not.

"Do you not ask me," said my guide, "who these spirits are. They are those of sinless men, whose virtue, nevertheless, does not suffice, for they never received baptism. I am one of these who, living before the time of Christ, could never worthily adore their God. The Son of God, crowned with a victorious diadem, came here once, surrounded by a great light, and led forth the souls of Adam, Abel, the patriarchs, and many others. Before that time no human spirit had been saved."

We had come but a short distance, when I saw a little point of brilliance; here dwelt those whose fame on earth had earned them such grace as to be marked out from the other suspended shades. Homer came forth to greet us, bearing a great sword, and with him were Horace, Ovid, and Lucan. They greeted my master with warmth, and I was allowed to walk a way with them and hear their conversation. We passed before a lofty, seven-walled citadel, moated by a river, which we crossed over, as if we were upon dry land. Within the seventh gate there was a fresh, green meadow. There I saw majestic spirits, whom to have seen were glory in itself. Plato was there, and Socrates also, Hector, Aeneas, Caesar in armor, and many more; my words are not sufficient for my theme. My guide and

I were once more alone. My leader led me from that place by another road, and then we came to where all light was gone.

Canto V: Second Circle: *Francesca da Rimini*

Between the first circle and the second sits the dread judge Minos. When a doomed soul comes before him, all transgressions are made known, and the demon coils his tail about himself, each turn denoting an added degree of punishment; each spirit speaks, hears its fate, and then is hurled below. Passing Minos, we came to a region of deafening winds, bellowing like the sea, wherein are blown about the shades of the incontinent.

> The infernal hurricane that never rests
> Hurries the spirits onward in its rapine;
> Whirling them round, and smiting, it molests them. . . .
> I understood that to such a torment
> The carnal malefactors were condemned,
> Who reason subjugate to appetite.
> And as the wings of starlings bear them on
> In the cold season in large band and full,
> So doth that blast the spirits maledict;
> It hither, thither, downward, upward drives them;
> No hope doth comfort them forevermore,
> Not of repose, but even of lesser pain.

Cleopatra, Helen, Paris, and Tristan passed us, with many more of antique fame; I nearly swooned from pity. I spoke with the ghosts of Paolo and Francesca, who paused for a moment at my request to tell us of their love. One day, while reading the romance of Launcelot, as she told me, Paolo had kissed her; that day they had read no further, and love at last led them to one death. Paolo's passionate weeping as Francesca told her tale overmastered me, and I fell swooning to earth.

Canto VI: Third Circle: *The Gluttonous*

When I recovered, new torments met my eyes, for I was come to the circle of eternal rain, where, upon the muddy, putrid ground, Cerberus, the three-headed monster, barks like a hound and tears the sinners with his teeth and claws. He would have served us in like manner, but that my master, picking up some earth, stopped his jaws with it, and we passed on unharmed. One shade arose with pain, to address me. His name, he said was Ciacco, a Florentine, who suffered there for the sin of gluttony; he prophesied that, after years of bloodshed, within three years the conquerors of my city should fall, the present faction be bitterly oppressed. Asking after others of my acquaintance, I learned that they were in deepest hell; Ciacco once more fell prone in the filth. Greatly moved, I asked my guide whether, after the judgment, the pangs of Hell should lessen or increase.

"True perfection has the greatest sense of pleasure, and hence, of pain"; he answered, "and these unfortunate souls will then be nearer perfection than now." Passing to that point where one descends below, we encountered Plutus, the accursed wolf in Hell.

CANTO VII: Fourth Circle: *Spendthrifts and Misers*

> "Papé Satàn, Papé Satàn, Aleppe!"
> Thus Plutus with his clucking voice began
> And that benignant Sage, who all things knew,
> Said, to encourage me, "Let not thy fear
> Harm thee; for any power that he may have
> Shall not prevent thy going down this crag."
> Then he turned round unto that bloated lip,
> And said, "Be silent, thou accursèd wolf;
> Consume within thyself with thine own rage."

With these words, we went down into the fourth abyss. Upon both sides of the ring, a screaming throng were rolling great weights toward one another; they came together with a shock, screaming, on the one side, "Why do you squander?" and, on the other, "Why do you hoard?" Then they turned, until, on the opposite side of the ring, they crashed together again. Among them I saw clerks, Popes, and Cardinals, tonsured men, who sinned more than most in their avarice. Here Vergil told me of Fortune, whose rule over material things is confirmed in Heaven, where with God's other angels she turns her wheel, moved by no human plaints, nor by those who wrongly abuse her for changing, whose very nature is change. We crossed the circle to the farther bank, passing on the way a boiling well, whose waters descend the precipice and spread into the marsh of Styx, the river of Sorrow. Descending the crag, we came into the fifth circle of Hell, where the sin of wrath is punished.

> Said my good master; "Son, thou now beholdest
> The souls of those whom anger overcame;
> And likewise I would have thee know for certain
> Beneath the water people are who sigh
> And make this water bubble at the surface,
> As the eye tells thee wheresoe'er it turns.
> Fixed in the mire they say, 'We sullen were
> In the sweet air, by which the sun is gladdened,
> Bearing within ourselves the sluggish reek;
> Now we are sullen in this sable mire.'
> This hymn do they keep gurgling in their throats,
> For with unbroken words they cannot say it."
> Thus we went circling round the filthy fen
> With eyes turned unto those who gorge the mire;
> Unto the foot of a tower we came at last.

Canto VIII: Fifth Circle: *The Angry*

Upon this tower were two signal-lights, answered by another far across the stream. Vergil compelled Phlegyas to row us across, and the boat seemed overladen by my mortal weight. One of the muddy souls arose to speak with me, but I, recognizing him, cursed him without pity; I was pleased when the others who were near him, crying, "At Filippo Argenti!" until he began to tear himself with his teeth and nails. We left him there, and now we could see the dread citadel of Dis, its mosques reddened by the fire of God's wrath.

At the city's iron gates, the cursed guardians, the fallen

angels, threatened my master and me, shouting, "Who comes to the land of the dead without feeling death?" He left me, terrified, while he went forth to hold parley with them. I could not hear his arguments, but soon, fleeing from him, they rushed back into the city and closed the gates in his face. He returned with troubled brow, but cheered me, saying that, even now, one was coming to open the gates for us.

Canto IX: *The Walls of Dis*

Once before, summoned by the witch Erictho, Vergil said, he had made this deadly journey, to summon up a soul from the circle of Judas; therefore, he knew the way. But just then, I saw arise over the wall the three dreadful Furies, who called up Medusa, that I might be forever lost. Vergil covered my eyes, saving me from certain death. Now there came over the water a sound as of thunder, and I saw one who walked dry shod over the Styx toward us—certain I was that he must come from Heaven. With scornful words, he caused the gates to be opened, then retreated, speaking no word to us, as one lost in graver cares than these.

Stepping within, I saw a wide plain covered with tombs, which glowed with wrathful fire.

Canto X: Sixth Circle: *Heresiarchs*

They were unsealed, although my leader told me that at the time of judgment, they should be closed forever upon the heresiarchs, who had led men from the faith, and their followers.

But now there came a voice from one of the tombs; Farinata, rising as if in disdain of Hell and all its torments, addressed me from his grave. Eyeing me scornfully, he asked of my ancestry, which I did not conceal; all, he said, had been bitter enemies to himself and his fathers, who had driven them forth twice in exile. "But they returned," I replied, "which is an art not so well learned by your faction!"

He answered, "If it is true that the Ghibellines have learned that art wrongly, yet, before she who reigneth here has fifty times rekindled her face, they must learn how heavy that art is of which you speak." He told me that once, alone, he had stood against the destruction of Florence, and, at my request, told me that, although the doomed souls had no knowledge of the present state of living men, they were still allowed imperfect glimpses of the future, which, however, should cease with all knowledge after the gates of the future should be closed upon them. Downcast by his dire prophecy, I returned to my guide, who promised me that all doubt should be cleared from me when I should stand before the radiance of "her whose lovely eyes can perceive all things."

CANTO XI: Seventh Circle: *The Three Kinds of Fraud*

> Upon the margin of a lofty bank
> Which great rocks broken in a circle made,
> We came upon a still more cruel throng;
> And there, by reason of the horrible
> Excess of stench, the deep abyss throws out,
> We drew ourselves aside behind the cover
> Of a great tomb, whereon I saw a writing,
> Which said, "Pope Anastasius I hold,
> Whom out of the right way Photinus drew."

Here we were forced to pause, to grow used to the sickening stench from below; and to occupy the time, my guide told me who lay in this circle: the fraudulent, separated into three groups. In the first inner circle lie the violent; violence is three-fold, so the ring is correspondingly divided, to punish those who sinned, respectively, against their God, themselves, or their fellow men. Hence, in the first round are murderers, thieves, and other such spoilers; in the second are those who despised God and His gifts—perverts, blasphemers, and scorn-ers of the Deity. In the next circle below are the fraudulent who have sinned where no special trust was placed—hypo-crites, sorcerers, liars, simoniacs and such filth. In the lowest circle of all are the traitors, for they have betrayed both natural affection and human confidence. I asked my guide why usury is so deep an offense against God; and he replied that, since man must, according to Genesis, make his way by industry or art, the usurer, setting his hope for wealth elsewhere, misuses both.

CANTO XII: Seventh Circle, First Ring: *Punishments of the Violent*

Terrible to look upon was the rugged descent between the rocks, and, at our place of passage, the dreadful Minotaur lay, biting himself in his wrath. Deliberately enraging the monster, my guide distracted his notice from our passage. As we walked over the shattered cliffs, Vergil told me that this, with many parts of lower Hell, fell into ruin when Christ had taken away his great burden from the topmost ring of Dis. Below me, there was a great moat, curved like a bow; between it and the base of the cliff galloped centaurs, armed with bows and arrows. Here lay Alexander and Dionysius, the scourge of Sicily, black-haired Azzolino, and Obizzo of Este, slain by his stepson. Telling Chiron, chief of the centaurs, of our mission, Vergil secured Nessus as our guide, and, thus escorted, we moved along the margin of the crimson flood, in which the souls of tyrants and murderers boiled. As we walked, the stream became shallower, until at last, it covered only the feet of the victims; beyond, the river's bed sloped downward again, deepening to join the place of tyrants. Nessus now returned across the ford, leaving us in a strange, dark wood.

CANTO XIII: Seventh Circle, Second Ring: *The Suicides*

The branches of the trees here were black, the limbs gnarled, and the thorns of the barren limbs laden with poison. Here the loathsome Harpies nest; they have human necks and faces, great wings, huge feathered bellies, and taloned feet. Hearing cries within the wood, I believed that there must be people hiding from us; Vergil told me to break a branch from one of the trees and resolve my doubts. No sooner did I obey than the tree began to cry out in pain, blood and words streaming together from the wound that I had made. Once, he said, he had been steward to Frederick, but an evil courtesan had turned away the prince's heart, and he had sought escape from shame in self-slaughter; so he, the just one, was unjust at last to himself. His condemned soul, falling hither, germinated and became a tree; the Harpies, feeding upon this grim foliage, gave pain, as well as an outlet for its expression. Since these shades had put off their bodies, they might never, he said, wear them again, but, at the judgment, each must bring his body here, where it should hang forever from the plant belonging to the soul that had wronged it. Suddenly, two naked men burst through the wood, pursued by gigantic black bitches; one of them tried to hide behind a tree, but the hounds found him out, and tore both him and his shelter to pieces.

"What good does it do you, Jacomo da Sant' Andrea," cried the mutilated bush, "thus to make a screen of me? How am I to blame for your sinful life?" At its request, we gathered up its severed branches, and it said that, as a man, it had been a Florentine.

CANTO XIV: Seventh Circle, Third Ring: *The Violent Against God*

Going on to the boundary which divides the second round from the third, we came to a barren plain of arid, burning sand, over which fell a rain of fiery flakes. Over the desolate ground ran a multitude of souls; others lay still in their torment, although their groans were louder than the laments of those who ran. One of these, Capaneus, who had been one of the Seven against Thebes, bore the torment with unflinching courage, but increased his own pain by his rage against his god.

We came on to a stream, which ran between stony banks, so red that even now it makes me tremble to think of it. Vergil told me that, within Mount Ida, there stands an ancient man, with head of gold, arms and breast of silver, trunk of brass, and legs of iron, save for his right foot, which is formed of clay. And from a mighty cleft, which penetrates every part of his body save the head, gush forth tears, which, collected, enter the cavern and, running to this vale, form the rivers of Hell—

Styx, Acheron, and Phlegethon, at which last we were then
looking, as it ran downward to form Cocytus. Lethe, he told
me, was outside Hell, for in it those are permitted to wash who
have repented of their sin. Though we had traveled far, turning always to the left, we had not completely encompassed any
circle, but had made our way downward. He warned me to
follow him closely, since only at the margins of the river were
the fiery sparks quenched, by a mist that protected the bank.

CANTO XV: Seventh Circle, Third Ring: *The Violent Against
Nature*

> Now were we from the forest so remote
> I could not have discovered where it was,
> Even if backward I had turned myself,
> When we a company of shades encountered,
> Who came beside the dike, and every one
> Gazed at us, as at evening we are wont
> To eye each other under a new moon,
> And so towards us sharpened they their brows
> As an old tailor at the needle's eye.

One of them, coming closer, seized my garment and cried out
in joy. Not even the crusting of his seared face could have kept
me from recognizing my teacher and friend.

"Do not be annoyed, my son," he said to me, "if Brunetto
Latini will turn back to walk with you a while." I would gladly
have sat with him, but learned that, should any of these souls
pause for rest, they must then lie a hundred years without
turning for relief. "Had I lived longer," he said, "I might have
comforted you a little in your work. But the Florentines will,
for your good deeds, become your enemies. Yet it were not
fitting for the fig to bear among the sour sorb trees." He bade
me see that I followed my star and cleanse myself of the foul
ways of my native city. Though I should be an exile, he said,
still my future was to be so honorable that both factions should
one day seek my support in vain.

"Had I my wish," I said, "you would not yet have taken leave of the race of men. For I remember well, and it strikes me to the heart, how kind and fatherly was your manner as you spoke to me of man's eternal goal, when you were on earth. How well I prize your teachings should be evident to you now." Seeing again what lay beyond earthly life, I was prepared for any possible blow of Fortune; her wages were no longer precious to me.

My old teacher went on to describe several of his more famous companions in damnation, but was interrupted by a new smoke which signaled the arrival of men with whom he might not travel. Into my care he commended his *Tesoro,* in which his name lives on. Turning away, he ran to join his companions.

CANTO XVI: Seventh Circle, Third Ring: *The Three Sinners*

We came then to a place where the crimson river poured down in a mighty cataract. From the horrid rain came a company of three spirits, who called to me as a Florentine. They never ceased their turning, for they formed themselves into a rolling wheel, turning their faces always toward me. Willingly I would have thrown myself among them, but the fire prevented me. They were Guido Guerra, Aldobrandi, and Jacopo Rusticucci, who in life had been powerful Guelphs, but who were condemned for their sins to eternal punishment. Swiftly they vanished, begging me to speak of them in the world above; but there was no time for a reply, not even for an Amen. Therefore my guide thought it best to continue our journey. I unfastened from my waist the knotted cord with which I had intended to snare the spotted leopard and gave it to my master, as he bade me. He turned to the right and cast it downward into the abyss.

CANTO XVII: *Downward to Malebolge*

Up from the depths there came a shape ghastly enough to freeze the most courageous heart. He had a face like a proper man, mild of aspect, but all the rest was fashioned like a serpent, spotted in many fantastic hues, with two great, shaggy paws, broad wings, and an enormous tail, tipped with a venomous fork.

While my guide parleyed with this dreadful beast, he sent me to converse with some people sitting near by.

> Out of their eyes was gushing forth their woe;
> This way, that way, they helped them with their hands
> Now from the flames, and now from the hot soil.
> Not otherwise in summer do the dogs
> Now with the foot, now with the muzzle, when
> By fleas, or flies, or gadflies they are bitten. . . .
> Not one of them I knew, but I perceived
> That from the neck of each there hung a pouch. . . .

The pouches were the symbols of usury and the love of money, the sins to which these damned souls had devoted themselves upon the earth; always they kept their eyes fixed upon the pouches, for in them they had kept their evil gains; and for a punishment they were condemned to wear them forever.

When I returned to my guide, he had already seated himself upon the back of the monster. As he instructed me, I mounted in front, so that the lashing tail might not injure me, and we began the horrifying descent. When at last Geryon set us down at the bottom, I had seen enough circling horror to rob me of speech and movement; unburdened of his load, the creature fled, and I felt able to follow my Guide.

CANTO XVIII: Eighth Circle: *Seducers and Flatterers*

The place through which we went was called Malebolge—"evil pouches," indeed; it is divided into ten concentric valleys, like rings of moats around a castle, and springing from the cliffs were bridges connecting them with the center, like the spokes of a wheel. Upon the right, I saw a troop of horned demons, who flogged their victims with heavy scourges to urge them on. I recognized one of them—Venedico Caccianimico—who responded to my greeting and told me, although it shamed him to do so, that it was he who brought Ghisola to give herself to the marquis' will, and that there were many Bolognese whose greedy hearts had brought them to this place. "Move along, pander!" cried the demon who pursued him; "there are no women here for your profit!" As we crossed the bridge, Vergil pointed out those who were running in the other direction; among these false deceivers of women we saw Jason, receiving vengeance for his seduction of Hypsipyle and Medea.

The path now crossed another arch; in the next valley, the horde of flatterers lay, submerged by their own filth, with which, in life, their tongues were never satisfied. Among them, my guide pointed out a shade:

"Thaïs the harlot is it, who replied
Unto her paramour, when he said, 'Have I
Great gratitude from thee?'—'Nay, marvelous!'"

CANTO XIX: Eighth Circle: *Popes Guilty of Simony*

O Simon Magus and your evil crew, greedy beasts who sell for gold the good things of God, now may the trumpet sound for you! We had reached the third pocket; standing upon the middle of the bridge which spans the gulf, I saw the dark gray rock pierced with many holes, the feet and legs of a sinner protruding from each. The soles of these feet were aflame, and the sinews writhed and crackled so that, had the limbs been mortal flesh, they must have broken. As my master directed, I moved down to the floor of the valley and spoke with one whose feet seemed licked by a redder fire. He cried aloud, "O Boniface, here already? Surely the prophecy erred by many years! Are you so soon satiated with the wealth for which you did not shame to wed the Lady [the Church], and then wrong her?" I answered that I was not the Pope Boniface, and asked for knowledge of his name and sin. "Know, I once wore the Mantle, and was so greedy that I pocketed gold above and pocketed myself here.

"Beneath my head the others are dragged down
Who have preceded me in simony,
Flattened along the fissure of the rock.
Below there I shall likewise fall, whenever

That one shall come who I believed thou wast,
What time the sudden question I proposed.
But longer I my feet already toast,
And here have been in this way upside down,
Than he will planted stay with reddened feet;
For after him shall come of fouler deed
From towards the West a pastor without law,
Such as befits to cover him and me."

"How much gold did Our Lord require of St. Peter before he gave the keys into his hands?" I demanded in scorn. "What is the difference between yourself and the idolaters, save that they worship one, and you a hundred?" His pain seemed increased by my words, and it seemed that my master was pleased thereat, for he embraced me. Still in his arms, I arrived at the top of the next embankment.

Canto XX: Eighth Circle: *Fortune-Tellers and Witches*

The people below had been strangely deformed, for their heads were turned about, so that their faces stared from between their shoulder blades, and their tears streamed down between their buttocks. I wept, and my master upbraided me, saying, "Here, pity thrives when pity is dead. Who is more to be blamed than he who weeps when he beholds the judgment of God? Lift up your head, and see Amphiaraus, who fled from the battle when he saw the earth open before his feet. Like the others, he sought to peer into the future; for this sin, his head is turned backward upon his shoulders, and he sees only what is past." Many another famous sorcerer was here, false prophets of alien deities; Vergil pointed out the seeress Manto, upon whose tomb, Mantua, his birthplace, was founded.

Canto XXI: Eighth Circle: *Bribe-Takers*

Passing from bridge to bridge, we reached the summit, and here we could see the next division of Malebolge, which was filled with a mass of boiling pitch. As we looked, a jet-black demon ran along the brink of the cliff, burdened with a sinner

from St. Zita, where nearly every man is a bribe-taker—except
Bonturo. He flung him over the cliff into the boiling lake below; other demons, jeering at their victim from the bridge,
prodded him with their rakes until he was glad to sink below
the surface to escape them. Vergil bade me hide, and went
forth to meet the demons; as they formed to attack him, he
cried to them to send forth an emissary, then to consider
whether they cared to grapple with him. When Malacoda,
leader of these Malebranche, came forward, my master daunted
him by telling of our mission, and he gave the signal to let us
pass. The demon told us that the bridge was broken at the
sixth arch, and sent some of his crew to escort us along the
precipice. I wished that we were going unattended, for these
creatures gnashed their teeth and grinned horribly at us. He
replied that I should have no fear, for they did so to terrify the
wretches in their charge. The demons whistled at their leader,
and he made a trumpet of his rump.

CANTO XXII: Eighth Circle: *Demons and Their Victims*

Many a time have I seen an army break camp and move, but
never have I traveled with such a wild and terrible company.
As we walked along the ridge, I watched the sinners in the
lake; now and again one of them, to ease his pain, would show
his back above the pitch as a dolphin arches through the water,
and as quickly hide it again. Some of them stood up in the
lake, but when we approached, they dived in, as frogs dive
into a pool. One luckless evil-doer was dragged up by his hair.
The demons amused themselves by tearing bits from his flesh.
I asked him whether there were any Italian companions of his
punishment; he replied that there was one he knew, a Friar
Gomita, a master bribe-taker. Then he offered to call up seven
other souls, for it was their custom, when one had got out of
the lake, to signal with a whistle. The devils, taken in by this
device, freed him; but instantly he dived to the bottom of the
lake. Two demons pursued him, so rapidly, indeed, that they
too plunged beneath the pitch; biting one another, half-cooked,
they were dragged forth by their comrades.

CANTO XXIII: Eighth Circle: *Hypocrites*

We had made them laughable, and I feared that they would not endure ridicule. Our fears were justified, for we soon saw them flying after us. Vergil seized me, and together we slid down the sloping cliff to the valley. Scarcely were his feet upon the ground than the demons reached the cliff above; but the limits of their power were reached, and they could not pursue us across the boundary of the fifth enclosure.

Below we found a painted crowd, moving with dragging paces beneath the weight of great mantles, gilded bravely without, but made of lead so heavy that Frederick's mantle might seem as a straw beside them. We spoke with two of these hypocrites, friars of Bologna, Catalano and Loderingo, who had outwardly conformed to their office of keeping the peace in Florence, but had secretly worked their will by misuse of power. I began to reprove their wickedness, but stopped short when I saw one man lying crucified with three stakes upon the ground, in the path of that heavy multitude; Caiaphas who first counseled the Pharisees that one man should be tortured for the people, formed a carpet for the feet of the hypocrites, along with every other evil adviser. Asking the way, we learned that the Malebranche had lied, for the Devil is father of lies, and that, beyond this valley, the bridge was sound.

CANTO XXIV: Eighth Circle: *Robbers*

That ascent along the ruins was no easy one, but, my master helped me up the rock, and as I was about to sink exhausted, he encouraged me, saying, "Now you must cast off sloth, for neither under quilts nor upon beds of down may men come to fame!" I heard, as we climbed, a faint cry of anger from the other side of the rampart, and asked Vergil to lead me into a position from which I might view the speaker. When he complied with my request, I saw one sinner bitten by a viper, and instantly the venom of the bite kindled his body to flames; but no sooner had he been entirely burnt to ashes, than he arose again, for fresh torment. He told us that he was Fucci of

Pistoia, confined here with other thieves because he had stolen the ornaments from a church; to wound me, he prophesied that Florence should renew the government of his native city, but that war should again break out, and every single White should suffer dire harm.

CANTO XXV: Eighth Circle: *Shape-shifters*

As he cursed his God with obscene gestures, two snakes cut off speech and motion alike, at which I rejoiced greatly. Cacus the Centaur came up; his back was full of serpents. Behind his shoulders I saw a dragon, who kindles into flame everything he touches. Cacus was punished here for his theft of Hercules' cattle. And then I saw one of the running sinners, a shade whom his companions addressed as Agnello; a six-legged serpent fastened itself to him, and, before my eyes, their two shapes blended, until they formed a dreadful creature that was neither two, nor one. But then a little serpent darted forth, which fastened itself to the navel of this monster, and, in smoke, the original shapes issued forth again—but the man had become a reptile, the snake taken human shape.

> The legs together with the thighs themselves
> Adhered so, that in little time the juncture
> No sign whatever made that was apparent.
> He with the cloven tail assumed the figure
> The other one was losing, and his skin
> Became elastic, and the other's hard.
> I saw the arms draw inward at the armpits,
> And both feet of the reptile, that were short
> Lengthen as much as those contracted were. . . .
> The one uprose, and down the other fell. . . .
> He who lay prostrate thrusts his muzzle forward
> And backward draws the ears into the head,
> In the same manner as the snail his horns;
> And so the tongue, which was entire and apt
> For speech before, is cleft, and the bi-forked
> In other closes up, and the smoke ceases.

The soul, which to a reptile has been changed,
Along the valley hissing takes to flight,
And after him the other speaking sputters.

The change here went on with infinite horrible novelty. Exult,
O Florence, that these thieves have spread your fame so wide
through Hell!

Canto XXVI: Eighth Circle: *Ulysses*

Laboriously we made our way up the cliff to the patch which
separated the pockets of this circle.

The next was filled with tall, pointed flames, which seemed
to roam fitfully about. My guide addressed one of these, an
ancient flame of double tip, in which were confined the souls
of Ulysses and Diomed, bound together for eternity. The
greater portion of the flame, in which was Ulysses, began to
speak, and to say why he was punished here with the other evil
counselors: he had urged his men to sail beyond the pillars
fixed by Hercules as a signal that no man should venture beyond them.

"I and my men were old and weary," he said, "when we
came to that ancient and narrow strait. Upon the right, we
passed Seville; upon the left, Ceuta. 'Brothers, who now have
reached the West,' I said, 'you who have endured a thousand
dangers, do not deny to your few remaining years of life experience of that uninhabited world which lies beyond the sunset. Consider the nobility of your origin; you were not created
to live, beastlike, in security, but to pursue knowledge!' So
eager were they made that I should have tried in vain to restrain them. We turned our stern toward the dawn, and bent
our oars forward. At night, I could see the strange, new stars,
that guard the other pole. Before us we could see a dark mountain, looming high in the distance; and from it came a whirl-
wind that turned our joy to weeping. It smote the bow of the
ship, and thrice it whirled us in water. Upon the fourth turn,
we sank, as was Another's will." Silent within his towering
flame, he turned away from us.

Canto XXVII: Eighth Circle: *Pope Boniface VIII*

Still further on, we met another flame, the dwelling of a soldier turned priest. He called to me, saying that if he could return to Italy he would bear the tale of his destruction. Pope Boniface had induced him, Guido da Montefeltro, to take up war again, though he had laid aside his sword when he entered the Franciscan Order, and had promised him absolution for the sin of bearing arms not against the infidel but against his fellow-Christians. On this promise of absolution, Guido did as he was asked; but when, at his death, St. Francis came to bear his soul to Heaven, a demon from the pit snatched it away and bore it before Minos, who eight times coiled his tail about himself. He who repents not cannot be absolved; to repent and then repeat the sin is a greater sin.

Canto XXVIII: Eighth Circle: *Schismatics*

Passing over the next span, we came to the valley where the sowers of conflict are punished; as they had maimed the body politic, so they themselves were constantly driven before a demon with a sword who dealt them dreadful wounds. These cuts healed by the time that they had, with great pain, made the round of the circle; but each time they were mutilated anew by the cruel blade. Among the bleeding throng we saw Mahomet, fomenter of schism and bloodshed, and Pier da Medicina, one of my own countrymen. The mutilations were appropriate to the crime: he who had aroused riot with his bold tongue had now no tongue to use; Mosca, who had once said that "a thing once done is done," and thereby brought woe to the Tuscans, held aloft the bloody stumps of his wrists; Bertrand de Born, who had estranged Henry of England from his people, bore his own brain separated from his body, carrying his head like a lantern in his hand.

Canto XXIX: Eighth Circle: *Alchemists*

My master, seeing me look below and weep, learned that I lamented for my own kinsman, Geri de Bello, who was here confined; he bade me have no further thought for him, although his violent death, still unavenged, had caused him to pass by and speak no word to me.

As we came to the last enclosure of Malebolge, the cries of woe caused me to cover my tortured ears. If all the hospitals of three nations were heaped together, the suffering and the dreadful stench would scarcely be equal to this. We spoke to one shade who sat upon the ground, tearing at his own scabbed flesh with his frantic nails; he was of Arezzo, and the practice of alchemy had brought him to that degrading fate.

> "But what I died for does not bring me here.
> 'Tis true I said to him, speaking in jest,
> That I could rise by flight into the air,
> And he who had conceit but little wit,
> Would have me show to him the art; but only
> Because no Daedalus I made him, made me
> Be burned by one who held him as his son.
> But unto the last *Bolgia* of the ten,
> For alchemy, which in the world I practised,
> Minos, who cannot err, has me condemned."

Canto XXX: Eighth Circle: *False Witnesses*

In this pocket we saw those who had impersonated others to gain their own ends afflicted with madness, so that they had lost possession of their own bodies and bit each other like rabid swine. Liars and slanderers smoked from fever. Of these the most notable was the Greek Sinon, who had persuaded the Trojans to draw the great horse within their gates, by which lying device he brought Troy to destruction. I became so absorbed in their quarrels and their varied punishments that my master had to reprove my curiosity, for to wish to hear such disputes, as he said, is a base desire.

Canto XXXI: *Down to the Pit*

Proceeding from that place of woe, we heard a sound like a trumpet but louder than Roland's horn, and I could see vast shapes like towers standing against the dim sky. As we came nearer, I saw that they were not towers, but giants, who stood within the pit, against its side, so that they were visible only from the navel upward. One of these was Nimrod, whose vile plan had created diversity of languages; therefore, his mouth could utter only meaningless, brutish bellows, nor could he understand the speech of another. Vergil spoke fairly to the giant Antaeus, opponent of Hercules, and persuaded him to lift us down into the lowest round of all, Cocytus, where the souls of traitors lie locked in eternal ice. Easily he picked up the two of us in one hand. Antaeus seemed to me like the side of a mountain; gladly would I have taken another way of descent. But he set us down lightly in the abyss which holds Judas and Lucifer; then rose, like the mast in a ship.

Canto XXXII: Ninth Circle: *Fratricides and Traitors*

So hard was the ice that, even should a mountain fall upon it, it would not have creaked beneath the weight. I saw a thousand faces made doglike by cold; even their own tears added to their pain, for they froze before they fell, sealing in ice the eyelids of these sinners. As I walked among the heads which protruded from the glassy lake, I struck one in the face with my foot. I asked his name, offering to add to his earthly renown by inscribing it among my notes; but he refused with ill courtesy, and angered me so that I threatened to tear his hair from his scalp unless he spoke. Already his locks were in my hand, and many of his hairs were missing, but I should never have known him, had not another shade cried to him by name. "Ah, Bocca," I cried, "now I need no speech of yours! Despite you I shall bear true tidings of you to the world!"

Canto XXXIII: Ninth Circle: *Ugolino of Pisa*

We had not gone far, when I saw two who were locked so closely within the ice that the head of one fitted above that of the other like a cap; viciously, he gnawed upon the scalp of the man beneath him, wiping his mouth upon the hair. When I questioned him he answered, "You renew my grief; yet if I may bring further infamy to him whose head I am chewing,

I shall speak gladly. I was once Count Ugolino, myself a
traitor; this creature was the Archbishop Ruggieri. I, trusting
him completely, was taken prisoner, with my young sons, and
thrown into prison. We were left without food, and I looked
upon my suffering children without tears, for my grief had
turned me into stone. In my anguish, I bit my own hands, and
they, believing that this act was caused by hunger, begged me
to eat them, who had given them life. They died before my
eyes, still looking to me for aid. O unfeeling earth, why didst
thou not rend thyself open at the sight? I watched all four
perish; and, myself already blind, yet I felt them with my
hands, and for two days called their names. On the third day
my agony was overcome by hunger." And again he seized upon
the wretched skull, with teeth as strong as a mastiff's upon a
bone. Ah, Pisa, foul blot upon your fair country, well might
your people perish! Though the Count betrayed you, yet his
sons should never have been tortured! Their tender age alone
made them guiltless.

We passed on to another crowd, lying upon their backs, so
that their eyes were completely filled with frozen tears to increase their agony. I thought that I could feel a wind, although
my face was nearly numb with cold; the cause of this blast, my
guide told me, I should soon see for myself. One of those in
the ice, who begged me to unseal his eyes, identified himself
as Friar Albergio, a man of infamy whom I had thought to be
still alive. He answered my confusion by revealing that the
souls of men of extraordinary wickedness are often snatched
away to Hell before the death of their bodies, which remain
inhabited by demons for the rest of their mortal span. I left
his eyes unopened; it was courteous to treat him so. O men of
Genoa, at war with virtue and full of all vice, how do you remain in the world?

CANTO XXXIV: *Bottom of the Pit*

"Vexilla regis prodeunt inferni—Forward move the banners
of Hell's King." Now I was in that part of the lowest circle
where the sinners are held below the ice; I saw them as if

through glass. Some were lying down, others upon their heads; one I saw frozen like a bow, his feet arched to his face. Now my master told me to arm myself with all my courage, for we approached Dis, the center of gravity and also of evil, where Satan munched forever the three arch-traitors, Judas, Brutus, and Cassius. If once Satan was as beautiful as now he is foul, yet turned against his Maker, fitting it is that all evil should come from him! His head had three faces, red, yellow, and black, and beneath each of the rear faces sprang two great, bat-like wings. With all six eyes he wept, and his tears, with the foamy blood of the traitors upon which he fed, ran from his three chins. For Judas, in the front, the biting was as nothing beside the clawing, for with his talons, Satan continually flayed away his skin, from every part save his head, which was within the dreadful mouth.

Grasping the hairy flank of Satan, Vergil climbed, and bade me follow. When we had reached that point where the thigh turned upon the haunch, my master, holding fast, turned himself completely around, so that his head lay where his feet had been. I feared that we were going back to Hell, but it proved otherwise; for, looking back, I saw Satan to be feet uppermost. We had passed the center, and climbed upon the side of the earth from which Satan had first fallen. Along a hollow tunnel of rock, my guide and I ascended, caring not for rest, until we came forth to see again the stars.

THE DIVINE COMEDY: THE STORY

II. Purgatorio

CANTO I: *Approach to Purgatory*

My little boat of wit has now left behind the cruel waters of
the deep ocean, to run on better seas. Now my song is of that
second kingdom, where the soul is cleansed of sin and made
fit to ascend to Paradise. O sacred Muses, I give myself wholly
to you; and let Calliope enlarge my song with harmony!

Blue as sapphire shone the serene heaven, and stars en-
kindled the eastern sky such as no mortal had seen since leaving Eden. Four there were in whose light the very heaven took
glory; bereaved indeed art thou, O northern hemisphere, deprived forever of their light!

Turning, I saw an old man with hoary locks and beard,
whose aspect demanded an even greater reverence than that
of a son for his father. He came toward us and asked how we
had been permitted to leave the place of damnation. "Are the
heavenly laws broken, or are there new laws there," he demanded, "that you dare come, thus doomed, to my rocks?"
My master, motioning me to kneel, explained his mission, begging Cato—for it was he—that he should, for his Marcia's sake,
let us pass.

"On earth," answered the noble shade, "so pleasing to my
eyes was Marcia that I obeyed her in all things. Now that she
dwells beyond the horrid river, she has no power to move me
further. Yet, if a heavenly lady guides you, you need not flatter
me, for it is enough that you ask me in her name." He bade
Vergil gird me with a smooth reed and wash away from my

face the grime of Hell; my master spread his fingers in the dewy grass, and I, understanding him, turned up a tear-stained face, that he might obey the command. Beside the shore, Vergil plucked a reed, and, where it had been, another sprang up at once in its stead.

Canto II: *The Angelic Ferryman*

The cheeks of dawn turned from white and rose to a deeper hue, and, as we walked beside that shore, a brightness came so swiftly over the sea that never might any flight match its speed. My master bade me kneel in prayer, and the whiteness revealed itself as a boat, piloted by an angel, who scorned all instruments, but propelled it with his great wings. In the bark sat more than a hundred souls, singing together of the departure of the chosen from Egypt. The angel made over them the sign of the Cross, and they sprang out upon the shore, whereat the boat departed, as swiftly as it had come. One of the pilgrims asked directions of us; my guide replied that we, too, desired to climb the mountain, but, being strangers as they were, did not know the way. The spirits, noticing by my breathing that I was alive, looked at me with wonder, as if they had forgotten their mission. One of them sprang forth to greet me; I tried to embrace him, but my solid arms passed through him as through air. I begged my friend, Casella by name, to stay and speak with me, which he did for friendship's sake; he sang, with his wonted sweetness, "Love, which pleads its cause within my mind," and all the souls listened with delight, until Cato cried out to them to make all speed to their purification.

Canto III: *The Base of the Mountain*

They scattered like frightened birds toward that mountain where reason cleanses our souls; I drew close to my guide, for how could I proceed without his aid? As we walked, I saw that he cast no shadow. "Marvel no more at this," he said, "than at the heavenly spheres, moving without obstructing each other's radiance. Had all things been explicable to you, there had been no need for Mary to bear a Son."

Approaching the mountain, we beheld a crowd of souls above us on the cliff, who showed us where to mount the slope. One of these was Manfred, grandson to the Empress Constance, who, dying, had given himself to God and had been saved; however, he said, those who die, though repentant, in contempt of the Church, must remain outside the gate of Purgatory for a term thirty times as long as the period when they lived in that state. He also told us that this time might be shortened by prayer, and asked me to tell of him on my return, since souls in Purgatory may receive much help from the worthy living.

CANTO IV: *The Ascent Begins*

We struggled upward through the rocky cleft, until we came out on the cliff's summit; my master advised that we continue to climb, until we should meet a guide. He pointed to a still-higher terrace, which we reached by pulling ourselves up with hands and feet; from this place, I looked backward to the east, where the sun was rising. We rested there, but I was dismayed by the height of the mountain, which seemed to reach to the stars; Vergil told me that the ascent was most difficult at the bottom, but toward the top became as easy as coasting in a skiff.

"Then, when it so appears to you," he said, "you will have reached your journey's end, and there you may expect to rest after your labor."

"Perhaps before then," said a voice near us, "you will have to sit down and rest." Turning, we saw a company reclining in the shadow of the rock; of one in particular I remarked to my master, saying that surely Sloth herself must be his sister. "Go up then yourselves, you who are so valiant!" he remarked.

"Belacqua," I cried, smiling a little, "now no longer must I grieve for you! But why do you sit here? Do you wait for a guide? Or do your old habits of sloth yet govern you?" He replied that he, with these others who had put off repentance until the last, must wait for admittance to the cleansing torments for a period as long as his lifetime, unless a prayer from a soul in a state of grace should remit some of the time. What, then, availed it to climb up, since the angel would refuse him passage?

CANTO V: *The Repentant*

Parting from these shades, we encountered another group, whose chant of the *Miserere* was broken off in surprised exclamations at the sight of my shadow. These were spirits of men who had died in violence, sinners until the last, but who, through grace, had received God's peace in time to win forgiveness. Jacopo del Cassero, slain by the Paduans in battle, begged me, should I return to Fano, to ask the prayers of his old neighbors, that his time before Purgatory might be shortened. Another was the shade of Buonconte da Montrefelto, who, falling by the Archiano, had died with Mary's name upon his lips; the Devil, seeing him borne to salvation, had vented his wrath upon his dead body, causing it to be carried, frozen, into the Arno, the crossed arms upon its breast torn apart by the flood, until it was buried, forgotten, upon the bottom.

CANTO VI: *The State of Italy*

The spirits crowded about me, plucking my garments, endeavoring to call themselves to my attention, that I might gain prayers for them on my return to earth. But I freed myself with promises, and we continued on our way. I asked my guide whether he denied, as he seemed to do, that prayer might avail to help these souls. He replied that if one considered the matter rightly, he must know that Love can work miracles, and that by Love these would be saved. The answer to my question I should have from Beatrice, who awaited me on the top of the mountain; and with his words, my feet, heavy before, grew light.

We had not gone far, before we saw a solitary shade, who spoke not, but watched us pass. Vergil asked directions of him, but he did not reply directly, asking us first of our lives and countries. Vergil had no sooner spoken the name of Mantua, than the other embraced him, crying, "O Mantuan, I am

Sordello, your countryman!" Even here, O Italy, one countryman welcomed another at the mere sound of his city's name—
while your living citizens still make war upon each other! O
German Albert, who have, for hope of gain, abandoned your
seat in the saddle from which you should control the wild
beast, may Heaven's just judgment fall upon you. Come, cruel
man, to see the tyrannical deeds of your own nobles; punish
them, and give your people back their Caesar! O Lord, Who
suffered for us upon the Cross, let me ask whether Thine eyes
have turned elsewhere, or whether this be a part of some
greater plan? For every town in Italy bears its own throng of
despots; every countryman who devotes himself to a party,
becomes a Marcellus! My Florence, this concerns thee not,
because thy people, in their pride and zeal, pick up the load
which the rightful bearers cast away; hence, wealthy art thou,
at peace, and full of wisdom. Yet how often hast thou changed
rule, coinage, laws, and population? Thou art in this like an
old crone, who finds no rest in her pain, but turns constantly
from one side to the other, hoping for ease.

CANTO VII: *The Approach of Night*
  Sordello, having learned my master's name, fell to his knees,
clasping him like a vassal.

  "O glory of the Latians, thou," he said,
  "Through whom our language showed what it could do,
  O pride eternal of the place I came from,
  What merit or what grace to me reveals thee?
  If I to hear the words be worthy, tell me
  If thou dost come from Hell, and from what cloister."

Vergil replied that he was in Limbo forever, for he had never
seen the Sun of Grace; and asked whether Sordello could
guide us to the beginning of Purgatory. On learning our mission, Sordello told us that, since it was not permitted to climb
the mountain by night, he would, with our permission, lead us
to some other spirits, near whom we might take our rest. Fol-

lowing him, we came, through a sloping passage, to a valley of surpassing loveliness, filled with brilliant flowers and shrubs, and scented with the fragrance of a thousand perfumes. Here a group of spirits rested upon the turf, singing "*Salve Regina*" amid the flowers; from the bank above the valley, we might see their faces clearly. These were the shades of great rulers— Ottocar, Emperor Rudolph, Henry of England, and many others of eternal memory—who had neglected their kingly duties, and who waited here for passage into Purgatory.

CANTO VIII: *The Evening Hymn*

Suddenly, as the light faded, I saw that noble company kneel, gazing upward in silence. From heaven, there came two angels, armed with blunted flaming swords; their garments and pinions were green, the color of hope, and their radiance dazzled my eyes. Both had come, Sordello told us, from Mary, to guard these spirits against the prowling Serpent. We descended into the valleys, but my eyes looked only above, where three brilliant stars had risen in that place where the earlier four had set. Suddenly, on that side of the valley where there was no barrier, we saw a serpent come, like an evil streak, through the grass and flowers. But no sooner did it begin to approach, than the heavenly guardians repelled it, and it vanished.

CANTO IX: *The Gate*

Soon after, I, still burdened by Adam's flesh, was overcome by sleep. Toward morning, I seemed to see, in a dream, a great eagle in the sky, who, descending, seized me and bore me upward to the realm of fire, whose flames seemed to scorch me, so that I awoke. I was now alone with my master, who explained that Saint Lucia had carried me to the gate of Purgatory, lighting with her lovely eyes the way for Vergil to follow. We had come to a gate, approached by three steps, one smooth and white, one rough and black, and one scarlet. Its guardian learned our mission; and, after I had fallen upon my knees and struck my breast three times, beseeching him to open for me, he let us pass. But first he traced with his sword's point seven P's upon my forehead, and warned me to be sure that, at the end of my journey, these scars had been wiped away; these letters, I later learned, stood for the *peccati* (sins) which were purged upon each level of the mountain. Then, from his ashen garment, he drew forth two keys, one silver and one golden; both, he said, were necessary, if the lock were to open. One of them was more precious, but the other required art and wit; they were given him in trust by St. Peter, who had instructed him to err rather in opening, than in shutting out, for all who should fall prostrate at his feet. We passed in, having been warned that any soul who looked backward must return outside; the heavy gate closed behind us.

Canto X: *The Sculptures on the Walls*

We ascended through a steep and rocky cleft, clinging to the stone wall of the mountain that we might walk with greater certainty. When we gained the ledge, we had both lost our way, and I was sorely weary. I think that, from the outer edge, the terrace would measure thrice a human body's length, and it seemed to be uniform in width, as far to right and left as eye could span. I saw that the mountain wall was of white marble, carved with a skill no human hand could match—indeed even Nature herself had been here surpassed. The angel, who had carried the great decree re-opening Paradise to mankind, first met my eyes, carved so perfectly that the Lady to whom he spoke seemed about to say, "*Ecce ancilla Dei.*" There also I saw a carving of David, dancing before the Ark of the Covenant; and the Emperor Trajan, saved by the intercession of St. Gregory for his justice to the poor widow.

Reader, do not flinch from the purification of Purgatory because of what I shall tell you of its suffering, for it cannot extend beyond the Day of Judgment. I saw there souls, bent beneath heavy weights; and he who seemed by his looks most patient under suffering seemed to say, "I can bear no more."

CANTO XI: *Pride*

They were reciting the Lord's Prayer, not, as they said, for themselves, who were now rescued forever from temptation, but for the living. If there so much good is done for us, how devoutly should we pray for them, that their blemishes may be speedily washed away. My guide asked if they knew a way by which a man burdened by a living body might possibly ascend, and one of them bade us follow them to the right, where he believed that there was such a passage. He was Omberto of Siena, whose pride not only caused his own death, but brought many of his race to misfortune; here he atoned for despising other men and forgetting that all mankind are brothers by a common birth and redemption. Listening, I bent down, and another shade, twisting his head beneath his burden, recognized me and called my name.

"Are you not that Oderisi," I asked, "who brought honor to Gubbio—honor to the art of painting which is called illuminating by the Parisians?"

"Brother," he answered, "Franco of Bologna's painted leaves are fairer by far than mine. His is now the honor that once was mine. Never, while I was alive, should I have striven so hard to excel, and it is for this pride that I labor here in expiation. Were it not that I repented before my death, while I was still capable of sin, I should not be speaking to you here."

O vanity of earthly fame! Once men admired Cimabue most of all painters; now they turn to Giotto; and, in later years, another shall obscure them both. If one should die very old, rather than as a babbling child, how much greater will his fame be in another thousand years? And what is a thousand years to the span of eternity? His words brought true humility into my soul, and crushed my pride.

CANTO XII: *The Carved Pavement*

Side by side, bent together like a yoked pair of oxen, we walked and conversed together, until my good teacher called me to move on. The pavement, like the mountain, was carved with representations of old stories; here, I beheld those who had fallen through pride—Niobe, weeping for her children slain; the Assyrian horde, fleeing at the death of Holofernes; Arachne, frozen in the middle of her sad metamorphosis. Be proud, ye children of Eve, and look not down, lest you behold the evil road you tread!

My master called me from my absorption, saying, "Raise your head, and dispose yourself to humility, for here is the angel who shall direct us higher." Glorious, the celestial minister approached us, and, wiping away one of the P's on my forehead, he showed us the stairway to the next terrace. As we turned to mount it, I heard voices singing, "Blessed are the poor in spirit," in tones sweet beyond description. And it seemed to me that I was lighter than before, and mounted with greater ease.

Canto XIII: *The Second Circle*

On this ledge we saw neither imagery nor figures; both walls and floor were starkly bare. My master prayed to the celestial light to guide us, and we came at last to a place where envy was punished by blindness. The multitude of shades sat upon the ground, touching one another for reassurance in their darkness, and through their eyelids ran an iron wire, sewing them shut. Through the hideous sutures each pressed out his tears.

"O spirits certain of beholding at last the Light on high," I said, "tell me if any of you is Italian."

One lifted her face to me and answered, "I am of Siena; sapient I was not, though Sapìa was my name. I rejoiced at the ills of others more than at my good fortune. Once, when my fellow-citizens fought near Colle, I asked God for what He later willed: our men were put to flight. Turning my face to the sky, I said, 'From this time, I have no fear of You.' Before my death, I made my peace with God; but even this would have been insufficient, had not Pier Pettignano, who out of charity mourned me, also prayed for me." She wondered at my good fortune, since my eyes were unsealed; I answered that I, too, should suffer here, but not for long, since envy was not my worst fault. When she learned that I, a living man, had come thither, she, like the others, implored that I secure the prayers of her countrymen.

Canto XIV: *The Degeneracy of Florence*

Two spirits asked me whence I had come; and I told them that my home was upon the Arno, a river whose course may be traced by the evil lives of those who dwell along it.

> "Virtue is like an enemy avoided
> By all, as is a serpent, through misfortune
> Of place, or through bad habit that impels them;
> On which account have so transformed their nature
> The dwellers in that miserable valley
> It seems that Circe had them in her pasture.
> 'Mid ugly swine, of acorns worthier
> Than other food for human use created,
> It first directeth its impoverished way.
> Curs findeth it thereafter, coming downward,
> More snarling than their puissance demands,
> And turns from them disdainfully its muzzle.
> It goes on falling, and the more it grows,
> The more it finds the dogs becoming wolves,
> This maledict and misadventurous ditch."

These spirits mourned with me the fraud and guile which pollute my country, and the grievous weakness and wickedness of its nobility.

When we were again alone, I heard a sudden voice in the air, crying, "Every man who finds me shall destroy me!" And, from the rocks, there came a cry like a burst of thunder, "I am Aglauros, who was turned into stone!" I pressed against my tutor in horror, and he reassured me, saying that these dire warnings were meant as a boundary to hold men in their alloted place, but that I, on higher summons, might ignore them.

Canto XV: *The Angel of Mercy*

We were walking with the setting sun in our faces, and I had made a shield of my hands to protect my eyes from the unaccustomed radiance of its glow; suddenly there came a light even more blinding, so that I was forced to avert my gaze entirely.

"Marvel not," said Vergil, "that you are blinded by the progeny of heaven. This is a messenger, who bids us ascend." As we mounted the stairs, someone was singing, "Blessed are the merciful," and then, "Rejoice, thou that art victorious!"

Vergil explained to me the meaning of envy, interpreting the words of the shade on the second level, who had told me of his delight in "things which can never be shared." Material things cannot be shared, but the love of God is such that, the more who share in it, the greater the good possessed by each, since it is infinite; and, even as a beam of sunlight upon a brilliant object, it gives according to the love it finds. I remained somewhat confused; but he told me that all doubts should be explained by Beatrice, and, at the sound of her blessed name, my zeal increased.

Before I could speak again, I came to the outer cornice of the ledge, and suddenly I beheld, as in a vision, a crowd of people in a temple. Upon the threshold stood a gentle Lady, who lamented, "My Son, why hast Thou treated us so badly? See, both Thy father and I have sought Thee sorrowing." This vision faded, to give place to that of another lady, who pleaded with her lord for vengeance against the ravisher of their daughter. He, mild of aspect, replied, "What, then shall we do to our ill-wishers, if he who loves us is condemned by us?" And next I saw an angry multitude, stoning to death a youth, St. Stephen; in his look was compassion and forgiveness for them all. When I came to myself, Vergil said, impatiently, that my steps had been vague, my eyes veiled by my arm, and bade me hasten. When I would have told him what had passed, he answered that he knew all that I had seen, and spoke but to lend vigor to my feet, that I might use my senses, now that I had regained them.

CANTO XVI: *Papal Ambition*

We came now to a region of dense smoke, which stifled sight

and breath at once. Vergil ordered me to stay close beside him, that we might not be separated. All about us, the spirits sang the *Agnus Dei,* "Lamb of God, Who takest away the sins of the world, have mercy upon us!" They were the souls of those who must expiate here the sin of anger. A misty shape ran after us through the gloom, and my leader told me to reply to his questioning, that I, in turn, might learn of him. He said that his name was Marco Lombardo, and that the sin of wrath was punished here; greatly did he reproach the evils of our generation, but added that, since we possess free will, we have ourselves, and no others, to reproach for our sufferings. In the old time, he said, that fair region where the Adige and the Po are flowing was the seat of peace, courtesy, and learning, until Frederick brought war into the land; henceforth, we must say that the Church, in its endeavor to wield both religious and secular rule, has fallen into the mire. We had now reached the boundary beyond which Marco might not pass, and we went forth from darkness into light.

CANTO XVII: *Ascent to the Fourth Circle*

Mingled in the smoke I saw the shapes of spirits who had sinned greatly in anger: Haman, crucified, and surrounded by Ahasuerus, Esther and Mordecai; Lavinia, too, whose mother had hanged herself, when she thought Turnus dead. As the light of day grew less, we ascended toward the next circle. A heavenly spirit, unasked, revealed the way to us; as we ascended, I felt the gentle touch of a moving wing upon my face wiping away another P, and a voice sang, "Blessed are the peacemakers." At the top, I looked for some distinctive sign, but, seeing none, asked my master where we were now.

"This is the place," he answered, "where the failure to perform duty is punished. But, before we proceed, let me enlighten you further. All human actions spring from love, but it may turn to wrong ends, or issue with too much or too little zeal, and then the creature acts in opposition to its Creator. In the circles below, misdirection of love so that it injures one's neighbor is atoned for; here, dilatory love is expiated. The love that turns too greatly toward the object, not toward its essence, is wept for in the three circles above us. Now let us proceed."

CANTO XVIII: *Love and Free Will*

As we went along, my guide tried to resolve in me my doubts concerning the nature of love. All love proceeds from and is contained in the Ultimate Love of God, he said; when I asked how this might be, unless all love was constrained by necessity, he answered me in veiled words, saying that reason, the faculty of discernment by which we might gather in the good and refuse the bad, had been placed in us to receive and return that love; hence, although the will was free, love could still be present over it all. My mind was still clouded, but again he assured me that Beatrice could resolve my uncertainty.

We came upon a company of souls running, urged on by will; one shouted, as he ran, "Mary ran in haste unto the hilly country!," while another said, "Caesar, to subdue Ilerda, thrust at Marseilles, and pressed quickly forward into Spain!" When we asked the way, they bade us follow quickly, for their desire would not let them pause for rest. Soon they were out of sight, and my eyelids closed from weariness, even as I saw the sun decline; my mind wandered aimlessly from thought to thought until I slept.

CANTO XIX: *Purgation of Avarice*

Near dawn, I saw in a dream an ugly hag, who came staggering and crooked, but sang with a voice of incredible sweetness, "I am that Siren who tempted the great Ulysses. Seldom does any who stays with me depart from me, so greatly do I give pleasure." Then Reason, a saintly lady, suddenly appeared, calling to Vergil, "Who is this?" He pulled aside the other's drapery, disclosing her belly, from which arose so foul an odor that I awoke. Vergil urged me to rise at once.

We had gone only a few paces, when a lovely voice said, "Here is the passage." He who had addressed us pointed out the way and, ascending, fanned us with his plumes, confirming the promise that they who mourn shall be blessed. My guide reproved my earthbound glance, and asked the cause of my delay. I told him of my dream, and he asked, "Have you seen that old witch, from whom man is to be saved?" We came through a narrow passage, and, reaching the next level, saw many people lying face downward upon the earth and weeping. One of these, who had been a powerful churchman, had, upon gaining the papacy he coveted, perceived the falsity of his greed, and so been saved. Here, with the other souls who had looked only upon the desirability of earthly things, he must forfeit the sight of the sky, fettered to the ground by his hands and feet. I had knelt down in reverence for his great office, but he, somehow perceiving it, bade me stand, saying that we were all brothers in God's service. At his request, we left him there.

Canto XX: *The Avaracious: Hugh Capet*

O Avarice, ancient wolf-bitch, who preys more upon us than any other beast, may you be forever accursed! When will he come who shall put the wolf to flight?

Spirits about us proclaimed the humility and poverty of Mary, Fabricius, and St. Nicholas. I spoke with Hugh Capet, founder of the French dynasty, who lamented that greed had so utterly enslaved his race. He foresaw yet worse evil, when the French standard should enter Alagna and seize the person of the Pope himself, mocking Christ anew, between two thieves. By day, he said, the spirits on this ledge recalled examples of holy poverty, while by night, they spoke of those destroyed by greed: Midas, Pygmalion, and Ananias and Sapphira.

We left him, and were about to fare forward, when suddenly, the entire mountain trembled like a thing about to fall, and all those about us shouted, "Glory to God in the highest!" We stood motionless until the quake and the song had passed. I remained torn by curiosity, nor did I dare to ask, such was our haste, what that happening had meant.

CANTO XXI: *Statius and Vergil*

We continued upon our hallowed path, until we found ourselves overtaken by a shade who had approached us silently,
and who now drew near, saying, "Brothers, may God grant you
peace!"

"In the high tribunals of Heaven," answered Vergil, "may
you be granted peace by that just authority which dooms me to
eternal exile!"

"But, if you are indeed unfit to go beyond," said the other,
"how does it happen that I meet you so high on His stairway?"
My master explained to him our goal and his commission, and
asked the reason for the earthquake.

"The mount itself is eternal and changeless," answered the
noble spirit, "but it trembles of itself when any soul feels itself
pure enough to rise from its torments to Paradise. I, confined
for five hundred years or more by the wish to expiate my sins,
have recently felt this free impulse toward a better place.
Therefore you felt that shock, and heard the spirits give praise
unto the Lord, Who, I pray, will soon speed them upward after
me."

"If it so please you," said my guide, "give us your name, and
tell us why you have been enchained here for so long."

"Rome summoned me," answered the shade. "My home was
in Toulouse. I earned the right to wear the myrtle crown. I
sang of Thebes, and of the mighty Achilles; it was the *Aeneid*
which gave birth to my second song, in which I failed to attain
my end. Without its guidance, I should never have been worth
a drachma. Would that I had lived below when Vergil lived;
for that, I would willingly remain upon this mount another sun
beyond my ordained limit!" I turned to look at my master,
whose face bade me be silent; but I could not help but smile.
The other questioned me about this, and, with Vergil's permission, I revealed his identity. Statius knelt before him, but
my guide bade him rise, since both were but shades.

CANTO XXII: *Statius' Conversion*

"Blessed are those who hunger and thirst after righteousness," sang the angel who ushered us into the next circle. Statius had told us that he had been redeemed from the sin of prodigality and recalled to eternal life by a passage in Vergil's *Fourth Eclogue*, which prophesies the rebirth of the world when a Virgin should bear a son, descended from Heaven. He asked our company in his pilgrimage. The two walked ahead, conversing like brothers, and I, following, listened to their talk, which was of the manner of Statius' conversion. He had mourned the persecution of the Christians by Domitian, and had been secretly baptized; but, because he had not the fortitude to own himself a Christian, he here expiated his sin of lukewarmness in religion. Then they spoke of the other poets of antiquity, who were, said Vergil, his companions in Limbo. We came to a tree which stood midway in our path, laden with fragrant apples; it was tapered like a fir tree in reverse, with its point near the ground and its laden wider branches upward. Near by was a pool of clear water. As we approached, a voice cried out from the tree, "Little of this fruit shall ye have!" it said. "Mary wished more to provide plenty at the wedding feast than for viands to feed her mouth, which speaks now for you." Naming many more examples of temperance, both classical and scriptural, it warned us away.

Canto XXIII: *Purification of Gluttony*

I was lost in fascination, but, following my master's direction, I looked and beheld a company of souls who approached, singing. They appeared in the last stages of starvation—incredibly thin, with sunken eyes and skin so dry that its appearance was like that of a leper. One of them spoke to me, and, when I heard his voice, I recognized Forese. He told me that he, for the sin of intemperance in appetite, was tormented here by hunger and thirst. In making the round of the circle, this company had to pass the fruit tree and the crystal spring, whose odors enticed perpetually, without promise of relief. I was surprised to find him here, only five years after his death, since he had postponed repentance until the last; he said that his Nella, by her tears and prayers, had remitted much of his time outside the gate. "As much more precious is my widow, my dear love," he cried, "in the sight of God, as alone she stands in her good conduct."

Canto XXIV: *Abstinence*

I asked after his sister Piccarda, and was told that she was already among the blessed. Forese asked when he should see me again; I answered that I could not know how long I should live, but that I feared, because of the wickedness of Florence, that I should desire to return long before the appointed time. When I lamented the wickedness of my city, he told me that justice should not delay long in striking the miscreants, then bade me farewell, since in that realm time was too valuable to waste in conversation. As we walked on, I saw yet another tree that spoke in parables of the excellence of temperance, and announced that it came from the seed of that tree of which Eve had eaten. So deep in thought was I that I failed to notice anything else around me, until a voice said in my ear, "What are you thinking, you three solitary ones?" Looking in the direction of the voice, I saw an angel who glowed as redly as if made of glowing metal or glass. I felt the gentle breeze as his wing wiped away yet another P from my brow, and heard him say, "Blessed are those whom grace so illumines that desire is in them ever moderate."

Canto XXV: *Birth in Death*

As we ascended the hill, I asked Statius how it was that spirits grew lean and pale, even in a place where food is not required. He replied that the spirit, after death, re-forms itself in the shape dictated by its nature and its own inclinations. It is formed, thus, into a new body, with all the members and faculties of the body; and with this spiritual form it feels and endures all that shall happen to it, though immaterial and bodiless, until the Day of Judgment. Thus it is that spirits can speak and laugh and weep; just as our nature and desires have been, so is this shape.

We had reached the turning of the ledge, and had to pay attention to our steps; for here a flame darts out from the cliff, and we must walk in the free space created by the upward blast that turns away the fire, if we were not to be scorched. In this fire walked the lustful, crying out within the embrace of the dreadful heat.

Canto XXVI: *The Two Crowds*

One of them inquired why I seemed to make a wall against the sun, as one who still lived; I would have answered, but another sight distracted my eyes. For against this group there came another multitude, walking within the fire's path, in the opposite direction. As the two peoples met, they hailed each other with opposing cries. "Sodom and Gomorrah!," said some; the others answered, "Pasiphaë entered the cow, that a bull might satisfy her lust!" Mingling their tears, they kissed each other in brotherly fashion, seeming contented with a brief salute. Then each group took once again its own way, uttering still the cry that suited their offenses. He who had first spoken said that his name was Guido Guinicelli, and, having died repentant, he here purged the sin of incontinence. I was deeply moved, for to me, as to all other poets who have used the language of love, the man who had spoken was a father in art. When I told him of my admiration, he indicated to me the shade of one who, he said, surpassed him, and all others, in the poetry of passion, one Arnaut of Provence.

Canto XXVII: *The Purifying Flame*

Suddenly an angel barred our path, singing, "Blessed are the pure in heart," and denying us entrance into the Earthly Paradise until we had passed through the flames. At these words, my heart grew faint with fear, and, gazing upon the fire, I recalled the sight of bodies burning at the stake. My guide assured me that, although suffering might lie here, I should come to no real harm; he even invited me to make a test of this statement with my own hands, upon the hem of my garment. But still I hesitated, until he reminded me of Beatrice. At her name, I mastered my fear, and entered the fire, with Vergil before and Statius behind me. So great was the heat that I would gladly have cooled myself by leaping into molten glass. My loving father, to encourage me, spoke constantly of Beatrice. "Already," he said, "I seem to see her eyes!" As we came forth, a voice was singing, "Come, ye blessed of my father," within a brilliant radiance before us. The road ascended between the cliffs, and, when darkness fell, each of us lay down upon one of the stairs. The stars seemed to shine more brilliantly here, and I fell asleep between my two friends. As the night drew to its end, I saw in my dream a lady of celestial loveliness, who walked in a meadow gathering flowers.

"Know," she sang, "that I am Leah, who bestir my hands to make myself a wreath of these blossoms, that I may deck myself to please me at the mirror. But my sister, Rachael, never leaves the glass in which she contemplates all day her lovely eyes. Work is my joy, and contemplation hers."

We had reached the highest step, when my guide said to me that I now had reached a place where he might aid me no further. Here, he said, I might pass the time as I pleased, but henceforth I should hear no speech or sign from him. "Thus do I crown you sovereign of yourself."

CANTO XXVIII: *The Earthly Paradise*

Eager to search the forest which lay before me, I set forth at once, slowly taking my way across the plain. A gentle breeze touched my face and rustled among the leaves, whose magic made sweet accompaniment to the voices of the birds within them. Soon I was so far within the wood that I could no longer find my place of entry; suddenly a stream cut across my path. Upon the other bank I saw a lady, divinely fair, who sang as she plucked the enameled flowers at her feet.

"O fairest lady," I called to her, "who now seem to bask in love's own rays—for I may trust your aspect, which so often in man reveals the heart's nature—I pray you, come this way, that I may hear your song."

Her eyes modestly downcast, she turned, with a dancer's grace, and came to the opposite margin of the stream, where

she raised her glance to mine and smiled. Courteously she
offered to answer all my questions. I asked her whence came
the breeze, since I had heard that earthly elements never disturbed this mountain, and she told me that it came from the
revolution of the spheres, and carried to other parts of the
earth seeds of all the plants in Paradise. The water, too, she
said, arose not, like earthly water, from the condensation of
vapors, but emerged from its unpolluted source by God's will
alone, and poured forth in two streams; the one, Lethe, takes
away memory of evil, while the other, Eunoë, restores memory
of good. Both streams must be tasted if either is to be effective.

> Those who in ancient times have feigned in song
> The Age of Gold and its felicity,
> Dreamed of this place perhaps upon Parnassus.
> Here was the human race in innocence;
> Here evermore was spring, and every fruit;
> This is the nectar of which each one sings.

CANTO XXIX: *The Apocalyptic Procession*

When she had spoken, she resumed her song, and wandered
along the bank, motioning to me to follow on my own side of
the river. Suddenly, she directed me to look about me; and
there came upon the air sweet music and brilliant light. May
Helicon now pour forth for me its waters, and may Urania aid
me with her chorus to sing in verse of ineffable things!

As the lights came closer, I perceived them to be seven
celestial candlesticks, whose radiance left banners of light upon
the air behind them, forming seven bands colored like the rainbow. Beneath came a band of twenty-four elders, robed in
white and crowned with fleur-de-lis, singing, "Blessed indeed
art thou among the daughters of Adam; may thy loveliness be
blessed forever!" When they had passed on, there followed
four beasts plumed with green foliage, and bearing triple
wings filled with eyes. Amid the four there came a chariot of
triumph drawn by a Gryphon of gold, white, and vermilion,
whose wings pierced the bands of rainbow color above him.

Surely never Scipio or Augustus had such a car; it far outshone even the fabled chariot of the sun. Three ladies danced about one of the wheels; one was red as fire, the second as if fashioned of living emerald, and the third as white as freshly fallen snow. Four others, robed in purple, followed the measure of one with three eyes, about the other wheel. Behind these walked two old men, one mild in aspect, like a healer [St. Luke], the other bearing a sword of deadly keenness [St. Paul]. Then came four others, humble in their aspect, then a solitary sage who walked as if in trance, though appearing keen of vision. These were crowned with roses instead of lilies, whose color resembled living flame. When the chariot drew opposite to me, there came a clap of thunder, and the whole throng stood still.

Canto XXX: *Beatrice*

Turning toward the chariot, all that throng called out to it, and from it rose a hundred angels, singing, "Blessed art thou who comest!" Among them I saw a lovely lady, dressed in green, white, and flame-red, whose very aspect commanded my reverence, though veiled.

I turned to Vergil, but he had vanished completely. Not all the joys of Paradise could prevent me from shedding a tear for him, to whom I had turned for inspiration in art and salvation in spirit.

"Weep not, Dante, at the departure of Vergil," a voice said to me, "for you must later weep for other woes." The words, I saw, came from that divine lady whom I had seen among the angels. Regally, yet with anger in her bearing, she continued, "Look well, for we, indeed, are Beatrice. Why did you think yourself worthy to climb this mountain? Do you not know that here man is happy?"

I bent my head in shame before her scornful pity; she was silent, and the angels sang, "In Thee, Lord, have I hope." At length some of those who sang seemed to pity me.

"I wish that he who stands there may weep, that he may understand," she said to them. "This man, gifted from birth with every natural aptitude, was for a short time upheld by my countenance. When, on the threshold of my womanhood, I changed from life to death, he forsook my memory and turned his steps upon an evil road. Even in dreams I tried to recall him, but at length he descended so low that no means of salvation might avail save showing him the damned in Hell."

CANTO XXXI: *Dante's Confession*

She called upon me then to answer her charges, but I, choked by tears, could not speak. My tears and my words burst forth together, with a great "Yes!" I confessed that the enticements of the moment had drawn me aside from contemplating her; and she replied that confession of one's sins blunts the edge of punishment. Then she bade me turn my face toward her. As she stood facing the Gryphon she seemed, though still veiled, fairer than before. The nettle of repentance so pricked me that I swooned.

When I recovered my senses, the lovely lady whom I had seen at first was above me, drawing me through the stream. As we neared the shore, she pushed me beneath the waves, so that I was forced to swallow some of the water. Emerging, she presented me, thus bathed, before the seven nymphs of the chariot, who led me to Beatrice. At their request, she unveiled to me. What man could tell your beauty, O living spirit of eternal light, as you stood revealed to me, with heavenly harmony your only veil?

CANTO XXXII: *The Suffering of the Church*

I stood, unaware of anything but the glory of her eyes, until the goddesses cried out that I had gazed too intently; indeed, I was for some time entirely dazzled by her radiance, and entirely bereft of vision. But, when my eyes awoke to lesser splendors, I saw that the heavenly procession had turned and was wheeling back to the right, facing the sunset, with the seven-fold flames moving before them. The damsel who had brought me across Lethe, Statius, and I followed the chariot with the others, beside the right-hand wheel. At length, Beatrice halted the caravan beside a great, barren tree, which, like the one in the seventh circle of Purgatory, tapered in reverse.

"Blessed art Thou, O Gryphon," the multitude chanted, "that Thou eatest not of the tree; for later must the belly convulse in agony."

"By this restraint is the seed of godliness preserved," responded the animal of two natures. Turning the pole of the chariot toward the tree, he there made it fast. Even as trees seem to renew themselves in a single instant, when the warmth of spring touches them, so did these bare branches at once put forth leaves and blossoms, showing lovely colors that ranged between the violet's and the rose's. I was lulled into a state like slumber, and, when I awoke unto myself, it seemed that the veil of sleep had been rent by a dazzling light, in which a voice cried out, "Awake! What dost thou here?"

Beside me was Matilda, my earliest teacher in the forest.

"Where," I cried in anguish, "is Beatrice?" Matilda indicated to me her seat, amid the newly grown foliage, at the root of the tree. Near her was the abandoned car; and the seven nymphs were gathered about her in a ring, bearing the seven holy lights in their hands.

"Although your stay here will be short," my lady said to me, "you will, with me, be a citizen of Rome forever, as is Christ. But, to help this misguided world, take careful note of what you are about to see, and fix your eyes upon the chariot."

Then there came, with divine swiftness, a great eagle, who, sweeping through the branches of the tree, so that the bark was stripped off, left the holy car feathered with his wings, upon his ascent, after he had put to flight the she-fox that appeared within it. From Heaven there came a voice whose accents were laden with grief, crying, "O my little vessel, how evil is thy load!" I thought that next the earth groaned, and cleft apart, and from that crack there came forth a dragon, who tore away a portion of the chariot's floor and wandered away again. Now the remaining part of the cart covered itself entirely with the plumage of that eagle, who, perhaps had offered it in most friendly wise; and from each part it put forth heads.

Like oxen were horned the three upon the pole, while the single head upon each corner had but one horn. Upon this monster there now appeared a brazen harlot, mistress to the giant of evil aspect who stood beside her. It seemed that she cast her wanton eyes on me; and, seeing this, the giant dragged her from her seat and began to beat her dreadfully. At last, he untied the beast from the tree and dragged both it and the woman within the wood, until they were lost to sight.

CANTO XXXIII: *The Purification of Dante*

The choir of goddesses, weeping, sang to Beatrice, while she responded with her sighs. At last, rising, she answered, with a countenance glowing like fire, "A little while and ye shall not see me; yet a little while and again ye shall see me."

Leaving her station, followed by her nymphs, she approached me, saying, "Brother, now that we are reunited, why not take heart and question me?"

"My lady," I answered, with downcast eyes, "you know my need, and what is fitting for me."

She bade me cast off all timidity and shame, and explained the mystic signs that I had seen.

"Know," she said, "that the vessel shattered by the serpent was and is not. Yet let its spoiler beware; for there are some stars, secure from impediment, conjoining in five hundred, five, and ten, that soon will slay both the female thief and the incestuous giant. Take care that you conceal not from living people that you have seen this tree, twice ravished, but still living; and, unless your intellect be somewhat impaired, you must divine the reason for its shape, so spreading at the topmost branches."

She asked that I see now, in its true light, my earlier-chosen doctrine and its faults, that never again might I estrange myself from her. When I, amazed, answered that I could never recall that I had wandered from her, since my conscience was free of remorse, she recalled to my mind the river Lethe which I had passed and its unique power. She said that, from hence, her words should be unveiled before me, and bade me drink of the second stream, which recalls memory of good. Matilda guided Statius and me to Eunoë, where we drank; the sweetness of that draught cannot be spoken.

Purified with this new life, as trees are renewed by spring foliage, I went forth, fit for my ascent to the stars.

III. Paradiso

Canto I: *Dante Ascends with Beatrice*

The glory of Him Who moves everything shines more in one place, less in another. And, as we ascend into comprehension, drawing near the vision, the mind so exceeds the power of reason, that memory cannot follow it. But as much of that holy realm where next I came as I have treasured up within my brain, my song shall tell. O good Apollo, make me thy vessel, that I may merit the prized wreath of laurel! O Power Divine, make me worthy of my exalted theme!

Fixing our gaze upon the sun, we stood at that place where three crosses conjoin with four circles, together with a more propitious star. The eyes of Beatrice were fixed upon the celestial spheres, and mine were fixed only on her. Before me lay incomprehensible vastness, and, gradually, I realized my thirst to know their cause and extent. Smiling, she told me that I no longer stood still, but was speeding to a new destination more swiftly than lightning in its course. As we moved, she spoke of the eternal order which is in things themselves, in which, too, all that moves—even the swiftness of the spheres—is contained in eternal, changeless tranquility. No more should I, she said, marvel at my ascent than at the flow of waters, springing forth to meet the depths; the waterfall seeks earth by its nature, while I, by the spark of divinity in me, sought God and Light. Now that the prison of my sins had been unlocked, it would be much stranger, had I remained below, than if a living flame should there remain motionless.

428 EPICS OF THE WESTERN WORLD

CANTO II: *The Moon's Sphere*

> O ye, who in some pretty little boat,
> Eager to listen, have been following
> Behind my ship, that singing sails along,
> Turn back again, to look upon your shores;
> Do not put out to sea, lest peradventure,
> In losing me, you might yourselves be lost.
> The sea I sail has never yet been passed;
> Minerva breathes, and pilots me Apollo,
> And Muses nine point out to me the Bears.
> Ye other few who have the neck uplifted
> Betimes to the Bread of Angels upon which
> One liveth here and grows not sated by it,
> Well may you launch upon the deep salt-sea
> Your vessel, keeping still my wake before you
> Upon the water that grows smooth again.

That innate love of God created in men moved us swiftly upward, until at last my lady said, "Give thanks to God, that he has brought us to the first star of Heaven!" It seemed as though we were within a cloud, were received into everlasting pearl. If I was then body, meditation upon the impossibility of body within body should the more enkindle us to worthiness, that such mysteries may at last be plain. Beatrice explained to me that the seeming diversity of illumination proceeded not, as I had guessed, from bodies of various rarity and density, but, as the farthest of three mirrors will reflect a stationary light in smaller proportion, but with equal brightness, it reflected the nature of that sphere itself. Diverse virtues, she told me, create different combinations with that unchanging, celestial Light which unites itself with Divine Love. Darkness and light here appeared to my eyes, thus, according to worth, and not rarity or density, as men know these qualities. Divine Intelligence, the force which turns all the nine spheres, is the source of all light, and Light Itself appears of various brightness.

CANTO III: *Female Spirits*

As a pearl, upon the pale skin of a beautiful woman, reveals itself in faint lustre, so did faces come before me in the translucent radiance of the moon. Great was my wonder; and my lady, smiling faintly as she might smile at a child, bade me speak with these souls, that I might be enlightened. Obeying, I addressed one of them.

"If thy memory is sufficient to the task," the spirit answered, "thou wilt recognize me as Piccarda; my greater beauty here will not hide me from thee." Because she, and her sisters in blessedness, had broken their holy vows, they were in the lowest sphere of all. I asked her whether she did not desire a higher place; smiling, she replied that it would be discordant to the Will of God to ask for more than they had, for His Will is their peace. I asked her then why she had not continued under vows to the end of life, and she told me that after she had submitted herself to the Rule of the Order of Santa Clara, she had been torn from the cloister by evil men. With her was Constance of Sicily, who, against her will, was returned to the world, though she had never, in her heart, renounced the veil. This speaking, and singing, "*Ave Maria,*" she vanished from my sight, as a stone vanishes into deep water.

CANTO IV: *The Abode of Spirits*

As a man might die of hunger before he could decide which of two dishes was the better, I stood silent, trying to puzzle out two questions. Seeing my confusion, Beatrice said, "Clearly, you do not understand why, if vows are broken by the violence of another, against the will of the votary, his merit is less; and whether the teaching of Plato, that souls return again to their star, is true. Plato errs, for all share in the Vision, though in greater or less degree. Perhaps he meant more than he said, and, if so, one must not deride him. If he meant that one must think better or worse of these spheres because of their influence on men, he may have spoken truth. Your other question is less hard to solve. Justice cannot be unjust: had these spirits, when on earth, resisted to the death, their place would have been higher. But the will cannot be forced. Though these ladies did, under duress, what they would not have done otherwise— made choice of the worse of two courses of action—their wills remained free. Piccarda, when she said that Constance never renounced the veil in her heart, spoke the truth, for no untruth can come here. She meant that the will remained free, and was not constrained to consent to an ill action."

I was yet unsatisfied, though they had answered me well; for I desired to know whether one may make reparation for broken vows.

Canto V: *Mercury*

"If, in the heat of my love, I seem to shed upon you flame beyond your endurance," said Beatrice, "do not wonder at it; its intensity is rooted in perfect understanding. And, if anything turn you now from this love, it is but some vestige of that same light, improperly understood."

Now she resolved my doubts on the freedom of the human will, and its relation to vows. "The greatest bounty of God, made in the image of His goodness, is freedom of the will, granted only to intelligent creatures. A vow is an agreement between God and man, in which man makes a sacrifice of his free will. Consider this matter carefully; it is not knowledge if you have only heard, and not retained it. The essence of the sacrifice is two-fold: one, the material thing or specific act promised; the other, the agreement, which cannot be canceled until it is complied with. Nor may any other act or agreement be substituted for that promised. A vow should never be undertaken lightly, but unreasoning faithfulness to it—like that of the Grecian monarch who sacrificed Iphigenia—may produce great evil." So said Beatrice to me, even as I write it.

Like an arrow that has left its bow, even with such swiftness were we translated to Mercury, the second sphere of Heaven. My lady was so joyful, on her entrance to that bright Heaven, that the star itself seemed more luminous.

As fish in a pond dart toward their food, so I beheld a myriad of glowing souls approach me. "Lo, here is she who shall increase our love!" sang one. I turned toward another which was visible in the radiance issuing from it, and desired to hear of its condition. Enfolded in its radiance, the figure replied.

CANTO VI: *Roman Spirits*

"Caesar was I," he said; "I am Justinian. Were it not for blessed Agapetus, I had yet believed that God's nature were but one. What he taught me I now see easily." He told me of the turbulent history of Rome, in which tranquility and war conflicted to produce an ensign before which half the world bent the knee. For the second Emperor's deeds, he said, Brutus and Cassius now wail in Hell, and Cleopatra still weeps. Under the third Caesar [Tiberius] living Justice granted the glory of vengeance for His wrath, in the death of Christ. And, much later, when the Lombard tooth had bitten Holy Church, Charlemagne saved her. "Let not this new Charles, and his Guelphs, strike it down!"

This little planet, he said, was adorned with those who had won fame and honor upon earth. Justice had so intensified love in them, that their desires could not turn to evil.

CANTO VII: *The Redemption*

"Osanna, God of Hosts!" he sang and, with his comrades, he was lost to me in the whirl of stars, while I was left alone with my sweet lady.

The words of Justinian, when he had spoken of a just vengeance itself avenged by Justice, perplexed me. Even before I could ask, Beatrice answered me, turning upon me that smile which would gladden even one being burned at the stake.

"Quickly I shall resolve your mind," she said. "When Adam fell, he damned all his offspring, and for many centuries they lived in error, until it pleased the Word of God to be joined, by a great act of Eternal Love, to human nature. When we consider the Person who suffered, having within Him both natures, there was never yet so great justice as the Cross or so great injustice. The act was pleasing to God and to the Jews; earth trembled, and Heaven opened. No longer should the problem of a just vengeance avenged by Justice seem difficult.

"But you say, 'This is true; but why did God will only this way of redemption?' When man was driven from Eden, he could have been granted pardon by God, or he could himself have made satisfaction. But man has no power of himself to do so; therefore, God, knowing that no other mode of justice was possible, humbled Himself in the Incarnation of His Son.

"So too, this land in which you are, and its angels, are informed by a created virtue; and your nature is such that it always desires the Supreme Beneficence. From this you may argue your resurrection."

Canto VIII: *Venus*

The ancients believed that Venus sent down mad love, even into the realm of the gods. I had not realized that we had risen to the next sphere, until I saw Beatrice appear even lovelier than before, and beheld a multitude of dancing lights about me. One of them detached itself from the throng to speak with me. He announced himself as Charles Martel. Had the world possessed him longer, it would have profited greatly thereby.

"How can such sweet seed father such bitter fruit?" I asked. He told me that heredity applied but to the outer form, not to the soul, although the Supreme Good foresees and contains all natures. He asked me if a man on earth would consider himself fortunate, deprived of citizenship; I, of course, said no. "Do not wonder, then," he responded, "that different estates are created for the happiness of all, here and upon earth. As men themselves differ, so do their spheres of happiness, and fortunate is he who knows this truth!" He seemed saddened because some born to holiness are forced into the life of this world, while some, inclined to worldly fame, must take the road to priesthood. If the living world would but fix its mind upon the natural order of things, such misfortunes might seldom occur.

Canto IX: *Quia Multum Amavit*

He prophesied to me also, O beautiful Clemence, the miseries that your progeny should undergo, but bade me be silent until the years should be finished. Then there came before me another light, which signified its desire to speak by growing brighter. As one that delights to do good, she sang of her life: her name had been Cunizza, sprung of the same stock as evil Ezzelino. Because of her course of life upon the earth, the vulgar might have thought her lost; yet, because she had greatly loved, she was among the blessed, and because of her life, she was in the sphere assigned to Venus. She brought before me another light, that of Folco, the poet whose poems, after half a millennium, were to become known again. And he explained that here also was the spirit of Rahab, the harlot, who had saved the emissaries of Joshua. Little of him, or of Nazareth, does the Pope think, but rather of the things of this world.

Canto X: *The Sun*

We ascended further, but I was not at once aware of the difference in station; then I saw that we had arrived at the sphere of the Sun. It was illumined by pure light; never can human spirit imagine its brightness. When my eyes had a little accustomed themselves to the light, I saw that in it there glowed other smaller lights, twelve in number, which seemed to move as in a dance. From one of them came a voice; it was that of St. Thomas Aquinas, the Angelic Teacher; and the other lights were the homes of blessed spirits who in this world had taught the Church—St. Dominic and St. Albert, of the later days, were among them, Boethius and Orosius from the earlier days of the Church.

Canto XI: *St. Francis*

St. Thomas spoke again to me of his companion, St. Francis of Assisi, who even while he was young gave to the world an example of virtue. Early in his life he wedded, as he said, Lady Poverty, and throughout his time on the earth he remained faithful to her—as no one had been for over a thousand years before. From Pope Innocent he had received the seal of approval on his Order; and from the time of its founding he went through the world, preaching, even so far as Constantinople, where he preached to the Sultan. But the pagans were not ready for conversion; and Francis returned to Italy. There he received the Stigmata of Christ's wounds, which he bore for two years. Many followed him into the Order of Friars, and to them he commended the spirit of Poverty. But see now how they are changed!

CANTO XII: *St. Dominic*

As he finished speaking, the circle of lights again began to revolve, and another circle joined it, the two wheeling together in harmony. Out of the heart of one of the lights there came a voice which drew me to listen, that of the Seraphic Teacher, St. Bonaventure. It was right, he said, to speak of the other leader, St. Dominic, because his own, Francis, had been well spoken of. It was Dominic who, when the armies of the Church were moving slowly, drew them together and inspired them. Even as a child he had shown himself so strong in faith that he might have been called an athlete of holiness. And as a man, he had set out not to gain benefices and rich livings, but to fight for the Church against her enemies. At one time, he and Francis might have been called the two wheels of the Church's chariot; but now the Franciscans have grown weak. Here with their leader were other great Dominicans, and the scholars from whom they had learned, Hrabanus Maurus and Hugh of St. Victor.

CANTO XIII: *St. Thomas Aquinas*

Think, if you can, of the constellations dancing in the heavens; even so was the movement of these lights which moved through the greater light. From another of them came the voice I had heard before, that of St. Thomas Aquinas, who told me why Solomon must be considered the wisest of men. Though Adam and Christ had been created directly by God, and must therefore have been wisest, yet Solomon asked for wisdom, and was divinely granted it. From this we learn that it is unwise to leap to conclusions—as the heresiarchs did—for a too-quick "Yes" or "No" may ignore all the distinctions which must be made if we are to answer truly and fully, and judgment on earth should never be too rigid, since from the briar there often springs a rose.

CANTO XIV: *The Resurrected Body*

My lady knew that a question, unvoiced, remained within me, and she asked whether, through eternity, these spirits should blaze with so great a glory. A voice within the heart of the circle spoke to her softly in answer: "When we shall be complete, with body and soul our glory shall flame; then more fittingly may we praise Him Who is the source of all glory."

O radiance of the Holy Ghost! How suddenly, how burningly, it vanquished my eyes!

When again I could see about me, we had been moved to a higher sphere. This planet seemed redder than the others, for it was the seat of God's warriors. From within, two rays of ruby light seemed to form a great Cross, Christ shining from it like lightning, and I gave thanks to God therefore. From arm to arm, there moved sparkling flames, and from that figure there flowed a melody of high triumph, which seemed to say, "Arise and conquer!"

CANTOS XV and XVI: *Early Days of Florence and Its Degeneracy*

Among the jewels studded in this emblem, I found the father of my own dynasty, who spoke of those happy days when Florence was a city of peace and dignity, content with simple wisdom, when every man became, with his baptism, "at once a Christian and a Cacciaguida." How small a thing seems our nobility of blood, compared to that greater nobility of spirit! The intermingling of population, he told me, was one of the prime sources of that evil which now threatened Florence. How glorious were once those families, now fallen through their pride! How easily is a crest conferred for gold, that was bought of old with piety and with feats of arms!

Canto XVII: *Exile of Dante*

Encouraged by Beatrice, I asked him to tell me, although I cared not now for Fortune's blows, what might be my future state on earth. He told me plainly that, even as Hippolytus, falsely accused by his stepmother, I should tread the paths of exile.

"All things most loved by you," he said, "you must leave behind. Next must you learn how bitter is the taste of others' bread, how toilsome the road upon another's stairs. But worst of all will be your discovery of the stupidity and wickedness of that company which you must keep—they, not you, must suffer for it at last. Well will it be if you keep yourself aloof from these, making of your own self a party!" He told me further of that Gascon prince who should be my friend, and of my other patrons after him. Yet, he said, for these evils, which should be done to me by my own countrymen, he would not have me hate bitterly those who were my neighbors, for my future should lie far beyond the just punishment of their disloyalty.

"Let your voice be bitter, like nourishing medicine," he advised. "For there may be some who will hear you, and will scratch the itch. For this reason, only those of greater fame have been singled out to speak with you, here, on the mount, and in the vale of woe; for never can the mind of any be set at rest with obscure examples."

Canto XVIII: *Jupiter*

As I stood, rapt in my own thoughts, weighing the bitter with the sweet, Beatrice again turned her lovely eyes on me, reminding me that she was very near to Him Who bears every heavy load. Looking only at her, I fell into a state like trance; until, at length, she bade me turn away my eyes; Paradise, she said, was not in her eyes alone. In this fifth sphere of Mars were the great warriors for good, Joshua and Judas Maccabeus, and of the Christians, Charlemagne and Roland, and Godfrey of Bouillon.

I turned then to Beatrice, whose heightened joy and radiance told me that we had been translated to yet another Heaven, that of Jupiter, the sixth that had received us. The radiant souls traced against the sky the words: *DILIGITE JUSTITIAM, QUI JUDICATIS TERRAM*—"Love Justice, you who judge the earth." Jupiter seemed to shine like silver, overlaid with gold, and the spirits of that sphere danced about like the sparks of a fire. When they had settled into place, I saw outlined a great eagle and, upon the last letter of *TERRAM,* a lily. O shining star, how did you then teach me that justice on our world comes indeed from Heaven!

Canto XIX: *The Eagle*

The eagle, outlined in lights that glowed like rubies, spoke to me; and I prayed that my hunger for justice might be satisfied. "He Who set the bounds of the universe is infinite in worth, and because of this the finite souls of men cannot plumb the depths of His justice. The first to fall, Lucifer, fell because he did not await enlightenment. You have often asked whether one born far away in India, where there is no one to teach him of the True God, yet who lives a just and blameless life, can be saved, though faithless, or must perish eternally? Who are you to judge this question, you who have knowledge only of human justice? Many there are who call upon Christ who, at the Last Day, shall not be known to Him; and there are many among the pagans whose name shall be in the Book of Judgment. What shall the rulers of your day plead, when their deeds are laid open for judgment? Then shall we know the greed and cowardice of the ruler of Sicily, and how Henry of Lusignan keeps pace in evil with greater kings!"

Canto XX: *The Eagle Continues*

Within the throat of the eagle spoke the souls of just men, of David, who had earned the reward of Heaven for his Psalms; of Trajan, whose soul had been saved for his charity to the poor widow; of many another, pagan and Christian, who in this world had done justly. I wondered that Trajan and the Trojan Rhipheus could be saved, but the eagle answered me, "These were souls naturally Christian, though they died before the Redemption. Because their eyes were ever fixed on right, Divine Grace brought them hither."

Predestination—how far thy doctrine lies from the understanding of those who see only a part, never the whole! Mortals, have care in your judgments; for even the souls in that great bird of Heaven told me that they had not yet knowledge of all the elect.

CANTO XXI: *Saturn: Contemplation*

My eyes turned again upon the face of my lady. She did not smile, lest the radiance of her smile should strike me dead, as Semele died before the glance of Jupiter. For we had arrived now at that place where I could see, amid the circling rays of the sun, a shining ladder. Ascending and descending it were such a multitude of splendors that my tongue can have no power to describe them. Here I heard not the music of the spheres, nor were there the songs which resounded in the other Heavens. A spirit who had descended the ladder told me that here the Heavens were silent, and Beatrice did not smile, because it was the abode of those who on earth had devoted themselves to contemplation. The spirit was that of St. Peter Damian, who had been satisfied with little earthly food, but was better fed with contemplating Eternal Good. He examined me, and, at the thought of earth's iniquity, he and the other cried out with such intensity that I was shaken unto my heart.

CANTO XXII: *St. Benedict*

Startled by his cry, I turned in bewilderment to my guide. Quickly she spoke to me, saying that the cry was not one of intended evil, for in Heaven there is no harm done, but was a prayer. She bade me then look at the lights which moved upon the ladder. Within one of them I heard a voice, "I am he who first brought to Monte Cassino the name of Him Who brought Truth. There, in the monastery, we fasted and gave our lives to contemplation." Then I spoke to St. Benedict, "Shall I ever see you with uncovered countenance?" And he replied that I should do so, in the final sphere, where all wishes are granted. But the ladder which he and the others climbed is no longer the path of those upon earth; the Rule remains, but it is worthless. Peter did his work without gold or silver, and Francis had with humility gone about the work of his Order. But now gold and silver are the only concern of religious, not pious contemplation. He ceased his talk, and vanished.

"Now you are so near salvation," said Beatrice, "that you should sharpen and clarify your vision." Here were all the seven spheres that I had crossed displayed to me in all their vastness. I saw entire that threshing-floor, from hills to harbors. And then my wearied eyes sought those of Beatrice.

CANTO XXIII: *The Company of the Redeemed*

As my eyes became accustomed to the sight of that which moves the spheres, I beheld the host of the redeemed, the harvest of all the spheres. Then my lady turned to me and said, "Look now upon me, see me as I am. For now you may bear the radiance of my smile."

Never, though I might be aided by all the Muses, could I hope to portray the least part of that smile. But he who meditates upon my theme can never blame me. This is no voyage for a little bark, nor for a self-indulgent pilot, this vast ocean where I steer!

"Does your love for my face blind you to the Rose which is the Word made manifest?" said Beatrice.

I saw a great host illumined from above by light, though no source of it could I see. A torch, shaped like a crown, descended from Heaven, crowning my lady, and the divine melody of the Archangel Gabriel flowed through Heaven, hymning the love of Mary. As a child throws its arms up to its mother in gratitude, so the light stretched upward, and in it I read infinite love. Still present with me is my delight in the song, *Regina Coeli,* which there I heard chanted.

Canto XXIV: *St. Peter*

Beatrice prayed for me: "O chosen company of the Lamb, you whose desires are all satisfied, give to this man some foretaste of your o'erflowing wisdom." The fairest of all the lights three times swept around Beatrice, and she spoke to it, "Master, to whom are given the keys of Paradise, ask this man concerning Faith, for your eyes see into all minds."

Then St. Peter turned to question me; and I was as a candidate who may not answer until the question has been put. "What is Faith?" he asked; and I drawing upon the wisdom of St. Paul, who had set the feet of Rome on the right path, answered, "Faith is the substance of things hoped for, the evidence of things not seen." The Saint was pleased with my reply, and asked the bases of my belief. I answered that on the earth the things which I had experienced in Heaven are yet closed to us, wherefore we must believe without argument. I had, I told him, Faith; it came to me from the Scriptures, both the Old and the New Testaments, and I knew that my Faith was from God, for He had proved it with His miracles. But, Peter objected, the miracles are attested only by the Scriptures; was I not arguing in a circle? No, I answered, for the conversion of the world by the humble band of the Apostles was a greater miracle than any in the Scripture; pleased with my answer, the Saint's light encircled me thrice, as it had encircled Beatrice.

Canto XXV: *St. James*

Then there moved toward us a radiance whom my lady knew for Saint James, the Apostle to whom Our Lord gave most light. "Be of good cheer," he said, "and tell me what is Hope, and how it came to you."

Beatrice answered for me, lest I should seem boastful in my hope, that no man had greater Hope than I; then she directed me to answer the Saint.

"Hope," I said, "is the sure expectation of future glory, which comes from Grace and preceding merit. From many have I received this illumination, but from David most of all, who sang, 'I will lift up mine eyes unto the hills, from whence cometh my strength.' It has come to me too from your Epistle, which bears greatest tidings of Hope."

The light grew brighter with joy at my answer; and nearer to the two radiances who had examined me a third approached, the light of him to whom the message was given from the Cross: St. John, the Apostle whom Jesus most loved. I turned to Beatrice; how great was my dismay that she was no longer with me!

Canto XXVI: *St. John*

For a time my eyes again were dazzled by the radiance of the lights; but St. John demanded of me what I knew of Love. I replied that the Good, which gave contentment to Heaven, was the Alpha and the Omega of Love. But the Saint asked that I speak more fully of what I felt and knew of this matter; I replied that because all nature is moved by the desire of all things for God, all forces which turn the heart and mind to the love of God work upon me and turn me from baser loves to this greater one. When I paused, my lady sang with the other spirits, "O Holy, Holy, Holy!" and as one awakes from slumber, I saw clearly again. Before me shrouded in light was the spirit of our all-father, Adam. He perceived, without speech from me, what I wished to know: how long it had been since his creation, why he had earned the wrath of God, and how he had spoken in the Garden of Eden. For only seven hours had he lived in the Garden before his fall; he lived for nine hundred and fifty years, and was in Limbo, until Christ descended into hell, for 4,232 years. His language in the Garden had been forgotten before Nimrod built the Tower of Babel.

Canto XXVII: *The Heavens of Crystal*

"Glory be to the Father, to the Son, and to the Holy Ghost!"

was the song of all Heaven, intoxicating me with its unspeakable joy. Then, as I beheld the four radiances who had spoken to me, one of them, Peter, began to glow with a crimson flame. "Marvel not at this color," he said; "for as I speak the others too will change their hue, for that one who usurps my place on earth has turned my sepulchre into a sewer of corruption, more pleasing to the Perverted One than to our ruler. It was not on gold that the martyrs were nurtured, or the Christians of old, nor were my Keys designed as an emblem for a warlike banner. From above we see that the fold is given over to the wolves. My son, when it is granted you to return, see that these things are made known."

The spirits of the blessed swirled about us as snowflakes fall on the earth, but these swirled upward. As my eyes followed them, Beatrice turned my attention again downward, so that I saw the whole Mediterranean laid before me. Then she spoke: "Here the world begins, for this is the Primum Mobile, the place where Divine Intelligence moves all spheres." And as she spoke, she carried me to the Heaven of Crystal.

CANTO XXVIII: *The Heavenly Host*

When she who emparadises my mind had finished her speech, I looked about me to see the whole universe turning. Then I beheld a point of Light so intense that vision could not endure it. About it swept the nine circles, those realms governed by the hierarchy of Heaven. From that Point the universe takes its origin, and from It streams the Light of goodness throughout. The first circles were those of the Seraphim, the Cherubim, and the Thrones; then the Dominations, the Virtues, and the Powers; and the outermost were the spheres of Princedoms, Archangels and Angels. Choir by choir they sang "Osanna!" about the Point, the universal Where.

CANTO XXIX: *Quomodo Scit Deus*

Smiling upon me, Beatrice began, "I tell and need not to ask what you would know; the center of Where and When. God said, 'I Am'; and He is, apart from time and space. The angels, whom He created, are pure Intelligence; His acts are pure Power. The fallen angels, who fell before one could count to twenty, were like the others, save that they suffered the sin of pride; these, who remain in Heaven, are the humble, circling God eternally. Because these have never turned their sight from the face of God, they need no memory, for they have eternal knowledge of what is, what was, what is to be. Men, who must depend on memory for what has been, fall into error—so that from many a pulpit vain stories are bawled out to astonish the ignorant. Christ did not come to preach idly, nor did He direct His followers to disgrace the pulpit with empty tales. On earth now men pay for counterfeit indulgences; St. Anthony's swine, the mendicants, grow fat from their empty beliefs. But enough: see how the stair climbs to Infinity; and remember how Daniel shows that the number who shall ascend it is unknown. The First Light irradiates all, and the various degrees of the angelic host perceive it as Love."

Canto XXX: *The Rose*
As the sun wheels about, bringing light to us and then fading into darkness with the night, so that Triumph Which forever whirls about that Point of Light seemed to fade from my vision. Love constrained me to turn my eyes toward Beatrice; could all that I have said of her be wrought into a single act of praise it would be too little; no poet can speak what I thought. My song has never ceased to be of her; but now I must cease, for the task is too great for me. She drew me to the ultimate Heaven, where she promised to show me the blessed, as they shall sit, robed for the Last Judgment. Now my eyes were prepared for the Vision, and I saw the River of Grace. She bade me plunge into it, that my sight might be the clearer; eagerly I did so, and as I dipped my eyelids, it seemed to swell into a lake. Then I beheld the Celestial Rose, the Courts of Heaven, the Light which, beheld, is Peace. God grant me the power to sing of it!

CANTO XXXI: *St. Bernard*

The saintly host displayed itself to me in the shape of this Rose, and even as a swarm of bees visits a flower, the Intelligences, with faces of living flame, and robed in white, plunged into it and returned again to behold the Triune Light. As a barbarian, who comes for the first time to Rome, wonders at the splendor about him, so I, a simple Florentine, gazed upon Heaven. Then I turned to Beatrice, to ask her of these things; I saw her not, but an old man, robed in light, approaching. When I asked where she was, he replied that I should see my lady in the third round of the Rose, seated on her throne. I invoked her protection, and it seemed to me that she smiled, but did not speak. "Because I am Bernard, Her faithful servant, the Queen of Heaven has sent me to your aid; now look about you, that your sight may be purified by what you see." My eyes went through the whole garden; then I lifted them up to the highest center; there, surrounded by more than a thousand angels, I saw a Beauty, which was the same joy that smiled in the eyes of the blessed. Bernard, when he saw my eyes fixed upon it, turned his thither also; and the depth of his contemplation inspired me to greater ardor.

CANTO XXXII: *The City of God*

In his office as teacher, the blessed contemplative Bernard showed me the petals of the Rose. "That wound which was anointed by Mary was opened by the fair woman, Eve, who sits at her feet. In the third order is Rachel, and beside her Beatrice. See there the holy women of the Hebrews, Sarah, Rebecca, Judith; see the great John, who hailed the coming of His Lord, and bore the martyrdom of Hell before the Redemption; and Benedict, Francis, and Augustine, ranked in the order assigned them. Near them are the souls of baptized children, who died before they sinned. No one is placed accidentally, for Law governs here absolutely; these are at higher or lower levels because of the greater or less clearness of their vision. Before the era of Grace, innocence sufficed for salvation; but since then, the unbaptized infants must be held in Limbo.

Those who looked to the coming Christ are in one part of the Rose; those who knew the Christ already come in another; yet all are infinitely happy with their stations. Look now upon the face most like to Christ's!" I saw, and before that glorious light a figure, spreading his wings, sang, "Hail, Mary, full of Grace!" This I knew for Gabriel, who had been granted the bliss of announcing the birth of her Son to Mary. Near her sat Adam and St. Peter, and opposite Peter were St. Anne and St. Lucy. Then Bernard bade me turn my eyes upon the Lady, and he began his invocation.

CANTO XXXIII: *The Beatific Vision*

"Virgin Mother, Daughter of thy Son, humble and exalted above all others created; who granted to human nature such nobility that its Creator did not scorn to use it for His manifestation; within whose womb was born the Love of which comes Peace—grant, I beseech, that this man may have for a moment a glimpse of the Great Joy. And I pray thee further, Queen, that after this Vision his affections be kept whole. See, Beatrice and the others clasp their hands, and join in my supplication!"

The eyes most loved of God turned toward us in benediction; and Bernard, knowing that his prayer had been granted, bade me look aloft. In Mary's name, all was opened to me, and I saw for a fleeting, yet enduring moment-in-eternity the end of all desire.

O Light Supreme, lend to my mind a little of Thy rays, that I may illumine that which is beyond human understanding! I saw, and yet could not penetrate to the end; and this limitation was in itself sweet to me. I knew that I should be forever lost, if once my eyes should turn away. I saw the universal form of everything commingling and being absorbed. I think, that is, that I must have seen all this; for even the memory brings joy past understanding.

There was but one likeness within that glory: yet it seemed that I saw three rings, one in dimension; yet of three colors, all equal. How powerless, alas, is human speech! At last, that circle seemed to show me a human face. I wished to see how that image joined to the rings, and how all three found place in one, but, suddenly, as in a lightning-flash, there came the fulfillment of all desire.

My will and my desire were now satisfied and resolved with that moving, yet stationary wheel. And, as a wheel is driven in even progress, so were both will and desire moved by that Love which moves the sun and the other stars.

Suggestions for Further Reading

Translations:

Longfellow, Henry W. *The Divine Comedy,* Boston, 1867

Sayers, Dorothy. *Inferno,* Penguin Books, 1951

Other Books:

Dinsmore, C. A. *Aids to the Study of Dante,* Boston and New York, 1903

Grandgent, C. H. *Dante,* New York, 1903

Ruggiers (tr. Barbi) *Life of Dante,* Berkeley, 1953

PARADISE

LOST

O mighty-mouth'd inventor of harmonies,
O skill'd to sing of Time or Eternity,
　　God-gifted organ-voice of England,
　　　Milton, a name to resound for ages;
Whose Titan angels, Gabriel, Abdiel,
Starr'd from Jehovah's gorgeous armouries,
　　Tower, as the deep-domed empyrean
　　　Rings to the roar of an angel onset!
Me rather all that bowery loneliness,
The brooks of Eden mazily murmuring,
　　And bloom profuse and cedar arches
　　　Charm, as a wanderer out in ocean,
Where some refulgent sunset of India
Streams o'er a rich ambrosial ocean isle
　　And crimson-hued the stately palm-woods
　　　Whisper in odorous heights of even.

——TENNYSON

PARADISE LOST: INTRODUCTION

John Milton began his epic poem, *Paradise Lost,* in seven-teenth-century England, during the turbulent period of the Puritan Commonwealth, and completed it after the restoration of the Stuart King Charles II, which took place in 1660. It is, in a very special sense, the product of its time; for only the violent social antitheses, the Puritan mode of thought, and the creative genius of Milton could have produced it.

Milton believed passionately in freedom of choice; his *Areopagitica* defends freedom of speech and maintains that the use of force to influence human decisions is one of the greatest of all crimes. Yet he was the foremost apologist for the theocracy of Cromwell, which gave its ruler unlimited powers and differed from the divine right monarchy of the Stuarts only in the method of selecting a leader. In this society, where individual rights were strictly limited, where publications were censored by the government, and where certain forms of worship were outlawed, Milton saw the ideal state in embryo. He also accepted in part the religious system behind it, the Reformed Catholicism of Calvin; this was a doctrine of strictest determinism, by which all men were damned save through Divine Election, and by the logic of which all human action was part of an established plan, which held man's will in complete bondage. These seemingly opposed ideas could, Milton thought, be reconciled through art. He abandoned his earlier plan for an Arthurian epic and turned his vast classical and scriptural learning to a poem which would "assert Eternal Providence, and justify the ways of God to men." The subject was to be the fall of man and his redemption through grace. The hero was to be mankind, represented by Adam and Eve, and the battleground earth, where good and evil should contend for the victory which could be granted only by man's decision.

But it is in the figure of Satan that one recognizes the qualities of the epic hero. At the opening of the poem, he is in Hell, immediately following his expulsion from Heaven. Magnificent in defeat, his pride and courage unbroken, he defies the power which has ruined him. Disinherited though he may be, he is still a king, with full consciousness of his own royalty; with powerful oratory, he gives his beaten forces hope and prepares to renew the fight. If he cannot vanquish his Enemy, he is resolved that at least he will deprive Him of joy in His conquest. Satan's virtues are not Puritan virtues; he is an Elizabethan hero-villain, in the Machiavellian tradition of greatness in evil. Structurally, Satan is not the hero of the epic; but the later dwindling of character which ends in his physical metamorphosis into a serpent carries relatively little emotional conviction. Since Adam, by comparison, does not attain epic stature, it may be said that *Paradise Lost* has no real hero.

It has been suggested that Satan personifies Milton's own spiritual temptation, and, for this reason, assumes proportions greater than his place in the poem justifies. During the last years of the Commonwealth, while Milton was still writing *Paradise Lost,* his blindness had become total, so that he needed assistance in his office of Latin Secretary. By 1635 his disability was so pronounced that his salary was reduced and he ceased attending Council meetings. Two years later his wife and daughter died. And in 1660, with the restoration of Charles to the English throne, he saw in ruins the cause to which he had devoted his life; he had to conceal himself with friends, and was later arrested and sent to prison. Surely he must have been tempted to rebel against a Providence which had so ordered his life.

The characters of Adam and Eve, though lacking the greatness of Satan, are beautifully drawn and reveal deep insight into human nature. They are, to a great extent, symbols of mankind as a whole; as such, their characters are generalized in order to convey ideas. Yet they are also real on a human level. Perhaps the chief reason for this naturalness is that Milton's dramatic sense would not let him pay more than token service to the Puritan idea that matter is evil in itself. He follows instead the rabbinical theory that matter and spirit, both arising from the same act of creation, are not to be divided; hence, the emotions of Adam and Eve gain solidity and conviction through their linkage with sensual values. They are not merely allegorical figures, but products of immediate and deeply felt experience. Milton's foolish and painful marriage to Mary Powell finds expression in the details of their relationship; yet there is neither contempt nor hatred in the portrait of Eve, who is one of the loveliest and most sympathetic of all feminine characters. Her description, like that of the Garden, is in the pastoral tradition of Spenser, deeply moving in its luxuriant beauty.

Adam and Eve are led to disobey God through the weaknesses which Milton considers typical of their sexes. She succumbs through vanity, curiosity, and restlessness for new experience; Adam follows her in sin through passion alone, which overwhelms his superior reason. Here, Milton follows an essentially Platonic concept of human moral nature, in which the center of right conduct is the reason, which should dominate other levels of the mind; a mind so ordered will make the correct use of free choice. Adam's complaint to Raphael that creation must have been imperfect since it leaves him susceptible to beauty, brings the warning that the will must be supreme over the passions. In Milton's later poem, *Paradise Regained*, Christ's victory over Satan is a victory of reason, atoning for the defeat of reason by Adam's sin; Satan's arguments are analyzed according to Socratic method and rejected because of their fallacies. Eve's temptation by Satan, on the other hand, reflects the Puritan distrust of Renaissance courtly love traditions, for Satan uses these conventions to beguile her vanity; the only proper relationship between men and women is that of marriage. Her sin also illustrates the Puritan concept of social freedom; if she had not been allowed to walk alone in the Garden, she would not have been exposed to Satan. Although freedom is the proper state of the individual, it must be modified, in practice, with respect to the immature or the foolhardy; those who have, by God's grace, been given wisdom, should, if necessary, compel lesser men to obey God's laws.

Although the proper use of freedom is obedience to divine order, Milton believes that the ability to choose is always present. What joy could God find in the creation of automata, and of what value would man's love be to God if he had not also the power to reject? Evading the Calvinistic theory of divine election, Milton reaffirms throughout the poem his belief in freedom of the will. Satan and the rebel angels are free to cry *"non serviam";* Adam and Eve are not only free to choose, but forewarned of their temptation by Raphael. God foresees the end of the struggle, but "foreknowledge had no influence on their fault, which had no less proved certain unforeknown." Since, however, mankind falls through misuse of freedom, he must be redeemed, decrees God, "not of will in him, but grace in Me, freely vouchsafed." This is not unqualified Calvinism, for God also says that those shall be saved who will. Milton goes no further in attempting to solve the paradox by philosophy; these statements are sufficient for the artistic purposes of the poem, and greater detail would upset its balance.

The misuse of freedom in government is expertly satirized in the debate of the infernal peers at Pandemonium, where the fallen angels decide their future course of action, as they believe, by free debate. Actually, none of the speakers is free; they are ruled, first by the will of God, which they ignore, and more immediately, by the Machiavellian statesmanship of Satan. The application to the weakening of parliamentary forms under Charles I is evident; the kingdom of Heaven, where the angelic hierarchy serves God by free choice, is intended as a parallel to the Cromwellian state. Abdiel, standing alone in resistance to Satan among the rebel angels, expresses this view magnificently:

"Unjustly thou deprav'st it with the name
Of servitude to serve whom God ordains,
Or Nature; God and Nature bid the same,
When he who rules is worthiest, and excels
Them whom he governs. This is servitude,
To serve th' unwise, or him who hath rebell'd
Against his worthier. . . ."

Milton shared with Dante the view that science is properly
a subdivision of theology; in *Paradise Lost*, this attitude is reinforced by a natural preference for a poetic, rather than
technically exact, description of nature, as well as a typically
Puritan distrust of empirical knowledge. Any question as to
the structure of the universe is referred to scriptural authority
or literary tradition. The Copernican system of astronomy was
certainly a part of Milton's vast reading; but he seems as willing to use in his work the older Ptolemaic and earth-centered
universe. In Books III and VIII he discusses both; in the latter
passage, the Archangel Raphael, in giving to Adam an account
of the universe, ends his speech,

"Heaven is for thee too high
To know what passes there; be lowly wise:
Think only what concerns thee and thy being;
Dream not of other worlds. . . ."

The ordered beauty of the older system is well suited to the
poem, and, in this context, has a feeling of rightness which
changes in cosmology can never alter. The awe and fear with
which nature is regarded are deeply poetic; a sense of wonder
is, perhaps, essential, not only to every epic poem, but also to
every great poem of any kind.

An almost lyrical aspect is presented in *Paradise Lost* by the
continual undercurrent of commentary, expressed or implied,
which colors the narrative. Milton's personality is seldom absent from the poem; several times, indeed, it breaks through
in intense, highly personal utterances. One of the most beautiful of these is the invocation at the beginning of Book III, a

prayer to God in the aspect of light; in tone and feeling, it is highly reminiscent of the famous Sonnet: "When I consider how my light is spent." His characterizations and descriptive passages are strongly colored by his opinions. This subjectivity of tone is deepened by the almost mystical effect of some of the imagery, and still other lyrical meanings are expressed through Milton's highly individual use of symbolism and allegory. The interval of divine creation following the war in Heaven, the divinely inspired instruction by which Adam is taught to contemplate the wonders of created nature, both express symbolically Milton's feeling that the works of peace are greater than the destruction of war; this attitude finds more direct expression in his sonnets to Cromwell and Fairfax. The militant Puritanism of the pamphlets is glimpsed, however, in the viciously anti-Catholic satire of one example, the "Paradise of Fools." Milton's attitude of resistance to the pressures and tribulations of the world shows up again and again, in the characters of Abdiel, Satan, and his selection of the trial of Adam and Eve in the Garden as the subject.

There is some evidence that Milton first intended to use dramatic form for *Paradise Lost*. In 1642, however, he decided to make use of the poetic form of Homer and Vergil. Perhaps the closing of the theaters in that year was the deciding factor; but the choice could have been made on artistic grounds alone, for the cosmic sweep of his theme requires epic form.

The poem is in twelve books, each preceded by a short prose "Argument" outlining the action. The classical epic form is employed with conscious, meticulous art and very little flexibility. Occasionally, in fact, it resembles a mold into which the material has been "poured." This rigidity of form sometimes involves Milton in technical difficulties which are almost impossible to solve. For example, the classical device of beginning the poem midway in the narrative and linking it to the beginning and end by exposition and prophecy often forces him to use long didactic passages with a minimum of action, in order to keep the machinery going. This method, which is not wholly suited to the content of the work, leads to a relatively weak ending.

The formal kinship of *Paradise Lost* with the classical epic can be traced in countless details of composition, as well as in the over-all structure. Milton's statement of theme in lines one to five follows the pattern of Homer and Vergil, as does his affirmation of purpose in lines twenty-four to twenty-five; his assertion of Providence, however, replaces the classical assertion of fate, and his invocation to the Muse (lines 6-23) is also altered in conformity with Puritan belief. The names of Greek and Roman deities, too, are interpreted as being names given by man to certain of the infernal peers who intervened in human affairs and were mistakenly worshiped as gods. The classical formula "what cause?" is used in lines twenty-six and twenty-seven, and its answer, "the infernal serpent" also conforms to the pattern. The infernal legions, like the heroes of the *Aeneid*, pursue "epic recreation" on the three levels of physical sport, poetry, and philosophy. Book IV closes with the figure of the scales of justice, from the *Iliad*. Like Aeneas at the court of Dido, Raphael sums up the antecedent action; and the prophecy of Michael to Adam at the close of the poem resembles the Sibyl's prophecy of the course of Roman history in Book VI of the *Aeneid*. Hanford, in his *Milton Handbook*, lists many other such correspondences. The most important of these are: alternation of scenes on earth with scenes in extraterrestrial regions; alternation of dramatic dialogue with extensive descriptive and narrative passages; enumeration of the hosts (Book I); a council of leaders (Book II) and a council of divinities (Book III); allegorical episodes, such as that of Sin and Death (Book II); descriptions of technical processes, such as the casting of cannon (Book VI) and the building of Pandemonium (Book II); a celestial visitant warning and advising mortals (Book V); and a war with episodes of single combat, challenge, and reply (Book VI).

But the true claim of *Paradise Lost* to epic stature lies not in its formal imitations of classical forms, but in the splendor of its verse. Milton justifies his selection of blank verse in a short preface to the poem, which cites ancient and modern authorities in support and defines "true musical delight" as consisting "only in apt Numbers, fit quantity of Syllables, and the sense variously drawn out from one verse to another, not in the jingling sound of like endings." Iambic pentameter is chosen as the heroic meter most natural to the English language.

The unit of construction in *Paradise Lost* is not the line, but what has been called the verse-paragraph, a device which aids in the organization of content and provides infinite opportunities for variation within the meter through the use of run-on lines and exchanged stresses. The internal rhyme-schemes are delicate and complex, and are handled with masterful subtlety.

The vividness and suppleness of the verse has a deeply dramatic quality. Milton is master of every device which may be employed to give color, music, naturalness, and variety to the interplay of sound and meaning between lines. Hanford has suggested that the almost material beauty of rhythm and rhetoric may have stemmed partly from Milton's blindness, the curtailment of one sense resulting in greater sensitivity of the others. Movement and sound are exquisitely accommodated to meaning; and the resonant quality of the lines attains an effect of dignity and grandeur which is completely appropriate to the theme. The first two books are superb and justify Matthew Arnold's assertion that Milton is the only English poet ever to sustain the "grand style." By comparison, the final books seem weak; actually, they contain many passages of rare beauty, and have received more criticism than they deserve. Relatively, however, they lack unity, contrast, and sustained dramatic power.

Paradise Lost was, we know, published on August 20, 1667, for it was entered on the Stationers' Register of that date. *Paradise Regained* appeared together with *Paradise Lost* in the edition of 1671, though there is a tradition that Milton had completed both poems before the first was published. The Quaker Ellwood is said to have remarked to the author, on seeing a manuscript copy of the earlier poem, "Thou hast said much here of *Paradise Lost;* what hast thou to say of Paradise found?" And Milton, after thinking the problem over for a time, showed Ellwood a copy of the second poem. This is a good story, but probably not true, for differences in style and meter indicate that the *Paradise Regained* was composed much later than *Paradise Lost*.

It is a shorter poem than *Paradise Lost*, in only four books, and deals with the temptation of Christ by Satan. In its own way it is a great poem; we have not included it here, however, because it does not rise to the sustained nobility of *Paradise Lost*. Had Milton written only *Paradise Regained*, he would still be recognized as an important poet of his time; but the greatness of *Paradise Lost* overshadows that of *Paradise Regained*.

PARADISE LOST: THE STORY

BOOK I: "The First Book proposes, first, in brief, the whole subject—Man's disobedience, and the loss thereupon of Paradise, wherein he was placed; then touches the prime cause of his fall—the Serpent, or rather Satan in the Serpent; who, revolting from God, and drawing to his side many legions of Angels, was, by the command of God, driven out of Heaven, with all his crew, into the great deep. . . ."

> Of Man's first disobedience, and the fruit
> Of that forbidden tree, whose mortal taste
> Brought Death into the World, and all our woe,
> With loss of Eden, till one greater Man
> Restore us, and regain the blissful seat,
> Sing, Heavenly Muse, that on the secret top
> Of Oreb, or of Sinai, didst inspire
> That shepherd, who first taught the chosen seed
> In the beginning how the Heavens and Earth
> Rose out of Chaos; or, if Sion hill
> Delight thee more, and Siloa's brook that flow'd
> Fast by the Oracle of God: I thence
> Invoke thy aid to my adventrous song
> That with no middle flight intends to soar
> Above th' Aonian mount, while it pursues
> Things unattempted yet in prose or rhyme.
> And chiefly thou, O Spirit, that dost prefer
> Before all temples the upright heart and pure,
> Instruct me, for Thou know'st; Thou from the first
> Wast present, and, with mighty wings outspread,

Dove-like, satst brooding on the vast Abyss
And mad'st it pregnant: What in me is dark
Illumine, what is low raise and support;
That to the height of this great argument
I may assert Eternal Providence
And justify the ways of God to men.[1]

In the deep Chaos, there was a place condemned to eternal darkness, awaiting the reception of those seduced by the leader of that foul revolt which opposed Truth, and fell by its own falsehood. Vain was the attempt, for the Almighty hurled these rebels headlong from the skies. In chains of adamant and dread fire, the Eternal Foe lay where he fell, planning his revenge.

No light, but rather darkness visible
Serv'd only to discover sights of woe,
Regions of sorrow, doleful shades, where peace
And rest can never dwell, hope never comes
That comes to all.

But Satan, archangel though in chains, led his fellows from the dreadful lake to higher ground. "Better to reign in Hell, than serve in Heaven," he cried, voicing the ambitions of tyrants forever, who would decree a special law unto themselves. Power alone had won the day, but the legions of Hell, better prepared, should one day triumph. Until then, to do evil, and to contravene, so far as possible, the purposes of the Creator, was to be their sole aim. "To be weak is miserable," said Satan, and to be strong, though racked with deep despair, was bliss beyond the glory of the angels who, as he believed, were forced to sing eternal praises to a God of might. Like the beast Leviathan, hugest of God's works, the Arch-Fiend had never raised his head from that burning lake, had not God willed it so, for His greater glory. But Satan, speaking with Beelzebub, his nearest lieutenant, believed himself free from

[1] The quotations from the poem are taken from the text of the edition of 1667. The spelling and punctuation have been modernized only slightly.

the power of the Omnipotent, Who had left him at large, that the decree of damnation might be certain. Yet all his malice served to bring forth good, beyond his perjured spirit's scope; infinite grace and mercy was to be shown upon man, by him to be seduced.

As an example to his astonished forces, the Fiend

> Was moving toward the shore; his ponderous shield
> Ethereal temper, massy, large, and round,
> Behind him cast; the broad circumference
> Hung on his shoulders like the moon, whose orb
> Through optic glass the Tuscan artist views
> At ev'ning from the top of Fesole,
> Or in Valdarno, to descry new lands,
> Rivers or mountains in her spotty globe.
> His spear, to equal which the tallest pine
> Hewn on Norwegian hills . . . were but a wand,
> He walked with to support uneasy steps
> Over the burning marl. . . .
>   . . . on the beach
> Of that inflamed sea, he stood and called
> His Legions, angel forms who lay entranced
> Thick as autumnal leaves that strow the brooks
> In Vallombrosa. . . .
> He called so loud that all the hollow deep
> Of Hell resounded: "Princes, Potentates,
> Warriors, the Flower of Heaven, once yours, now lost,
> If such astonishment as this can seize
> Eternal spirits! or have ye chos'n this place
> After the toil of battle to repose
> Your wearied virtue, for the ease you find
> To slumber here, as in the vales of Heaven?
> Or in this abject posture have ye sworn
> To adore the Conqueror? Who now beholds
> Cherub and Seraph rolling in the flood
> With scattered arms and ensigns, till anon
> His swift pursuers from Heaven-gates discern

The advantage, and descending tread us down
Thus drooping, or with linkèd thunderbolts
Transfix us to the bottom of this gulf?
Awake, arise, or be for ever fallen!"

They heard, and were ashamed. Up they rose upon their
singed wings to obey their general, as sleeping sentries awaken,
when found by him whom they dread. Innumerable they were,
like the locusts summoned by Amram's son; never did such a
multitude pour forth for any human cause, worthy to grace any
throne on earth, though blotted forever from the Divine Books
of Life.

All the heathen gods were in that host; all the heroes who
ever rebelled against Divine Law, all the creatures worshiped
by man in his blindness were with that army of Anti-Christ.
But they were sad and injured by God's wrath. Yet, seeing
their Chief not downcast, they rejoiced; in his usual pride,
Satan received his warriors. Azrael, Satan's cherub, claimed
the right to be the standard-bearer, and, to the Doric mode, the
infernal legions followed their Prince. In perfect phalanx they
moved, and, "instead of rage, deliberate valor breathed, firm
and unmoved." Through united thought and purpose, they
breathed in spiritual unison. Happy had they been, if they had
never ventured further against their King! Satan's heart
swelled with pride, as he beheld his minions rally to the pen-
non.

> . . . He, above the rest,
> In shape and gesture proudly eminent,
> Stood like a tower: his form had yet not lost
> All her original brightness, nor appeared
> Less than Archangel ruined, and th' excess
> Of glory obscured. . . .

> . . . Let none admire
> That riches grow in Hell; that soil may best
> Deserve the precious bane. And here let those
> Who boast in mortal things, and wondering tell

> Of Babel, and the works of Memphian kings,
> Learn how their greatest monuments of fame,
> And strength, and art, are easily outdone
> By Spirits reprobate.

What mortal hands could never perform in many centuries, the legions of Satan achieved in one night's space, or less. Never was any earthly structure so magnificent as the palace at Pandemonium, where the leaders of the evil host were to assemble. But the towers that Satan had built in Heaven, though greater than these, should never avail him more.

Satan's peers were summoned, and, within that archangelical work, they swarmed on the air and in the ground, thicker than bees. But, since, outside the realm of Eternity, all places are limited, these spirits, giants in the limitless Empyrean, were forced to reduce their stature to the narrow room left for them.

BOOK II: High on a throne of royal state, which far
> Outshone the wealth of Ormus and of Ind,
> Or where the gorgeous East with richest hand
> Showers on her kings barbaric pearl and gold,
> Satan exalted sat, by merit raised
> To that bad eminence; and from despair
> Thus high uplifted beyond hope, aspires
> Beyond thus high, insatiate to pursue
> Vain war with Heaven; and, by success untaught,
> His proud imaginations thus displayed.

The council was begun, and Satan debated whether to fight or surrender. Since the debate was open to all, Moloch, "sceptered King," arose, and with his clever discourse begged, as fitted his reckless and fierce-minded soul, for open war. Upon the other side arose Belial, who seemed

> For dignity composed, and high exploit:
> But all was false and hollow; though his tongue
> Dropped manna, and could make the worst appear

The better reason, to perplex and dash
Maturest counsels; for his thoughts were low;
To vice industrious, but to nobler deeds
Timorous and slothful; yet he pleased the ear. . . .

In persuasive accents, he pleaded for peace with Heaven. God, having made all, could, he said, annihilate all, including consciousness for thought and action, "this intellectual being, those thoughts that wander through eternity." He argued that, since God is omnipotent, further struggle would be useless, and that it would be better to stand upon the ground of their defeat, to endure, and not stir the Omnipotent to greater punishment.

But the assembly listened to Mammon, highest of Satan's peers, swayed neither by too much reason nor by too much passion, who derided as vain the hope of conquering Heaven, and argued that if

". . . He should relent
And publish Grace to all, on promise made
Of new subjection,"

their state in Heaven would be servile. Then it would be better to seek

"Our own good from ourselves, and from our own
Live to ourselves, though in this vast recess,
Free, and to none accountable, preferring
Hard liberty before the easy yoke
Of servile pomp. . . .
Our torments also may in length of time
Become our elements. . . ."

As Mammon concluded his advice, a murmur filled the assembly like the sound of the wind in hollow rocks. Great was the applause, for the fear of Michael and his sword was still within them.

When Beelzebub saw their terror, he arose. None greater than he, save Satan alone, had ever sat in the infernal council. God, he said,

> ". . . still first and last will reign
> Sole King, and of His Kingdom lose no part
> By our revolt, but over Hell extend
> His Empire, and with iron scepter rule
> Us here."

Nor could they hope for peace: peace would be only punish-ment; and what peace could they have, save plotting revenge? Would it not be better to find some easier enterprise? Perhaps the new creature called Man, whose creation had been decreed in Heaven, could be attacked, or seduced to their party, so that God should become Man's enemy. The bold design pleased the assembly, and they voted their assent.

Again Beelzebub spoke, asking whom they should send in search of the new world. It would be well guarded, and their last hope lay upon the one who should make the journey. None answered, for they pondered the danger of such an at-tempt. Satan, great in valor as in degeneracy, offered himself; as chief, he must accept both hazard and honor. Thus they ended their consultation; and the result was announced by the fallen Cherubim. To pass the irksome hours until the return of their chief, they pursued their favorite pastimes; some engaged in contests of arms; some sang to the harp the story of their Fall; others argued

> Of Providence, Foreknowledge, Will, and Fate,
> Fixed Fate, free will, foreknowledge absolute,
> And found no end, in wand'ring mazes lost.

Meanwhile, Satan flew through the ethereal substance of his own domain, until he came upon the Gates of Hell. Upon either side of the threefold gates there sat a horrible shape.

> The one seemed woman to the waist, and fair,
> But ended foul in many a scaly fold. . . ."

Around her middle, a great number of hellish monsters bel-lowed, and, as fast as they were born, they sought her womb again, where they barked and howled still. Upon the other

side, there sat a Shape (if shape it might be called), that all
creatures dreaded:

> . . . Black it stood as Night,
> Fierce as ten Furies, terrible as Hell,
> And shook a dreadful dart: what seemed his head
> The likeness of a kingly crown had on.

But Satan soon established his kinship with these—Sin, his
daughter, and Death, her son. Sin opened the gate with little
argument; Sin's fatal key, unknown as yet to man, was our
eternal woe.

With difficulty, Satan passed through Chaos, directed by the
Power that ruled it, to the new World which he had never
yet seen.

Book III:

> Hail, holy Light, offspring of Heaven first-born!
> Or of the Eternal coeternal beam
> May I express thee unblamed? since God is light,
> And never but in unapproached light
> Dwelt from eternity, dwelt then in thee,
> Bright effluence of bright essence increate! . . .
> Thee I revisit now with bolder wing,
> Escaped the Stygian pool, though long detained
> In that obscure sojourn, while in my flight,
> Through utter and through middle darkness borne,
> With other notes than to the Orphean lyre
> I sung of Chaos and eternal Night. . . .
>   . . . but thou
> Revisit'st not these eyes, that roll in vain
> To find thy piercing ray, and find no dawn;
> So thick a drop serene hath quenched their orbs,
> Or dim suffusion veiled. . . .
>   . . . Thus with the year
> Seasons return; but not to me returns
> Day, or the sweet approach of even or morn,
> Or sight of vernal bloom, or summer's rose,

Or flocks, or herds, or human face divine;
But cloud instead, and ever-during dark
Surrounds me, from the cheerful ways of men
Cut off, and for the book of knowledge fair,
Presented with a universal blank. . . .

Now had God, from His seat in the Empyrean, looked down upon all things, and, enthroned high above all height, He saw our first parents,

. . . yet the only two
Of mankind, in the happy Garden placed,
Reaping immortal fruits of joy and love,
Uninterrupted joy, unrivaled love,
In blissful solitude.

Next He looked upon Hell and the gulf of Chaos, and He beheld Satan, warily coasting the wall of Heaven, on the rim of the world. Sorrowing, He spoke to His Son, who stood at his right hand; seeing past, present, and future in His Eternal Present, He foretold the fall of man.

. . . Whose fault?
Whose but his own? Ingrate, he had of Me,
All he could have; I made him just and right,
Sufficient to have stood, though free to fall.
Such I created all the Ethereal Powers
And Spirits, both of them who stood and them who failed.

But, although both must bear the responsibility for sin freely committed, man, since he fell through deceit, should have mercy, while those who first fell from Heaven, being "self-tempted, self-depraved," should find none. But only through God's Grace should any of mankind return to their lost estate. Yet, that justice should be satisfied, even in mercy, God called upon another to bear the punishment of death for all the world of men. But all the heavenly host stood mute; and all mankind had been forever doomed to death and Hell, had not the Son of God, through fullness of love, offered Himself in man's place, to pay to death all of Him that might die, confident of eventual victory over His conqueror. God sealed with His decree this most perfect sacrifice:

> . . . So Man, as is most just,
> Shall satisfy for Man, be judged and die,
> And dying, rise, and rising, with Him raise
> His brethren, ransomed with His own dear life.

Because love, more than the glory of His birth, had declared His merit, the Son of God was exalted in eternal supremacy over every other creature in the universe; after sitting in final judgment on every soul, by His might the Gates of Hell should one day close for ever, death should be no more, and the golden days of eternal truth, joy, and love should come again.

> "Then Thou Thy regal sceptre shalt lay by;
> For regal sceptre then no more shall need;
> God shall be all in all."

Then the multitude of angels threw their crowns at His feet; crowned again, they sang praises to God and to the Son.

Meanwhile, Satan alighted, brooding, upon the bare convex of the world's outermost orb; he was yet alone, but in future, this barren space should be occupied by all those who built their hope and their glory upon nothing but vanity and the vain praise of the world, with the souls of embryos and unbaptized children and idiots. This Limbo should be called the Paradise of Fools. Satan next passed the Gate of Heaven, the stairs of which were then let down, and from the lowest step, he might survey all the world at once. Not attempting to climb further, he plunged through the still spaces among the stars toward the sun; undazzled by its glory, he beheld a radiant angel stand near him—that same Uriel whom John saw in the sun. Disguising himself as a youthful cherub, Satan approached the archangel, and, greeting him fairly, with expertly humble flattery, said that he had come to view the new Creation, in order to praise God with greater fitness. Uriel was deceived, for only God can see through hypocrisy, and graciously pointed out the way for Satan. Bowing to Uriel, Satan sped to earth, nor stayed until he alighted on the top of Mount Niphates.

BOOK IV:

> O for that warning voice, which he who saw
> The Apocalypse, heard cry in Heaven aloud,
> Then when the dragon, put to second rout,
> Came furious down to be revenged on men,
> *"Woe to the inhabitants on Earth!"* that now,
> While time was, our first parents had been warned
> The coming of their secret foe, and 'scaped,
> Haply so 'scaped his mortal snare; for now,
> Satan, now first inflamed with rage, came down,
> The Tempter, ere the accuser of mankind,
> To wreak on innocent frail man his loss
> Of that first battle, and his flight to Hell.

Envy, fear, and despair seethed within Satan, for he might never escape the true Hell which was his own soul.

> "Which way I fly is Hell; myself am Hell;
> And in the lowest deep a lower deep
> Still threat'ning to devour me opens wide,
> To which the Hell I suffer seems a Heaven.
> O then at last relent! Is there no place
> Left for repentance, none for pardon left?
> Disdain forbids me, and my dread of shame
> Among the spirits beneath, whom I seduced
> With other promises and other vaunts
> Than to submit, boasting I could subdue
> The Omnipotent. . . ."
>   Thus while he spake, each passion dimmed his face
> Thrice changed with pale, ire, envy, and despair,
> Which marred his borrowed visage, and betrayed
> Him counterfeit, if any eye beheld.
> For heavenly minds from such distempers foul
> Are ever clear. Whereof he soon aware

Each perturbation smoothed with outward calm,
Artificer of fraud; and was the first
That practised falsehood under saintly show,
Deep malice to conceal, couched with revenge;
Yet not enough had practised to deceive
Uriel once warned; whose eye pursued him down
The way he went, and, on the Assyrian mount
Saw him disfigured, more than could befall
Spirit of happy sort. . . .

But he steeled himself in his evil plan and proceeded toward
Paradise, where, crossing the boundary, he took his seat upon
the Tree of Life, the highest in the Garden, disguising himself
as a cormorant. Near the Tree on which he sat, which bore
ambrosial golden fruit, he saw the Tree of Knowledge, whose
fruit gave "knowledge of good, bought dear by knowing ill."
Southward through Eden, a crystal stream flowed with ambrosial water, and, issuing forth from the hill, rose to join the
fountain, which watered the Garden, from which united flood
arose four rivers. The tiny, fresh brooks from the fountain
above fed the flowers of Paradise with their nectar. Every
aspect of nature was perfect here; no creature had as yet any
thought of harming another. And, among the beauties of Paradise, among the gentle beasts,

Two of far nobler shape, erect and tall,
God-like erect, with native honor clad
In naked majesty, seemed lords of all,
And worthy seemed, for in their looks divine
The image of their glorious Maker shone,
Truth, wisdom, sanctitude severe and pure—
Severe, but in true filial freedom placed;
Whence true authority in men. . . .
         . . . the loveliest pair
That ever since in love's embraces met,
Adam, the goodliest man of men since born
His sons; the fairest of her daughters, Eve.

In innocent love and beauty, they feared nothing, for they
knew no evil. As they ate their evening meal of fruits yielded
by the submissive branches,

> About them frisking played
> All beasts of the Earth, since wild, and of all chase
> In wood or wilderness, forest or den;
> Sporting the lion ramped, and in his paw
> Dandled the kid; bears, tigers, ounces, pards
> Gamboled before them; the unwieldy elephant,
> To make them mirth used all his might, and wreathed
> His lithe proboscis. . . .

Satan beheld them with envy, wonder, and sympathy; the
unperverted part of his angelic nature shrank from wronging
their spotless innocence, yet, finding an excuse for his purpose,
put down these nobler feelings:

> "Hell shall unfold,
> To entertain you two . . .
> . . . if no better place,
> Thank Him who puts me, loath, to this revenge,
> On you, who wrong me not, for Him, who wronged.
> And should I at your harmless innocence
> Melt, as I do, yet public reason just,
> Honor and empire with revenge enlarged,
> By conquering this new world, compels me now
> To do what else, though damned, I should abhor."

Alighting among the animals, he sought what shape might
best serve his ends, and prowled, now as a lion, now as a tiger,
watching Adam and Eve as they talked together, recalling
God's kindness and wisdom, and the first day on which they
had seen one another.

> Thus talking, hand in hand alone they passed
> On to their blissful bower; it was a place
> Chosen by the sovereign Planter, when he framed
> All things to man's delightful use. . . .

Thus at their shady lodge arrived, both stood,
Both turned, and under open sky, adored
The God that made both sky, earth, air, and Heaven,
Which they beheld, the moon's resplendent globe,
And starry Pole. . . .
    This said unanimous, and other rites
Observing none, but adoration pure
Which God likes best, into their inmost bower
Handed they went; and eased the putting-off
These troublesome disguises which we wear.

As they went to their flowery couch to enjoy their innocent, lustless love, Satan turned aside in jealous torment. But Satan had learned from Adam's own mouth the single command imposed upon them by God, and determined to excite their minds with thirst for knowledge.

Meanwhile, Uriel sought Gabriel, chief of the angelic guards, where he sat watching the unarmed youth of Heaven in their heroic sports. In haste, he reported that the seeming cherub had, when he first alighted, returned to his original form. Gabriel replied that whatever peril might lurk within the walls of the Garden should be discovered. He dispersed his forces over Eden to search, and Ithuriel and Zephon came upon Satan, squatting in the form of a toad, close to the ear of the sleeping Eve. When forced to resume his original shape by the touch of Ithuriel's spear, he scorned to answer until he should be conducted to their leader.

"Know ye not then," said Satan, filled with scorn,
"Know ye not me? Ye knew me once no mate
For you, there sitting where ye durst not soar;
Not to know me argues yourselves unknown. . . ."
To whom thus Zephon, answering scorn with scorn,
"Think not, revolted Spirit, thy shape the same,
Or undiminished brightness, to be known,
As when thou stood'st in Heaven upright and pure. . . ."
    So spake the Cherub; and his grave rebuke,
Severe in youthful beauty, added grace

Invincible; abashed the Devil stood,
And felt how awful goodness is, and saw
Virtue in her shape how lovely, saw, and pined
His loss; but chiefly to find her observed
His lustre visibly impaired; yet seemed
Undaunted. "If I must contend," said he,
"Best with the best, the sender not the sent;
Or all at once; more glory will be won,
Or less be lost."

Gabriel was not deceived by Satan's plausible words, but
ordered him from the Garden within the space of an hour, on
pain of a forced re-imprisonment. Receiving defiance as his
answer, Gabriel marshaled his forces for the attack, while
Satan's figure grew until it towered to the sky. But God, to
prevent such a horrid war in Paradise, hung out in Heaven his
golden scales,

Which Gabriel spying, thus bespake the Fiend;
    "Satan, I know thy strength, and thou know'st mine,
Neither our own but given; what folly then
To boast what arms can do, since thine no more
Than Heaven permits, nor mine, though doubled now
To trample thee as mire. For proof look up,
And read thy lot in yon celestial sign,
Where thou art weighed, and shown how light, how weak,
If thou resist." The Fiend looked up, and knew
His mounted scale aloft: not more; but fled
Murmuring; and with him fled the shades of night.

Book V: With the coming of dawn, Adam awoke, and, seeing
Eve still asleep, with tumbled hair and glowing cheeks, signs
of unquiet rest, spoke gently to her. Waking, she told him of
her troublesome dreams, in which a soft voice had urged her
to forbidding knowledge, even seemed to hold the fruit before her mouth. Adam disliked her story, so portentous of evil,
yet he knew of no possible source of evil in her or in Paradise.
He explained her visions as merely the working of idle fancy,

unrestrained by sleeping reason; reassuring her with the hope
that what she had dreamed, waking she would even less consent to do, he led her to the door of their bower. After their
simple morning prayer, they went out to their pleasant employment among the luxuriant plants. God, beholding them,
sent Raphael, "the sociable spirit," to converse with Adam and
to warn him of his enemy. Nor did the wingèd saint delay, but
sped with glorious wings through the eternal host, which
parted to make way for him. To the fowls of the air, he seemed
as a phoenix flying, until, reaching his destination, he resumed
his proper shape; Adam, beholding the six-winged seraph, like
a second sun, called in wonder to Eve, who was preparing the
savory fruits for the midday meal. God-like, Adam walked
forth to greet his guest; nor did our first parents feel shame or
fear, for then did angels descend freely to mingle with the
creatures of earth. Arriving at the bower, Raphael addressed
Eve by the holy salutation, "Hail!", used "long after to blest
Mary, second Eve." The angel ate with them, for the partly-
spiritual foods of Eden were of relish to him.

> . . . A while discourse they hold,
> No fear lest dinner cool. . . .

Adam asked Raphael to tell him

> Of things above his world, and of their being
> Who dwell in Heaven, whose excellence he saw
> Transcend his own so far, whose radiant forms
> Divine effulgence, whose high power so far
> Exceeded human. . . .

And Raphael replied that all things proceed from God, and, if
not depraved, return to him, though the various beings have
differing natures. But, asked Adam, how can we be anything
but obedient?

> . . . Can we want obedience then
> To Him, or possibly His love desert
> Who formed us from the dust, and placed us here
> Full to the utmost measure of what bliss
> Human desires can seek or apprehend?

Raphael answered that some spirits are fallen; and Adam asked how that had come about. Then Raphael told how the spirits had all been summoned to a great conclave, and God the Father addressed them:

> "Hear, all ye angels, progeny of Light,
> Thrones, Dominations, Princedoms, Virtues, Powers,
> Hear My decree, which unrevoked shall stand.
> This day I have begot Whom I declare
> My only Son, and on this holy hill
> Him have anointed, Whom ye now behold
> At My right hand; your Head I Him appoint;
> And by Myself have sworn to Him shall bow
> All knees in Heaven, and shall confess Him Lord;
> Under His great vice-gerent reign abide
> United as one individual soul
> Forever happy; Him who disobeys
> Me disobeys, breaks union, and that day
> Cast out from God and blessed vision, falls
> Into utter darkness, deep ingulfed, his place
> Ordained without redemption, without end."

But Lucifer, in evil jealousy against the Son of God, believing his own desert as heir and lord of the heavenly host to be greater, first assembled his legions in the north. Calling together his associates, the Powers who were his regents, he proposed open violence against the Omnipotent. All obeyed him, for he was, under God and His Son, greatest in all creation.

The Father saw all these preparations, and, smiling, entrusted to His Son the power to quell the pride of the rebel angels. But, as God's Heir promised fealty and service, the forces of Lucifer were far advanced toward the place of combat; for, in his palace upon the Mountain of the Congregation, the rebel peer had called his chiefs in council and, with golden speech, persuaded them to throw off their chains of forced adoration and share with him the realm of Heaven. None opposed Lucifer, save for one Abdiel, a seraph, who dared upbraid him for his audacity:

"Shalt thou give law to God? shalt thou dispute
With him the points of liberty, Who made
Thee what thou art. . . .
How provident He is, how far from thought
To make us less; bent rather to exalt
Our happy state, under one Head more near
United. But—to grant it thee unjust
That equal over equals monarch reign—
Thyself, though great and glorious, dost thou count,
Or all angelic nature joined in one,
Equal to Him . . . ?"

Seeing that none other seconded this defiance, Lucifer spoke
boldly: "Remember'st thou thy making, while the Maker gave
thee being?" he asked; for himself, he held that, knowing not
when he was otherwise than at that moment, he found cause
to suspect God's truth in claiming himself creator of angels.
The faithful Abdiel replied;

"O alienate from God, O Spirit accursed,
Forsaken of all good! I see thy fall
Determined, and thy hapless crew involved
In this perfidious fraud, contagion spread
Both of thy crime and punishment . . .
Yet not for thy advice or threats I fly
These wicked tents devoted, lest the wrath
Impendent, raging into sudden flame
Distinguish not; for soon expect to feel
His thunder on thy head, devouring fire.
Then Who created thee lamenting learn,
When Who can uncreate thee thou shalt know."
So spake the Seraph Abdiel faithful found;
Among the faithless, faithful only he. . . .
And with retorted scorn his back he turned
On those proud towers to swift destruction doomed.

BOOK VI:

All night the dreadless Angel, unpursued,
Through Heaven's wide champaign held his way, till Morn,
Waked by the circling Hours, with rosy hand
Unbarred the gates of Light. . . .

. . . From whence a voice,
From midst a golden cloud, thus mild was heard:
  "Servant of God, well done! Well hast thou fought
The better fight, who single hast maintained
Against revolted multitudes the cause
Of truth, in word mightier than they in arms. . . ."
  So spake the Sovereign voice; and clouds began
To darken all the hill, and smoke to roll
In dusky wreaths, reluctant flames, the sign
Of wrath awaked; nor with less dread the loud
Ethereal trumpet from on high 'gan blow;
At which command the Powers militant
That stood for Heaven, in mighty quadrate joined
Of union irresistible, moved on. . . .
                                    . . . at last
Far in the horizon, to the north appeared
From skirt to skirt a fiery region, stretched
In battailous aspect, and nearer view
Bristled with upright beams innumerable
Of rigid spears, and helmets thronged, and shields
Various, with boastful argument portrayed,
The banded Powers of Satan hasting on
With furious expedition. . . .

The first battle was joined by the encounter of Abdiel and
Satan, who was struck by the faithful spirit; then, after a general
fight, Satan and Michael engaged in single combat:

            . . . the sword
    Of Michael from the Armory of God
    Was given him tempered so, that neither keen
    Nor solid might resist that edge; it met

The sword of Satan with steep force to smite
Descending, and in half cut sheer; nor stayed,
But with swift wheel reverse, deep entering, sheared
All his right side; then Satan first knew pain,
And writhed him to and fro convolved. . . .

Spirits cannot receive in their texture a mortal wound, but
Satan retired from the fight, and when evening put a stay to
the day's battle, the rebellious angels disappeared to their own
place, where they held a council of war. Confident that, having
for one day withstood the might of the Omnipotent, they could
continue their rebellion, Satan directed his angels to prepare a
weapon of his invention:

"Such implements of mischief as shall dash
To pieces, and o'erwhelm whatever stands
Adverse, that they shall fear we have disarmed
The Thunderer of his only dreaded bolt."

Without argument, they flew from the council to dig up
metals for guns and materials for gunpowder, and prepared for
the next day's battle.

As the two armies joined battle, Satan ordered his right and
left side to fall back, disclosing in the center

A triple-mounted row of pillars laid
On wheels (for like to pillars most they seemed
Or hollowed bodies made of oak or fir
With branches lopped, in wood or mountain felled). . . .
    . . . At each, behind,
A Seraph stood, and in his hand a reed
Stood waving, tipped with fire; while we suspense
Collected stood within our thought amused;
Not long, for sudden all at once their reeds
Put forth, and to a narrow vent applied
With nicest touch. Immediate in a flame,
But soon obscured with smoke, all Heaven appeared,
From those deep-throated engines belched, whose roar
Embowled with outrageous noise the air,

And all her entrails tore, disgorging foul
Their devilish glut, chained thunderbolts and hail
Of iron globes, which, on the victor host
Leveled, with such impetuous fury smote
That whom they hit, none on their feet might stand. . . .

The angels of God were forced back, for they had no knowledge of these new weapons; the angels of darkness laughed
among themselves, thinking how they had discomfited their
enemies. But throwing away the arms which they had previously used, now found impotent, the legions of Light

. . . plucked the seated hills with all their load,
Rocks, waters, woods, and by the shaggy tops
Uplifting, bore them in their hands: Amaze,
Be sure, and terror seized the rebel host,
When coming towards them so dread they saw
The bottom of the mountains upward turned,
Till on those cursed engines triple-row
They saw them whelmed, and all their confidence
Under the weight of mountains buried deep,
Themselves invaded next. . . .
The rest in imitation to like arms
Betook them, and the neighboring hills uptore;
So hills amid the air encountered hills,
Hurled to and fro with jaculation dire. . . .
            . . . Now all Heaven
Had gone to wrack, with ruin overspread,
Had not the Almighty Father where He sits . . .
Consulting on the sum of things, foreseen
This tumult, and permitted all, advised,
That His great purpose He might so fulfill,
To honor His anointed Son. . . .

On the third day of battle, the Son, armed with His Father's
thunderbolts, led the embattled seraphim to war, and by His
sole might defeated the rebel angels, and cast them into outer
darkness, into the place prepared for them.

> Hell heard the unsufferable noise; Hell saw
> Heaven ruining from Heaven, and would have fled
> Affrighted; but strict Fate had cast too deep
> Her dark foundations, and too fast had bound.

Hell closing at last upon the entire rebellious host, the Messiah returned, glorious in victory, to His Father. Thus ended Raphael his terrible example.

Book VII: Descend from Heaven, Urania, if I call thee rightly; it is the meaning, not the name itself, that I invoke. Inspire my voice, that I fall not, as once did Bellerophon from his flying steed, in this, my heavenly story.

Adam and Eve heard with admiration and deep thought this story of things so high and strange. Yet, his interest kindled, Adam begged Raphael for more knowledge about the Creation. Raphael, willing to relate all that was permitted to man's knowledge, began,

> "Know then, that after Lucifer from Heaven
> (So call him, brighter once amidst the Host
> Of Angels than that star the stars among)
> Fell with his flaming legions through the Deep
> Into his place, and the great Son returned
> Victorious with His Saints, the Omnipotent
> Eternal Father from His throne beheld
> Their multitude. . . .

To His Son, the Father declared that though some angels had fallen, there remained sufficient to people Heaven; and that He was determined to

> ". . . create
> Another world; out of one man a race
> Of men innumerable, there to dwell,
> Not here, till by degrees of merit raised,
> They open to themselves at length the way
> Up hither, under long obedience tried,
> And Earth be changed to Heaven, and Heaven to Earth."

For this new task, He sent again His Son, to accomplish in six days the work of creation. All the hierarchies of angels sang the praise of this decree, to bring into the place of unworthy, outcast spirits a better race. Raphael then related for the first time on earth the wondrous restraint of Chaos into a Light-impregnated and living unity.

"Let there be Light," said God; and forthwith Light
Ethereal, first of things, quintessence pure
Sprung from the Deep. . . .
    Again, God said, "Let there be Firmament
Amid the waters, and let it divide
The waters from the waters." And God made
The firmament, expanse of liquid, pure,
Transparent, elemental air. . . .
                                    . . . God said,
"Be gathered now ye Waters under Heaven,
Into one place, and let dry land appear!" . . .
The dry land, Earth, and the great receptacle
Of congregated waters He called Seas:
And saw that it was good, and said, "Let the Earth
Put forth the verdant grass, herb yielding seed,
And fruit tree yielding fruit after her kind. . . .
    Again the Almighty spake: "Let there be lights
High in the expanse of Heaven, to divide
The day from night; and let them be for signs
For seasons, and for days, and circling years." . . .
    And God said, "Let the waters generate
Reptile with spawn abundant, living soul:
And let fowl fly above the earth, with wings. . . ."
    The sixth, and of Creation last arose
With evening harps and matin, when God said,
"Let the earth bring forth fowl living in her kind,
Cattle and creeping things, and beast of the earth,
Each in their kind!" . . .
There wanted yet the master-work, the end
Of all yet done; a creature who, not prone

And brute as other creatures, but endued
With sanctity of reason, might erect
His stature, and upright with front serene
Govern the rest, self-knowing, and from thence
Magnanimous to correspond with Heaven . . .
And worship God Supreme, who made him chief
Of all His works; therefore the Omnipotent
Eternal Father (For where is not He
Present?) thus to His Son audibly spake:
   "Let us make now Man in Our image, Man
In Our similitude, and let them rule
Over the fish and fowl of sea and air,
Beast of the field, and over all the earth,
And every creeping thing that creeps the ground."
This said, He formed thee, Adam, thee, O Man,
Dust of the ground, and in thy nostrils breathed
The breath of Life."

Then Raphael told Adam of the Garden, and especially of
the Tree of Knowledge of Good and Evil. The fruit of this Tree
only he might not taste, for to taste it brings death.

Unwearied, the Creator returned, said Raphael, to His Father in Heaven; He had seen the perfection of His work, and
He knew that it was finished. His angelic train led His way
with rejoicing hymns, and the gate was opened to Him. And
in silence sanctified by the sound of the harp and the pipe, the
glorious Son rested from His labor.

BOOK VIII: "What thanks have I," said Adam, "sufficient to thy
friendship, divine historian?" But his thirst for knowledge was
so great that he begged yet greater instruction. Raphael solved
some of his doubts as to the structure and movement of the
universe, telling him that which suited the human mind. Adam
agreed that knowledge of useful things at hand, things on a
lower plane, not unreasonable to ask, would be more in keeping with Raphael's great favor of reply. Nor did our first father
lack eloquence in his speech, for grace of tongue was natural

to him. The Archangel, who had been absent upon the day
when man was created, leading a force to bar the Gates of Hell,
asked Adam to relate his memory of his day of awakening;
with this request, Adam gladly complied, speaking with innocent, yet instinctively knowing tongue of his first day in Eden.
He told of his wonder, his awe, and, finally, his growing loneliness. In vain did God require him to be content with the companionship of the creatures of the earth; these, though "in
reason not contemptible," awakened in him no feeling of kinship. Adam's state on earth had been, in fact, like that of God
among all created beings; yet Adam had humbly begged of
God a mate; for he, not all-knowing and all-seeing, needed true
fellowship, but could never find it for himself, or within himself. So God created Eve, having seen by trial that Adam, even
in his own mind, was no fit consort for beasts alone.

> ". . . I, ere thou spak'st,
> Knew it not good for man to be alone,
> And no such company as then thou saw'st
> Intended thee, for trial only brought,
> To see how thou couldst judge of fit and meet."

Adam went on to relate how, though sleeping, as if in trance he
saw brought forth from his own flesh a creature,

> "Man-like, but different sex, so lovely fair
> That what seemed fair in all the world seemed now
> Mean. . . ."

Only here, with the movement of passion, did Adam feel weak;
of all other joys save his joy in hers, he was master.

> . . . "Wisdom in discourse with her
> Loses, discount'nanced, and like folly shows;
> Authority and reason on her wait. . . ."

"Accuse not Nature!" answered Raphael, "she hath done her
part." Wisdom, he said, had been placed in man with reason.
"She deserts thee not, if thou dismiss not her." The position
of love, he added, is but to refine upon the thoughts and to

give them greater scope—never to replace them. The angel took his leave, courteously, but with reiterated warning:

> ". . . Stand fast; to stand or fall
> Free in thine own arbitrement it lies.
> Perfect within, no outward aid require;
> And all temptation to transgress repel."

BOOK IX:

> No more of talk where God or Angel guest
> With man, as with his friend, familiar used
> To sit indulgent, and with him partake
> Rural repast, permitting him the while
> Venial discourse unblamed: I now must change
> Those notes to tragic; foul distrust, and breach
> Disloyal on the part of man, revolt
> And disobedience: On the part of Heaven . . .
> Anger and just rebuke, and judgment given
> That brought into this world a world of woe,
> Sin and her shadow Death, and Misery,
> Death's harbinger. . . .

Satan, unobserved, had circled the earth; and guilefully he had re-entered Paradise, through the subterranean channel of Tigris. Having considered every creature, he had decided upon the serpent, "subtlest beast of all the field" as the most appropriate vessel for his purpose. In none of the beauties of earth might he find refuge; but no longer did he seek a dwelling for his exiled race. In doing evil lay his good, in marring within a few seconds what God had taken six days to make lay his triumph. And so he descended into the sleeping serpent.

On the next morning, Eve proposed that she and Adam labor apart, in order to accomplish more, unhindered by the temptations of each other's presence. Adam protested that, though her thought was good, yet God had not enjoined labor so strictly upon them as to prohibit the smiles that spoke of the interchange of reason. But, fearing that so much of his presence might cause her to weary of him, he consented to brief separation, fearing, however, that some harm might befall his love.

Eve replied that he should not doubt her faith and love, for their Enemy could do her no violence. Adam, deeply moved, consented immediately to her request, and the two separated for the day.

Eve walked toward the groves, like an ancient wood-nymph, yet lovelier far. And soon the Arch-Enemy beheld her,

> Veiled in a cloud of fragrance, where she stood,
> Half-spied, so thick the roses bushing round
> About her glowed, oft stooping to support
> Each flower of slender stalk, whose head, though gay
> Carnation, purple, azure, or specked with gold,
> Hung drooping unsustained.

Herself a graceful, unsupported flower, she stood, far from her best support, and facing the greatest of all storms. At the sight of her, for a time, the Evil One remained bemused, abstracted from his own evil; her very beauty silenced his malice. But the Hell burning within him permitted no long delay. He realized that all joy was lost to him forever, save the pleasure of destruction. In the form of the serpent, he approached her,

> . . . not with indented wave,
> Prone on the ground, as since, but on his rear,
> Circular base of rising folds, that towered
> Fold above fold, a surging maze; his head
> Crested aloft, and carbuncle his eyes;
> With burnished neck of verdant gold, erect
> Among his circling spires, that on the grass,
> Floated. . . .

None of the serpent breed had ever been more lovely of shape. And, feigning admiration, he enticed Eve from her labor. Appealing to the vanity that had first led her to admire her reflection in the pool, he addressed her in human speech, persuading her that he himself had tasted the forbidden fruit, and had found wisdom above that of beast or man. Should she taste it, he continued, her estate should be indeed godlike. Only to test the boldness of herself and her husband had the injunction been given; for only the bold were fit to be gods. But she resisted his advances until, it being late and her appetite keen, she began to desire that fruit above all, and to muse upon the idea:

"How dies the Serpent? He hath eaten, and lives,
And knows, and speaks, and reasons, and discerns,
Irrational till then. For us alone
Was death invented? or to us denied
This intellectual food, for beasts reserved?" . . .
　　So saying, her rash hand in evil hour
Forth reaching to the fruit, she plucked, she ate;
Earth felt the wound, and Nature from her seat
Sighing through all her works gave signs of woe
That all was lost. Back to the thicket slunk
The guilty Serpent, and well might, for Eve,
Intent now wholly on her taste, naught else
Regarded; such delight till then, as seemed,
In fruit she never tasted, whether true,
Or fancied so, through expectation high
Of knowledge, nor was God-head from her thought.

Elated, as if by wine, she sang in praise of the fruit; yet, fearing death still, resolved that, should she die, Adam must never live to enjoy another Eve. Seeing him approaching, she addressed him sweetly, telling him that the Tree was not of death, but of life, entreating him to eat of it.

Speechless he stood, and pale, till thus at length
First to himself he inward silence broke:
　　"O fairest of Creation, last and best
Of all God's works, creature in whom excelled
Whatever can to sight or thought be formed,
Holy, divine, good, amiable, or sweet!
How art thou lost, how on a sudden lost,
Defaced, deflowered, and now to Death devote!

Rather, how hast thou yielded to transgress
The strict forbiddance, how to violate
The sacred fruit forbidden! Some cursèd fraud
Of enemy hath beguiled thee, yet unknown
And me with thee hath ruined, for with thee
Certain my resolution is to die.
How can I live without thee, how forgo
Thy sweet converse and love so dearly joined,
To live again in these wild woods forlorn?
Should God create another Eve, and I
Another rib afford, yet loss of thee
Would never from my heart. No, no, I feel
The link of Nature draw me; flesh of flesh,
Bone of my bone thou art, and from thy state
Mine never shall be parted, bliss or woe."

Seeking to comfort her, he hoped that the fruit, first pro-
faned by the serpent, might not now be deadly; that God, at
so great labor to produce man, should not lightly destroy him
for one error; that the Adversary should not be given such
great power. However, since, at Eve's creation, he had bound
himself with her, he was determined to share her fate. And,
charmed by her reassurance, he ate. But no sooner had he
eaten than both were, for the first time, moved by lust. Within
the freshest, softest lap of earth, covered by violets and asphodel and hyacinth, they loved one another; and, when the
potence of that dreadful fruit had dispelled itself, they fell
asleep. But they rose again, divested of their innocence, to
upbraid each other. They sought covering for their nakedness,
and from the fig they took leaves.

"... Thus it shall befall
Him who to worth in women overtrusting
Lets her will rule; restraint she will not brook,
And left to herself, if evil thence ensue,
She first his weak indulgence will accuse."
Thus they in mutual accusation spent
The fruitless hours, but neither self-condemning,
And of their vain contest appeared no end.

Book X:

> Meanwhile the heinous and despiteful act
> Of Satan done in Paradise, and how
> He in the Serpent had perverted Eve,
> Her husband she, to taste the fatal fruit,
> Was known in Heaven; for what can 'scape the eye
> Of God, All-seeing, or deceive His heart
> Omniscient, who in all things wise and just,
> Hindered not Satan to attempt the mind
> Of man, with strength entire, and free will armed,
> Complete to have discovered and repulsed
> Whatever wiles of foe or seeming friend.
> For still they knew, and ought to have still remembered
> The high injunction not to taste that fruit,
> Whoever tempted; which they not obeying
> Incurred—what could they less?—the penalty,
> And, manifold in sin, deserved to fall.

When the guardian angels led by Gabriel knew of man's sin, they forsook their posts and returned to Paradise; in Heaven, their vigilance was approved, for they could not have been man's guardian against himself. God, by His grace, sent His Son, who would be both God and Man, to judge man in his fall.

> . . . From His presence hid themselves among
> The thickest trees, both man and wife, till God
> Approaching, thus to Adam called aloud:
> "Where art thou, Adam, wont with joy to meet
> My coming seen far off? I miss thee here,
> Not pleased, thus entertained with solitude,
> Where obvious duty erewhile appeared unsought.
> Or come I less conspicuous, or what change
> Absents thee, or what chance detains? Come forth!"
> He came, and with him Eve, more loth, though first
> To offend, discount'nanced both, and discomposed;
> Love was not in their looks, either to God
> Or to each other, but apparent guilt,
> And shame, and perturbation, and despair,

Anger, and obstinacy, and hate, and guile.
Whence Adam, faltering long, thus answered brief:
    "I heard Thee in the Garden, and of thy voice
Afraid, being naked, hid myself." To whom
The gracious Judge without revile replied,
    "My voice thou oft hast heard, and hast not feared,
But still rejoiced. How is it now become
So dreadful to thee? That thou art naked, who
Hath told thee? Hast thou eaten of the Tree
Whereof I gave thee charge thou shouldst not eat?"
    To whom thus Adam, sore beset, replied . . .
"This woman, whom Thou mad'st to be my help . . .
She gave me of the tree, and I did eat."
    To whom the Sovereign Presence thus replied:
"Was she thy God, that her thou didst obey
Before His voice? Or was she made thy guide,
Superior, or but equal, that to her
Thou did'st resign thy manhood? . . .
    "Say, Woman, what is this which thou hast done?" . . .
    "The Serpent me beguiled, and I did eat."
    Which when the Lord God heard, without delay
To Judgment he proceeded on the accused. . . .
And on the Serpent thus His curse let fall:
    "Because thou hast done this, thou art accursed
Above all cattle, each beast of the field;
Upon thy belly groveling thou shalt go,
And dust shalt eat all the days of thy life.
Between thee and the Woman I will put
Enmity, and between thine and her seed;
Her seed shall bruise thy head, thou bruise his heel. . . ."
And to the Woman thus His sentence turned:
    "Thy sorrow I will greatly multiply
By thy conception; children thou shalt bring
In sorrow forth, and to thy husband's will
Thine shall submit; he over thee shall rule."
    On Adam last thus judgment He pronounced . . .
"Cursed is the ground for thy sake; thou in sorrow

Shalt eat thereof all the days of thy life;
Thorns also and thistles it shall bring thee forth
Unbid; and thou shalt eat the herb of the field,
In the sweat of thy face shalt thou eat bread,
Till thou return unto the ground; for thou
Out of the ground wast taken—know thy birth—
For dust thou art, and shalt to dust return."

In mercy, He clothed the pair, and left them alone.

Sin and Death, learning of Satan's victory, left their appointed places, and built over Chaos a great bridge, following the track that Satan first made. On their way, they met the Fiend, flushed with his success.

When Satan returned to Pandemonium, he assembled all his followers in a general council:

"Thrones, Dominations, Princedoms, Virtues, Powers—
For in possession such, not only of right,
I call ye and declare ye now, returned
Successful beyond hope, to lead ye forth
Triumphant out of this infernal pit
Abominable, accursed, the house of woe,
And dungeon of our Tyrant: Now possess
As lords, a spacious world, to our native Heaven
Little inferior, by my adventure hard
With peril great achieved. . . .
                                    . . . I found
The new-created world, which fame in Heaven
Long had foretold, a fabric wonderful
Of absolute perfection; therein man
Placed in a Paradise, by our exile
Made happy; Him by fraud I have seduced
From his Creator. . . .
                              . . . Ye have the account
Of my performance: What remains, ye Gods,
But up and enter now into full bliss!"
      So having said, a while he stood, expecting
Their universal shout and high applause

To fill his ear, when contrary he hears
On all sides, from innumerable tongues
A dismal universal hiss, the sound
Of public scorn; he wondered, but not long
Had leisure, wondering at himself now more;
His visage drawn he felt to sharp and spare
His arms clung to his ribs, his legs entwining
Each other, till supplanted down he fell
A monstrous serpent on his belly prone . . .

                 . . . he would have spoke,
But hiss for hiss returned with forkèd tongue
To forkèd tongue; for now were all transformed
Alike, to serpents all as his accessories
To his bold riot; dreadful was the din
Of hissing through the hall. . . .

Before them appeared a vision of the Tree with which man had
been deluded; but, reaching for its fruits, they found themselves chewing nothing but dust and ashes. Incredible was the
din—for every serpentine monster imagined by man, and many
beyond his mind's fathom, squirmed there upon the floor of
Hell. At last, long plagued by famine and thirst, they were
permitted to resume their old shapes.

Meanwhile, Sin and Death, arriving in their new kingdom of
Paradise, hoped to devour all things. But God smiled, knowing
that these were His Hell-hounds, called there to remove the
filth polluted by the sin of man, until,

                  ". . . at one sling
Of Thy victorious arm, well-pleasing Son,
Both Sin and Death, and yawning grave, at last
Through Chaos hurled, obstruct the mouth of Hell
Forever, and seal up his ravenous jaws.
Then Heaven and Earth renewed shall be made pure. . . ."

Adam, perceiving the divinely-ordered alterations in everything, at first rejected Eve with bitterness, but she at last ap-

peased his anger. She proposed that they die at once, but
Adam, remembering the prophecy, persuaded her:

"What better can we do, than to the place
Repairing where He judged us, prostrate fall
Before Him reverent, and there confess
Humbly our faults, and pardon beg, with tears
Watering the ground, and with our sighs the air
Frequenting, sent from hearts contrite, in sign
Of sorrow unfeigned, and humiliation meek?
Undoubtedly He will relent and turn
From His displeasure; in Whose look serene
When angry most He seemed and most severe,
What else but favor, grace, and mercy shone?"
  So spake our father penitent, nor Eve
Felt less remorse: they forthwith to the place
Repairing where He judged them prostrate fell
Before Him reverent, and both confessed
Humbly their faults. . . .

Book XI:

Thus they in lowliest plight repentant stood
Praying, for from the Mercy-seat above
Prevenient Grace descending had removed
The stony from their hearts, and made new flesh
Regenerate grow instead, that sighs now breathed
Unutterable, which the spirit of prayer
Inspired, and winged for Heaven with speedier flight
Than loudest oratory. . . .
  . . . To Heaven their prayers
Flew up, nor missed the way, by envious winds
Blown vagabond or frustrate; in they passed
Dimensionless through Heavenly doors; then clad
With incense, where the golden altar fumed,
By their great Intercessor, came in sight
Before the Father's throne; them the glad Son
Presenting, thus to intercede began . . .

Although the Son of God interceded for Adam and Eve, God decreed that they must no longer live in Eden, but, fulfilling the words spoken to them, dwell in sorrow until their final victory through Faith and faithful works. He sent Michael, with a band of cherubim, to expel them:

> "Haste thee, and from the Paradise of God
> Without remorse drive out the sinful pair,
> From hallowed ground the unholy, and denounce
> To them and to their progeny from thence
> Perpetual banishment. Yet, lest they faint
> At the sad sentence rigorously urged,
> For I behold them softened and with tears
> Bewailing their excess, all terror hide.
> If patiently thy bidding they obey,
> Dismiss them not disconsolate; reveal
> To Adam what shall come in future days
> As I shall thee enlighten, intermix
> My cov'nant in the woman's seed renewed.
> So send them forth, though sorrowing, yet in peace;
> And on the east side of the Garden place,
> Where entrance up from Eden easiest climbs,
> Cherubic watch, and of a sword the flame
> Wide waving, all approach far off to fright,
> And guard all passage to the Tree of Life . . ."

In the Garden, Adam and Eve spoke together, Adam expressing his conviction that they were not utterly condemned:

> "For since I sought
> By prayer the offended Deity to appease,
> Kneeled and before Him humbled all my heart,
> Methought I saw Him placable and mild,
> Bending His ear; persuasion in me grew
> That I was heard with favor; peace returned
> His promise, that thy seed shall bruise our Foe;
> Which then not minded in dismay, yet now
> Assures me that the bitterness of death

Is past, and we shall live. Whence hail to thee,
Eve rightly called, Mother of all mankind,
Mother of all things living, since by thee
Man is to live, and all things live for man."

Eve replied that she was unworthy of so high a title, and
reminded Adam that they must begin their daily work, for
daily labor was enjoined upon them. While they dwelt in Paradise, what could be laborious? But Adam, perceiving an eagle
drive before him two smaller birds, and a lion pursuing deer,
knew that the signs of their expulsion had been given. Then
Michael appeared; Adam bowed humbly before him; but

          he kingly from his state
Inclined not, but his coming thus declared:
    "Adam, Heaven's high behest no preface needs;
Sufficient that thy prayers are heard, and death
Then due by sentence when thou didst transgress
Defeated of his seizure many days
Given thee of grace, wherein thou may'st repent,
And one mad act with many deeds well done
May'st cover. Well may then thy Lord, appeased,
Redeem thee quite from death's rapacious claim;
But longer in this Paradise to dwell
Permits not; to remove thee I am come,
And send thee from the Garden forth to till
The ground whence thou wast taken, fitter soil."

Eve wept, but he bade her resign with what cheer she might
that bliss which she had, through justice, lost. Adam pleaded
for some sign, that he might at least tell his children where
the Lord once sat; Michael, with benign countenance, reassured him:

    "Adam, thou knowest Heaven His, and all the earth,
Not this rock only; His omnipresence fills
Land, sea, and air, and every kind that lives,
Fomented by His virtual power and warmed;
All the earth He gave thee to possess and rule,

No despicable gift; surmise not then
His presence to these narrow bounds confined
Of Paradise or Eden. . . .
Yet doubt not but in valley and in plain
God is as here, and will be found alike
Present; and of His presence many a sign
Still following thee, still compassing thee round
With goodness and paternal love; His face
Express, and of His steps the track divine.
Which that thou may'st believe, and be confirmed,
Ere thou from hence depart, know I am sent
To show thee what shall come in future days
To thee and to thy offspring; good with bad
Expect to hear; supernal Grace contending
With sinfulness of men; thereby to learn
True patience, and to temper joy with fear
And pious sorrow, equally inured
By moderation either state to bear
Prosperous or adverse; so shalt thou lead
Safest thy life, and best prepared endure
Thy mortal passage when it comes. Ascend
This hill; let Eve (for I have drenched her eyes)
Here sleep below while thou to foresight wak'st,
As once thou sleptst, while she to life was formed."

The angel led Adam, submissive, to the top of a high hill,
where he revealed to him the future: Cain's murder of Abel,
from which Adam learned the fact of death. Michael told him
that death could come in many shapes, many of them the result of man's own sinful nature, or, to the virtuous and temperate man, it could come after many years

      "till like ripe fruit thou drop
Into thy mother's lap. . . .
                  . . . To whom our Ancestor:
"Henceforth I fly not death, nor would prolong
Life much, bent rather how I may be quit
Fairest and easiest, of this cumbrous charge,

Which I must keep till my appointed day
Of rend'ring up." Michael to him replied:
"Nor love thy life, nor hate; but what thou liv'st
Live well, how long or short permit to Heaven. . . ."

Then Michael showed Adam the vainglories of this world,
the lusts of the flesh and the evil thereof; the wars of men, and
their iniquities until the Flood. Michael explained that God
permitted the building of the Ark for the preservation of the
just man; Adam spoke:

". . . Far less I now lament for one whole world
Of wicked sons destroy'd, than I rejoice
For one man found so perfect and so just . . .
But say, what mean those colored streaks in Heaven,
Distended as the brow of God appeas'd,
Or serve they as a flowery verge to bind
The fluid skirts of that same wat'ry cloud,
Lest it again dissolve and shower the earth?"
    To whom th' Archangel, "Dextrously thou aim'st;
So willingly doth God remit His ire . . .
And makes a covenant never to destroy
The earth again by flood, nor let the sea
Surpass his bounds, nor rain to drown the world
With man therein or beast; but when He brings
Over the earth a cloud, will therein set
His triple-color'd bow, whereon to look
And call to mind His cov'nant. Day and night,
Seed time and harvest, heat and hoary frost,
Shall hold their course, till fire purge all things new,
Both Heaven and earth, wherein the just shall dwell."

BOOK XII: Seeing Adam in perplexity, Michael, relenting to
the limit permitted him, revealed the course of man after the
flood. Speaking of Abraham, he

*"comes by degrees to explain who that Seed of the Woman
shall be which was promised Adam and Eve in the Fall:*

His incarnation, death, resurrection, and ascension; the state of the Church till his second coming."

As they descended the hill together, the angel directed Adam

"Let her with thee partake what thou hast heard,
Chiefly what may concern her Faith to know,
The great deliverance by her seed to come. . . .
That ye may live, which will be many days,
Both in one Faith unanimous though sad,
With cause for evils past, yet much more cheered
With meditation on the happy end."

They found Eve still asleep, and Adam gently raised her. But now the flaming angel approached them, and the cherubim descended from the hill.

. . . High in front advanced,
The brandished sword of God before them blazed
Fierce as a comet, which, with torrid heat,
And vapor as the Libyan air adust,
Began to parch that temperate clime; whereat
In either hand the hast'ning Angel caught
Our lingering parents, and to the Eastern Gate
Led them direct. . . .
Some natural tears they dropped, but wiped them soon;
The world was all before them, where to choose
Their place of rest, and Providence their guide:
They, hand in hand, with wand'ring steps and slow
Through Eden took their solitary way.

SUGGESTIONS FOR FURTHER READING

Editions:

Beeching, H. C. Oxford, 1926
Hughes, M. Y. New York, 1935

Milton's works have been published many times; the editions above are the easiest to obtain.

Other Books:

Hanford, J. H. *A Milton Handbook*, New York, 1946
Abercrombie, Lascelles. *The Epic*, London, 1914

INDEX

(To Persons and Places in the Stories)